BRUNEL

in

SOUTH WALES

BRUNEL
in
SOUTH WALES

VOLUME II
COMMUNICATIONS AND COAL

STEPHEN K. JONES

TEMPUS

To Siân

Thanks for everything

Front cover illustration:
Bridgend station, a view from a coloured lithograph print depicting the station on, or shortly after, opening in 1850. (SKJ collection)

Back cover illustration:
Company seals for South Wales Mineral Railway and South Wales Railway. (Courtesy of GWR Museum, Swindon)

First published 2006

Tempus Publishing Limited
The Mill, Brimscombe Port,
Stroud, Gloucestershire, GL5 2QG
www.tempus-publishing.com

© Stephen K. Jones, 2006

British Library Cataloguing in Publication Data.
A catalogue record for this book is available from the British Library.

ISBN 0 7524 3918 9
978 0 7524 3918 1

Typesetting and origination by Tempus Publishing Limited
Printed in Great Britain

Contents

INTRODUCTION   8

FOREWORD TO VOL. II   10
Communications and Coal

PREFACE AND ACKNOWLEDGEMENTS   12

1   ACHIEVEMENTS AND ASPIRATIONS   15
'Ceir gweld cledrffordd newydd,...'[1]

2   CELTIC CROSSOVER   35
'pedwar llew tew'[1]

3   A LINE OF COMMUNICATIONS   55
'... the requisites and character of a good line.'

4   WESTWARD TO WALES   69
'... is 1,100ft practicable'

5   CAPITAL CREATION   88
'Well I'll go to Cardiff'

6   THROUGH THE GARDEN OF WALES   125
'... calculated to destroy the trade of the Town'

7   FINAL DESTINATION   152
    'Letter from Skibbereen'[1]

8   RETURN TO THE IRON CAPITAL   176
    '… the difficulties were insurmountable'

9   LANDSCAPE AND INDUSTRY   207
    'One must not think of the beautiful, but of the useful,
    with a capital U'

10 LAST LINES   227
    'And if the income should appear to be advantageous
    to the South Wales Rly…'

11 BEYOND BRUNEL   241
    '… the continued existence of the double gauge is a national
    evil'

    INDEX   253

Communications and Coal

From lines of communication to keeping the wheels of industry turning
– continuing the story of Brunel in South Wales.

ISAMBARD KINGDOM BRUNEL.
Born 9th April 1806.   Died 15th September 1859.

Isambard Kingdom Brunel.
(From G.A. Sekon's A History of the
Great Western Railway, *1895, London)*

INTRODUCTION

The contribution made by Isambard Kingdom Brunel to the economy of south Wales cannot be underestimated. Others may have developed the steam locomotive from its Penydarren origins, but Wales has Brunel to thank for turning the railway into an effective economic tool.

As Volume 1 of the *Brunel in South Wales* series showed, Brunel was an engineer with a prolific output and seemingly tireless energy. During the course of railway construction much of his time was spent on the move, travelling in his britzska coach, known to the navvies as the 'Flying Hearse', or on horseback. Such a commitment continued throughout his career and, naturally, had a detrimental effect on family life and his health, and no doubt contributed to his premature death. Brunel's engineering skills can still be seen throughout south Wales – on his broad-gauge lines, such as the South Wales and the Vale of Neath Railways, the Taff Vale Railway and elsewhere. His concept for lines of communication was based on the broad gauge, with level and straight sections of track to achieve the highest possible speeds, principles kept alive today with the Eurostar/TGV family of high speed trains and the HST in daily use by First Great Western. But while much of the emphasis of the 'Brunel effect', as far as articles and books are concerned, is on his lasting engineering work, there are at least two other major areas that impacted on life in south Wales and beyond.

In the financial field, the structure of companies and the raising of enormous amounts of capital were a direct result of the railway's requirements. The need to establish a strong legal framework and identify risk for investors led to the legislation which created the limited liability company. Before the railways, the level of transport investment was relatively small, even for the funding of the canal network. There was now a need to fund a risk assessed means of transferring money from those who had it (the landed gentry and wealthy merchants) to those who wanted to spend it (such as Brunel and the Great Western Railway Co. Ltd). The banking system had to react quickly to this need. No longer could the old banking partnerships cope with such, often, high risk ventures.

The other significant effect of Brunel and, indeed, the railway network of the mid-nineteenth century, was on society. Journeying across Britain had, until the railways, been long, arduous and dangerous. The train made a major impact on such journey times and would continue to do so; what had once been a six-day journey by stagecoach would soon be achieved in six hours. The wealthy saw new opportunities opened up by the railway as it was now possible to have an estate in Wales and one of the new, rather grand, houses then being built in and around Paddington. The size of these properties is still evident. The new middle classes (of clerks and managers) felt a need to imitate their wealthy neighbours. The railway catered for all but the poorer sectors of society and it created different classes of travel in terms of standards of comfort. Travelling for work purposes (on business or commuting) was soon followed by travelling for fun, to seaside resorts and inland spas, whose health-improving qualities were to feature in another new industry spawned by the railway – that of advertising.

While Volume I concentrated on engineering, Volume II also deals with the legislative and business aspects: the structure of the companies; how they were established by Act of Parliament; the markets they served and the raising of finance. The amounts of money by the standards of the day were frightening; relatively local railways needed to raise sums of £550,000 (for an equivalent sum today you need to multiply by fifty), making the Vale of Neath Railway a £27.5 million investment. An even higher magnitude of cost would be to look at contemporary costs as a percentage of contemporary GDP, in which case an expenditure of, say, £1 million in 1833 would be equivilant to £3.6 billion today (£1 million being equal to 0.24 per cent of GDP in Britain at that time). A useful present-day comparison is the estimated £80 million cost of rebuilding the Conwy Valley line for freight operation.

The funding of the Channel Tunnel (£8 billion) and the links to London (£4 billion) are equivalent of the level of funding that Brunel's railways required. These figures frighten today's bankers – it was no less frightening during the 'railway mania' of the mid-1840s. The political machinations of the day illustrated the power of Parliament over the development of the railways in Wales, England, Scotland and Ireland. Each new scheme required an Act of its own specifying the route, the funding and other details.

The first two volumes are, therefore, largely internal to the railway – the engineering and the financial aspects. Volume III promises to be just as fascinating in its consideration of the impact the railway had on society and social life and the maritime and shipping connections. The trilogy will then be complete.

Professor Stuart Cole,
Wales Transport Research Centre, University of Glamorgan

FOREWORD TO VOL. II
COMMUNICATIONS AND COAL

Brunel's first foray into south Wales – the Taff Vale Railway – had been very much a one-off commission – local, isolated, 'narrow' (i.e. standard) gauge, and with no aspirations to form part of a wider network. Its original purpose was simple and straightforward – to provide a more efficient transport link between the iron producing area around Merthyr and the sea at Cardiff. The movement of coal was a later complication to this basic plan.

Brunel's next incursions into the principality were on an altogether grander scale and followed on logically from his work on the Great Western Railway. In selecting a route for the GWR via the Vale of White Horse and Swindon, Brunel had clearly recognised the potential for a branch from this line to Gloucester, with the possibility of an extension onwards into south Wales. The link to Gloucester came via the Cheltenham & Great Western Union Railway (C&GWUR), promoted in 1835 with Brunel as engineer, and authorised by an Act of 1836. From Gloucester, Brunel's activities were to focus on the promotion of two heroic trunk routes, both seen as part of a strategic link from London through to Ireland:

Through mid Wales to Porthdinllaen on the Lleyn peninsula; and
Across south Wales to the shores of Pembrokeshire.

The former was to come to nothing, despite a later attempt at revival. The latter – initially in the form of the Gloucester & South Wales Railway (G&SWR) of 1836 – was eventually to see completion as the South Wales Railway (SWR), opened in stages between 1850 and 1856. However, the combined effects of the Irish Famine, financial difficulties and the need to serve intermediate centres of population produced a somewhat diminished grand trunk route – a legacy that has persisted down to the present day.

Brunel's report to the promoters of the of the G&SWR on possible routes through south Wales, completed in September 1836, provides a valuable insight into the mind of the great engineer at work – clear in vision, examining the alternatives, assessing the costs and benefits and wider implications, and providing a well-argued recommendation on the course to be followed. The scale of this exercise is also significant. Not only did Brunel identify the route which was to provide the basis for the SWR as eventually completed, he also set the terms of the debate on the nature and extent of the railway network throughout south Wales, which continued over the next quarter-century, with many of the potential routes he explored eventually bearing rails.

The G&SWR failed to get very far in the context of an unfavourable financial climate. Delay in completing the C&GWUR did not help and it was not until 1844 that a firm proposal emerged in the form of the SWR. Brunel was able to return to his survey, completed nearly eight years earlier, and so the proposal was able to progress rapidly. However, instead of starting out at Gloucester, Brunel proposed a direct route from the C&GWUR at Sandish, with a bridge over the Severn at Hock Cliff, between Fretherne and Awre. However, this feature proved over-ambitious, falling foul of the Admiralty's views on the need to safeguard the interests of shipping in this important estuary. A revised proposal, involving either an enlarged bridge or a tunnel under the Severn at the same place, also came to naught. Elsewhere, greater success was evident, with the bridge over the river Wye providing the test bed for the design concept which Brunel was to bring to such magnificent effect at Saltash. Many of the original structures on the SWR were of timber, reflecting the need for economy in difficult times, and included one over the Usk at Newport, which burnt down in 1848, and Landore Viaduct on the approach to Swansea.

The SWR was to provide the spine from which a number of mostly independent broad-gauge feeder lines were to be built. These were relatively modest in ambition and scope and included the somewhat anachronistic South Wales Mineral Railway incorporated in 1853, with its inclined plane harking back to that provided by Brunel on the Taff Vale Railway above Abercynon. The SWR got off to a difficult start and was not to realise its full potential until after the removal of the broad gauge in 1872 and the subsequent completion of the Severn Tunnel and the direct line to Swindon avoiding Bristol. Today, Brunel's SWR continues to perform its intended role as the trunk route for south Wales, although the Irish connection has long since faded away.

A stated aim of this series is to highlight Brunel's achievements in south Wales and in so doing promote a better balance, in terms of public perception, with his more widely known works between London and the West of England. The sheer scale of Brunel's contribution to the SWR and its associated lines in south Wales is apparent from Stephen's text. This volume should, therefore, go a long way to achieving this important aim.

Colin Chapman

PREFACE AND ACKNOWLEDGEMENTS

Whilst Brunel's works can be found in many other locations outside south Wales, it was south Wales that provided the location and the proving ground for some of his greatest works. Brunel, like others before him and since, was challenged by the landscape of Wales to develop innovative engineering solutions, working with Welsh industry in his pursuit of excellence. This year 2006, offered a national opportunity to look back on his achievements through the celebration of the 200th anniversary of his birth, and it was important to ensure, therefore, that at least one of the proposed three volumes of *Brunel in South Wales* should appear in 2006. As it turns out the middle volume, *Communications and Coal*, is the 2006 volume, which is most appropriate as it covers work that had the widest impact, in both a physical and social sense, on south Wales. Brunel's railways made up a considerable part of the transport infrastructure necessary to exploit the mineral wealth of south Wales which in turn led to the creation of new communities in the mining valleys. Even within his professional field, Brunel went well beyond what was accepted as the normal remit of the role. He acted as an intermediary between the South Wales Railway (SWR) and the GWR, seeking viable solutions and coming up with alternatives to address problems of funding. To play such a role he was fully aware of the concerns of industrialists in Wales and, indeed in the case of the SWR route around Bridgend, may have paid too much attention to certain industrials! Whilst it is true that for the major works he relied on a tried and tested team, some of whom, like William George Owen and George Frere, had Welsh connections, he also encouraged local contractors and enlisted the services of engineers who would go on to work on the next generation of transport improvements in south Wales. Such a pattern can be seen with his earlier work on the Taff Vale Railway (see Volume 1). Despite this railway being a minor work, as far as Brunel is concerned, we can see his innovative genius here, particularly with his skew crossing of the river Taff at Goitre Coed. The Brunelian solution here was a graceful six-arched viaduct that did not look like a conventional skew viaduct, the spans springing from octagon piers. The Taff Vale Railway could not, however, be called a line of communications, but Brunel was to address such a need, not only for Wales but as part of a strategic route to Ireland, when he returned with the broad gauge. This, following a review of the interim between the two phases of his work, is the opening scenario of *Communications and Coal* – looking at the mail route proposals through Wales. It continues with the main line that was actually built and the mineral railways that followed. Conveying the relevant history of so many railways in this volume has not been an easy task and should not be seen as a substitute for the many excellent railway company histories already available, but as an attempt to give an insight into Brunel's contribution to these lines and his engineering legacy. There is still much to be told, including dock works, shipping facilities and the many maritime connections with his ships in Wales. These, and the other wide and varied links with the engineer, all of which are part of the story of *Brunel in South Wales*, will be taken up in the final volume, *Links with Leviathans.*

For this volume of *Brunel in South Wales*, I wish to repeat my thanks to everyone mentioned in the first volume for their help and assistance. For this volume I am grateful to the following for their constructive suggestions on the text: Colin Chapman, Paul Reynolds, Stuart Cole and Stephen Rowson. For help with information, access to archives and illustrations I would like to thank the following: the Hon. Sir William McAlpine; Colin Lucas (formerly Western Region bridge engineer); Ian L. Wright; Michael Hale; Richard Morris; Peter Griffin; Ben Barr; Larry J. Schaaf; Gwyn Griffiths; Brian L. James; Neil Perry; Robin O'Brien and Angus Low of Arup; Fairfield-Mabey Co. Ltd; Katrina Coopey of Cardiff Central Library, John Davies of the Carmarthenshire County Record Office, the Pembrokeshire County Record Office; the Public Record Office, Kew; the National Railway Museum, York; Newport Reference Library; the Royal Institution of South Wales and Swansea Museum: Leticia Ferrer of the Science Museum: Susan Edwards of the Glamorgan Record Office; Kaye Moxon of CADW; John Edwards and Rosie James of Cardiff City Council; Michael Richardson, Nick Lee and Hannah Lowery of the University of Bristol (University Library Brunel Collection); Andrew Kelly of Bristol Cultural Development Partnership (Brunel 200); Carol Morgan and Mike Chrimes of the Institution of Civil Engineers (library and archives); Einion Wyn Thomas of the University of Wales, Bangor; Phillip Mutter of the Royal Mint; David Jenkins, Kay Staffen and Charlotte Topsfield of the National Museum and Galleries of Wales; Brian Davies of Pontypridd Museum; Scott Reed of Cyfarthfa Castle Museum; Caroline Jacob of the Merthyr Tydfil Reference Library; Rachael Anderton and Roger Cucksey of the Newport Museum and Art Gallery; Richard Rossington; Meinir Huws and Chris Daw of the Welsh Assembly Government.

Keith Thomas, the Welsh representative of the Panel for Historical Engineering Works (Institution of Civil Engineers) has been extremely supportive of *Brunel in South Wales* and I was particularly pleased, therefore, that the Institution of Civil Engineers (Wales) and the South Wales Institute of Engineers, led by Denys Morgan, decided to commemorate the Welsh dimension of his work in 2006. This would be undertaken through the bilingual plaquing of landmark structures and by a generous contribution to the cost of the exhibition 'Brunel: Gweithiau yng Nghymru – Works in Wales'. The exhibition, compiled by Andrew Deathe, opened at the National Waterfront Museum at Swansea in time for Brunel's birthday on 9 April 2006 and is now travelling around venues in south Wales. The plaques presented commemorated his work on the Taff Vale Railway, the Newbridge viaduct over the river Rhondda at Pontypridd and Goitre Coed viaduct over the river Taff near Quackers Yard. What suddenly became apparent in terms of the former structure, even though the information was in Volume 1 with quotes from Samuel Downing's paper, was that Brunel had decided that the span of his skew crossing of the river Rhondda would be recorded as 140ft and not as 110ft which is the accepted measurement of the span, i.e. the span of the arch measured at right angles to the inside of the arch of the structure, irrespective of the skew. Samuel Downing quotes 140ft as the span in his 1851 paper, which presumably was measured diagonally from the two 'outside' faces of the arch, i.e. the widest possible measurement of the span. Why did Brunel want this measurement to be the official one as far as he and his assistant engineers were concerned? Could it be that he did not want to be outdone by William Edwards' famous 140ft single span across the Taff at Pontypridd? A third plaque at Bridgend station marked his work on the broad-gauge South Wales Railway where Brunel himself (or rather his lookalike Chris Cade of the National Railway Museum, York) was present to support the ceremony and demonstrate the superiority of the broad gauge. Further plaques are proposed at Chepstow and Loughor. I would wish to acknowledge those not already mentioned who have been involved in plaquing and other events to commemorate the Brunel anniversary in Wales, namely: Angus Buchanan; Elaine Davey and John Griffith of the Victorian Society; Ian Fostick and Andrew Clayton of Network Rail; Chris Gray, chairman of ICE Wales, Gwyn Griffiths, past president of SWIE and Gordon Masterton, ICE president.

As before special thanks go to Owen Eardley for his creative input, in particular for designing three maps especially for this volume and the logo used for the exhibition. At Tempus Publishing I am grateful to Amy Rigg, Nicola Guy and Sophie Atkins for their patience and help in completing this volume. My greatest debt is to my wife, Siân, for her patience and in assisting me with the research. Our daughters, Kathryn and Bethan, also deserve recognition, with granddaughter Chloe being the youngest at the launch of the first volume! In this capacity thanks also go to Lee Griffiths and Simon Gatheridge, with my sincere apologies to anyone I have inadvertently omitted. All errors are regretted and entirely my own.

Stephen K. Jones, 2006

A 1973 story from the South Wales Echo's *long-running* Ponty and Pop *cartoon serial by Gren. The name of the bridge builder, 'Isambard Kingdom Brunel Pugh', may have been unlikely but Herbert Isambard Owen was christened with a middle name from his godfather. (Courtesy of the* South Wales Echo *and Gren)*

1

ACHIEVEMENTS AND ASPIRATIONS

'CEIR GWELD CLEDRFFORDD NEWYDD,...'[1]

Marking a year of accomplishment for Brunel, 1841 saw the validation of his style of engineering with the completion and opening of a number of major railway works. Foremost amongst these was the completion of the Great Western Railway between London and Bristol with the opening of the final section from Chippenham to Bath on 30 June 1841. The heaviest and the most significant engineering work on the whole of the GWR was to be found here in the shape of the longest tunnel in the country, carved through the oolite limestone for almost two miles.[2] Labelled as monstrous and impracticable, the formidable tunnel, known as Box, presented a high profile when it came to receiving the attention of critics, '… whose only qualifications were a classical education and a desire to become amateur engineers in those days of novel and rapid expansion'.[3] The cost of the tunnel exceeded Brunel's estimate financially and proved to be extremely costly in human terms, claiming almost 100 lives out of the 4,000 workmen employed at the peak of its construction.[4] Box has a well deserved place in Brunel folklore, due mainly to the legend of the sun shining through the tunnel on 9 April, Brunel's birthday.[5] In 1841 the broad gauge would no longer to be confined solely to the GWR, following the opening of Cheltenham & Great Western Railway between Cirencester and Swindon on 31 May and the completion of the first section of the Bristol & Exeter Railway, from Bristol to Bridgewater, on 14 June.

Wales in 1841 witnessed the opening throughout of the original main line of another of Brunel's lines, the Taff Vale Railway (TVR), on 21 April. Brunel, 'the great railway magician' as *The Times*[6] called him, had not done everything single-handedly. His resident engineer on the TVR, George Bush, received glowing praise from Sir Frederic Smith, the Inspector General of Railways, when he inspected the line for the opening of the final section from Abercynon to Merthyr, remarking on the '… skilful manner in which Mr. Bush has grappled with the professional difficulties he has had to contend with in the formation of this railway'.[7]

There were few similarities between the two sections to be opened to complete the GWR and the TVR, except that both had tunnels and the TVR had a rope-hauled incline which the GWR almost had. The TVR's incline was on the main line between Abercynon and Quakers Yard with gradients of 1 in 19 for a quarter of a mile and a similar distance at 1 in 22.[8] In 1839 it was reported to the Parliamentary Select Committee on Railways that the use of stationary engines might be used to work the 1 in 100 gradient of the Box Tunnel incline, but this idea had been discounted by 1840 with the improved performance of locomotives capable of working such gradients.[9] Wootton Bassett also had a 1 in 100 gradient, which, like Box, would be worked by auxiliary power, if necessary.[10] At a fraction of the length of the Box Tunnel, the Goitre Coed tunnel had been utilised back on 8 October 1840, when a major portion of the TVR was opened between Cardiff and Abercynon. Then it was lit up by numerous candles by Bush to allow a party from the inaugural train to walk through the tunnel and on to the Goitre Coed viaduct. A precedent for this had been the Wapping tunnel at the Liverpool end of the Liverpool & Manchester Railway, in which the tunnel walls were whitewashed and gas lighting installed when it was opened in July 1829.[11] This, and the candle illumination of Goitre Coed, no doubt helped to offset the discomfort early travellers had in travelling through tunnels; Lady Charlotte Guest commented on the effect of the candles as, '… exceedingly striking and picturesque.'[12] Brunel had considered lighting Box Tunnel with reflector lamps and had a number made and fixed inside the tunnel, a measure that Sir Frederic Smith felt, '… would add essentially to the comfort of the travellers, and in some degree to their safety…'[13] Brunel was forced to abandon this idea but pointed out that his main concern was trying to throw a light on to the rails, for workmen then engaged in packing the rails with ballast and to enable engine drivers to see ahead, rather than an attempt at general illumination, adding in a letter to the GWR directors in September 1841 that, 'I am afraid that there are no means of remedying the evils of darkness in tunnels…'[14]

The year 1841 was also the first year of the decennial census-taking of Great Britain in which people were individually identified by the census. Such a development reflected the march of social progress, and an attempt to measure it that had not taken place since the last census of 1831. The electoral base had increased as a result of the 1832 Reform Act and further Acts of Parliament, such as the Poor Law Amendment Act of 1834 and the Births and Deaths Registration Act of 1836, were to put in place the systems and administrative machinery necessary to record the more detailed census of 1841.[15] Brunel had witnessed first-hand the clamour for reform when the second Reform Bill was rejected in October 1831 precipitating bloody riots in Bristol. Sworn in as a constable, Brunel was involved in protecting Bristol Mansion House and its contents, an action in which he first met Nicholas Roch (1786–1866), the Welsh merchant and successful Bristol businessman who was to figure prominently in helping to establish Brunel's career as an engineer.[16] The passing of the 1832 Reform Act would not eliminate discontent as the vast majority of the working population would still not have the vote.

In Wales radical fervour had gripped Merthyr in June 1831, with wide-scale rioting leading to troops being brought in to clear the streets. With regard to the events of 1831 there was a connection with an individual destined to work very closely with Brunel.

Portrait of Brunel by John Calcott Horsley. This is a version of a portrait originally painted by Horsley (Brunel's brother-in-law) around 1844. (Courtesy of the National Portrait Gallery)

The individual was Daniel, later Sir Daniel, Gooch (1816–1889), although the two would not meet until August 1837.[17] In February 1831, the fourteen-year-old Daniel had moved with his family to Tredegar to enable his father, John Gooch, to take up the post of bookkeeper at the Tredegar Ironworks. Gooch began work in the foundry of the ironworks, and while living and working in Tredegar he claims to have been forced to join a body of men marching through Tredegar from Nantyglo and Ebbw Vale on their way to Merthyr, 'I was amongst the unwilling ones, and with the others was placed in front, the men behind having sticks with spikes in the end to push us on. There were eight or ten thousand altogether'.[18]

Soldiers blocked the way of the men at the top of the Dowlais ridge and prevented them from meeting up with the Dowlais and Merthyr men on the other side. The Monmouthshire rebels dispersed when the Riot Act was read or, as Gooch commented, when, '… the soldiers were ordered to "present" – unpleasant sound to us in front…'[19]

SIR DANIEL GOOCH.
Born 24th August 1816.   Died 15th October 1889.

Daniel Gooch 1816–1889 (From G.A. Sekon's A History of the Great Western Railway, *London, 1895)*

Gooch escaped back to Tredegar and later that week, on the morning of Friday 3 June 1831, the soldiers and an angry crowd of 2,000 confronted each other outside the Castle Inn in Merthyr. Troops opened fire and, after a protracted struggle in which twenty protestors were killed and 100 injured, the street was eventually cleared.[20] Gooch wrote, '… but I seemed to enter into the spirit of the march and the excitement of the shouting and noise, and I had no real occasion to get into the mess' which appears to indicate that he was not such an unwilling recruit.[21] Working-class radicalism was not given up so easily and within a few years industrial south Wales would take up the cause of Chartism. Merthyr was to establish a 'Working Men's Association' in October 1838 and quickly became the most active of all the Welsh branches, playing an important role nationally.[22] The Merthyr Chartists would be involved in the armed struggle that took place at Newport on the night of Sunday 3 November 1839, marching with Chartists from the surrounding iron- and coal-mining valleys to a mass public meeting in the town demonstrating against the imprisonment of the Chartist leader, Henry Vincent.[23] The more militant members of a crowd of some 7 or 8,000, then attempted to storm the Westgate Inn in the town, where other Chartists were being held (Vincent was being held in Monmouth Goal). The Westgate was a busy coaching inn used by travellers in these pre-railway times; indeed, only a month before the uprising Lady Charlotte Guest had rested there for a few hours on her way to the opening of the Bute Dock in Cardiff on 8 October 1839.[24] Lady Charlotte had been writing in her diary a few months previously about the Chartists that were congregating on Merthyr, finding them, '… perfectly orderly… They seem quite different in tenets, etc., from the rabble of Birmingham'.[25] The conflict, however, that occurred on the morning of 4 November 1839 has gone down in history as the most serious clash between the people and government in modern industrial Britain. Such a strategy for forcing the release of fellow Chartists had worked before as at Llanidloes when on 30 April 1839 a Chartist meeting learnt that three of their supporters had been arrested and were being held at the Trewythen Arms in the town. An angry crowd attacked the inn and released the incarcerated Chartists. Newport, however, was to be a much bloodier encounter and the tactics of Llanidloes would not work there as soldiers stationed in the Westgate fired on the crowd, causing some twenty-two deaths and wounding fifty. The Newport ringleaders, including John Frost and Zephaniah Williams, were arrested and sentenced to death, but this was later reduced to transportation for life.[26] As well as Chartism, rural Wales would also espouse its own brand of protest, taking its name from the manner in which the protest was conducted. On 13 May 1839 the first of the 'Rebecca' Riots occurred when farmers and agricultural labourers dressed or disguised as women attacked the turnpike gate at Efailwen, near St Clears.[27] Between 1839 and 1844, a time of growing discontent among the rural and urban poor who faced poverty as a result of bad harvests and falling stock prices, rural south and west Wales was witness to the physical response of 'Rebecca' – a response aimed at, what had become a representation of much local grievance, the tollgates of the turnpike trusts.

Sunday 6 June 1841, was census day. George Bush, with all the frenetic exertions to get the last section of the TVR opened just a few weeks earlier now behind him, was enumerated in an entry for the Gabalfa area of Cardiff.[28] At thirty years of age he was five years younger than Brunel and poised at the start of an independent engineering career that, unfortunately, was not to be. With the completion of the TVR Bush appeared to have had a number of options to continue his engineering career, from the first proposals for a Brecon & Merthyr Railway to railway surveys in the Swansea Valley. Even at the start of his engagement with the TVR Bush had sought to complete earlier work and was receiving tenders for the construction of Llanelly dock at his office in the Maindy TVR works in Cardiff. Sadly, 'the talented engineer Mr. Bush' as the local newspaper referred to him, was not to pursue any further work, dying of natural causes in the November of what, for him, had been a year of accomplishment.[29] Brunel was 'captured' by the enumerators in Bath where he was staying at the Lion Hotel in High Street.[30] Bath was a convenient stop-over for Brunel in the course of his work, which on this occasion was almost certainly in connection with the opening of the final section of the GWR between Chippenham and Bath on 30 June 1841. Relying on stage coaches to get around the country, it was natural that Brunel stayed at inns such as the Lion, all of which, ironically, were now under threat of their coaching livelihood because of railway engineers like Brunel. Brunel and his contemporaries were laying the foundations of a new transport system that the world would soon be changing to, leaving roads and its reliance on horse-drawn traffic behind. The historical accuracy of Tennyson's *Locksley Hall*, first published in 1842, may have been flawed, but the sentiment expressed the transport revolution taking place, 'Let the great world spin for ever down the ringing grooves of change'.[31] A revolution was to create a new category of traveller, the railway passenger, the first of this new breed being captured by the 1841 census on Southampton railway station.[32]

Brunel's relations with the TVR after the opening throughout of the line on 21 April 1841 would be more distant and far removed from the early assumptions that the TVR and the GWR would be natural bedfellows. Both companies had started, of course, with the same engineer and the projected line from Merthyr to Cardiff was included on a map accompanying the second prospectus of the GWR in 1834.[33] It was also considered in 1836 as part of a possible Great Western extension into south Wales (see Chapter 3). However, in 1838 the TVR adopted the 4ft 8½in gauge, ironically on Brunel's recommendation, and as a narrow-gauge railway it would not be a natural ally of the broad-gauge Great Western.[34] Brunel still responded to requests for his professional attention, as in 1843 when he reported on the condition of the railway, in particular to report on the maintenance contract taken out by the TVR in December 1841.[35] It was not long before there was conflict between the TVR and Brunel over railway incursions into the Aberdare or, more correctly, the Cynon Valley. Any traffic originating in the Cynon Valley was seen by the TVR as rightfully theirs as the river Cynon flowed into the river Taff. In 1844 Brunel was not consulted on or commissioned to build the Aberdare Railway, a railway which, like the TVR, had Sir John Guest as its first chairman, and a railway that would be worked by the TVR from 1 January 1847.[36] Brunel was behind a rival project, the broad-gauge Aberdare Valley Railway which was to come in to tap the rich coal seams from the top end of the valley via the Vale of Neath Railway (VNR). It was not surprising, therefore, that the TVR should oppose the VNR Bill, but what is interesting is that they chose as their engineering witness Robert Stephenson, Bute's advisor in his opposition to the TVR's Ely Dock scheme (see Chapter 8).

The TVR opened in a period of general economic depression, which had hit industry and railways hard, a consequence of which the TVR was unable to settle fully with the contractors who built the line. It also, with much disgrace, held out with payments due, in the form of wages and expenses owed, to the executors of George Bush's estate and which it was not to settle until some seven years after his death and then only about a fifth of what was owed.[37] The general workforce was also suffering with the downturn in trade to which the employers response was to lay off men and impose wage reductions. In January 1842, as a result of the falling price of bar iron, Dowlais laid off 150 men.[38] At one stage in this period Guest considered liquidating the whole of the plant and property of the TVR to settle with its creditors.[39] Against such a background the working classes were drawn to the aspirations of the Chartists and took up their political demands. A confrontation with the State as well as industry seemed inevitable, coming to pass in August 1842 as the 'Great Strike'. Involving up to half a million workers, from the Scottish coalfields to Cornwall and including south Wales, it was to last twice as long as the General Strike of 1926. Despite this force of strength the strike failed at both local and national levels and as a consequence the Chartist movement would be driven underground. Elements of the movement, known as the 'Moral Force' Chartists, favoured acts of civil disobedience while the 'Physical Force' faction wanted more direct action and called for a co-ordinated armed struggle. The growing economic revival that ushered in the 'large' railway mania of 1845 meant that such calls largely went unheeded and the Chartism movement as a whole was to wither away.

As with the country at large, things were looking up for the TVR in 1845 and an upbeat meeting was presided over by Walter Coffin, acting as chairman in the absence of Sir John Guest, at its half-yearly meeting in August 1845.[40] Coffin confirmed that a double line was now being formed, for which there was some criticism as they were not authorised to do this and they had not yet carried out all the original intentions of their Act of Parliament, such as the branch line to Dowlais. This point was made by George Overton several times during the meeting. One of the original twelve TVR directors, R.H. Webb, was pleased that a dividend of £3 14s 6d per cent per annum had been declared (to the holders of the original shares), stating that the dividend would benefit the shareholders at large and further:

> He would not exchange his Taff Vale shares, for an equal number in the Great Western Railway. (Cheers). He stated that four years ago; since which time they (the proprietors of the Taff Vale Railway) had exercised a great deal of patience and perseverance, and they had also taken a little water gruel as well. (Laughter). They were now as prosperous as any railway could be. (Hear).

Joseph Price of Neath Abbey, who had enquired about the double line now being formed on the TVR, asked when the directors' attention would be turned to opening the line up the Rhondda Valley, to which the chairman announced that arrangements had been made with the landed proprietors of the Rhondda Valley for the, '… formation of a line through it in connection with the Taff Vale Railway, and which branch line was to be a public one, and would shortly be carried into execution by the Taff Vale Railway Company. (Loud cheers)'.

Previously Walter Coffin, as the largest coal proprietor in the Rhondda, had been content with his own arrangements for transporting coal (using his tramroad to the TVR railhead at Dinas) and this announcement was widely appreciated by the meeting who gave it the only 'loud cheers' reported at the meeting. However, to the annoyance of George Overton, the TVR directors were stubbornly resisting their obligation to build the Dowlais branch, because they no doubt saw a greater return on capital through the extension of the Rhondda branch and the following year (1846) obtained an Act of Parliament to do just this.

There were a number of references to the Welsh Midland Railway at the TVR meeting; this line was being promoted in April 1845 as a standard-gauge line from Worcester, through Hereford, Hay and Brecon to Carmarthen, the prospectus of which was embellished as:

> The Welsh Midland Railway, to connect Birmingham and the Mumbles Roadstead, in the Bay of Swansea, and to communicate either by the main line or by branches with Worcester, Leominster, Ludlow, Shrewsbury, Hereford, The Hay, Brecon, Llandovery,

Llandilo, (with a branch to the present terminus of the Llanelly Railway,) Llanelly, Swansea and Carmarthen…[41]

Plans for the Welsh Midland Railway deposited in November 1845 were comprehensive; the Mumbles Head extension shows a line running to a steam packet landing place; there was a connection with the Swansea Vale Railway and the junction with the TVR was to be formed at Roed y rhiw gwmrwg [Troed y rhiw]. The alternative line from Neath to Swansea shows a line running up the Vale of Neath.[42] Despite the effort made to maximise support from the narrow-gauge interests, the Welsh Midland Railway Bill was rejected by Parliament on 3 March 1846. One of those interests was the Newport, Abergavenny & Hereford Railway (NA&HR), which was to gain its Act of Parliament on 6 August 1846. The NA&HR would form an alliance with the TVR to complete a link between that line and its own line across the Glamorgan and Monmouthshire valleys by the construction of the Taff Vale Extension (TVE). As a cross-valley railway, the line had to overcome some major natural obstacles, such as the Ebbw Valley at Crumlin, where a substantial viaduct was required. The opening of the line in 1858 ended the TVR's isolation from the standard-gauge railway network, one implication of which was that it had to run its trains on the left instead of the right as it had done previously.

Whilst his official connection with the TVR may have been in decline at this period, Brunel was still a frequent visitor to south Wales, and one story of a visit and his encounter with the 'incorruptible guard, Meyrick' at Dowlais station in the early 1850s has already been recorded in Volume 1.[43] Richard Price Williams, then a young engineer, was responsible for writing down these reminiscences, which had included the story of Brunel's visit to the Dinas collieries belonging to Walter Coffin. The only time Brunel could spare for this visit was at night and a special train was organised to take him from Cardiff to Dinas in the Rhondda, accompanied by Coffin, the general manager, George Fisher and Price Williams. It was on this trip that Brunel told Coffin of the incident with Meyrick, and believing that in the present company he would be allowed to smoke, he lit up one of his favourite Lopez cigars, 'Now I have the Chairman and the General Manager of the Company with me I can have a good smoke without any fear of that terrible Guard Meyrick'.[44] Coffin personally objected to the habit of smoking and in normal circumstances objected to anyone smoking in his company, or indeed on the TVR, but on this occasion allowed Brunel to enjoy his cigar whilst telling the story. The object of his visit to Dinas was to examine the methods of compressing coke that Coffin was experimenting with – the process turned out to be a complete failure.[45] During the railway journey Brunel was asked by Coffin which seat he felt was the safest seat in a railway carriage. Brunel replied, 'Not where you are sitting, Mr Coffin, right over the front wheel. One of my friends was sitting in that position when the end of a rail ran up the tyre of the wheel and spitted him like a trussed fowl'.[46]

Coffin immediately responded to Brunel's comment by vacating, '… the perilous position and occupying, as Brunel said he always did, a middle seat'. A special journey of another kind took place in 1843 when the Crown Prince of Wurttemberg made a visit to Wales organised by the engineer Charles Blacker Vignoles (1793–1875). Prior to

Charles Blacker Vignoles 1793–1875. (Courtesy of the Institution of Civil Engineers)

'Not where you are sitting, Mr Coffin'. Walter Coffin, the coal owner and TVR chairman. (SKJ collection)

going out to Germany in connection with plans for railways in Wurttemberg, Vignoles was to organise this visit by a German delegation to travel on the TVR and examine its operation first hand. Vignoles recorded the event, on 5 and 6 June 1843, in his diary:

> I joined HRH and suite at Clifton this evening, and the next day we went by steamer to Cardiff, where we met Mr. Crawshay, of Cyfarthfa, and Sir John James [sic] Guest. After examination of Cardiff Docks and railway terminus etc I accompanied HRH on a locomotive up the Taff Vale Railway to Merthyr Tydfil. I was much struck with the laying out of the lines, and especially the curves. The royal party thought the Taff Vale similar in character to the valley of the Neckar. In the evening we visited Mr Crawshay's "Cyfarthfa" ironworks…[47]

The party would visit Dowlais the following day. Guest later informed Lady Charlotte that the party had expressed, '… great desire to go upon the engine itself, which he gave leave for them to do'.[48] Vignoles was working with Brunel on the Porthdinllaen proposals at this time and Brunel was no doubt more than happy for Vignoles to take this party around the TVR. It would not go Vignoles' way, however, and despite the understanding that he should be engineer-in-chief of the proposed line in Wurttemberg, with his nineteen-year-old son Hutton as assistant, the commission to design and construct the work was given to German engineers.

Robert Stephenson 1803–1859. (SKJ collection)

Brunel and Vignoles had met some years earlier, probably as early as 1827 when they met in Liverpool, and despite an unfortunate episode in which Vignoles attempted to take over from Marc Brunel as engineer on the Thames Tunnel, the paths of the two engineers were to cross over throughout their careers. As well as railways, the two engineers had a common interest in packet ports as part of the strategic extension of the railway network. Wales itself offered markets and opportunities for trade – and beyond was Ireland. It was therefore both a market in itself and a stepping stone to wider markets. There was also the possibility of through traffic travelling from London to New York via Wales and Ireland but the march of technology by Brunel's entry into steam navigation negated this consideration. You could now travel non-stop from, say, Bristol to New York. There was not just one route, however, even as far as Brunel and the GWR was concerned. Over a ten-year period from 1836, Brunel was working on two main routes in Wales with various options through south, mid and north Wales which he was to survey or support. There was competition from narrow-gauge interests, particularly in reaching that wider market and securing the subsidies that the Irish mail contracts would bring. One of Brunel's contemporaries would remark that he felt the principal objective of the route eventually built, the South Wales Railway (SWR), was competing with the London & North Western and the Chester & Holyhead Railways for the Dublin traffic.[49] The reality was that the SWR would have to satisfy itself for many years with the traffic and trade of its locality. As a trunk route the origins of the SWR can be traced back to a scheme George Stephenson was to propose at the end of 1824 as the 'London and South Wales Road'.[50] This was one of the many schemes that would mark 1825 out as the year of the 'company mania', with proposals for trunk lines linking Bristol with Yorkshire, south Wales and London. Considering that the most ambitious railway to date, the Stockton & Darlington Railway, would not open until 1826, such schemes can be seen, in retrospect, as somewhat ambitious. Stephenson's London and South Wales Railroad proposal was to come to nothing, although a revival of interest followed on from news of a Bristol to London railway proposal, a proposal that would become the Great Western Railway (GWR). The Bristol to London railway soon became the London & Bristol Railway, a proposal driven by two committees, the Bristol committee meeting for the first time on 21 January 1833. They were to appoint Brunel on 7 March and hold their first public meeting on 30 July. The title 'Great Western Railway' was adopted at a meeting of the London and Bristol Committees on 19 August 1833. It is significant that this title was adopted in line with what has already been said, as it offered a considerably wider remit than 'London & Bristol Railway'.[51] Brunel was completely behind these aspirations and had probably pushed the idea forward in the first place as he is credited with coining the name 'Great Western Railway', but it was not an entirely new name, as a proposal for a 'Great Western Railroad', from Bristol to Exeter, had been raised in 1825.[52] In the weeks following the Great Western Railway news, local newspapers such as the *Glamorgan, Monmouth and Brecon Gazette, Merthyr Guardian* and *The Cambrian*, reported on proposals or meetings promoted variously as the 'Cambrian and Gloucester Railroad', the 'Cambrian, London and Gloucester Railway' and the 'Cambrian, Gloucester, Birmingham and London Railway', depending on which town or region the idea was being sold to. On 24 August 1833, the *Cambrian* reported that a correspondent at Newport had forwarded the following information:

> A gentleman is at present in our vicinity, whose object is to form a Railroad from Glamorganshire (through Gloucester) to London, to be called *The Gloucester and Cambrian Railroad;* thus leaving Bristol entirely out of the question. Landed property on the line will increase by at least 15 per cent.

A week later a fuller report gave details on the 'Cambrian, London & Gloucester Railroad':

> From Gloucester the line will be through Usk, to join the Merthyr Tramroad near Troad-y-rhyw, [sic] by Pontypool, Crumlyn, Panllwyn, Panellti, and Cawch Mill, with a branch to take the Cynon Valley; from Usk the line comprehends that beautiful country by way of Newport, Cardiff, Landaff, Lanharran, Ewenny, Newton and Briton Ferry, to Swansea, from whence by way of Lanstephan (where there will be a short tunnel and a bridge across the Towy river), thus terminating a line of above 250 miles at Milford, of unequalled level in the United Kingdom...[53]

The intention to leave Bristol out of this route remained strong; indeed, a correspondent commenting on the proposal in the same issue raises the question, '... what does Bristol create? We answer nothing. What then is to supply a railroad from Bristol to London?'. The answer given is the produce of Wales and Welshmen are urged to support this scheme without beholding themselves to Bristol, to, '... raise ourselves by our natural resources, industry and ingenuity'. The railway is mentioned in the next two issues and on 7 September it is said of the Cambrian, London & Gloucester Railroad that, '... this spirited undertaking is under the superintendence of Mr. W. Brunton, whose talents as an engineer are too well known in this neighbourhood to admit a doubt of success'.[54]

This reference to William Brunton (1777–1851) is interesting as the name of William Wooddeson appears after this as the engineer of the scheme. Wooddeson is present at the meetings called to promote the proposal. He is described as a surveyor and architect in reports of October 1833 and as a civil engineer in November 1833.[55] Brunton's name does not appear in any reports of these meetings and, indeed, there is no attempt by him or anyone else to counteract the claim. *The Cambrian* actually states that, 'Mr. Wooddeson, in October last adduced his plan for a Railway from London via Gloucester and Swansea to Milford Haven'.[56] We know nothing of Wooddeson's track record, but Brunton has a higher profile, being behind a Bath to Bristol Railway in 1830 and the first practical proposal for a line between London and Bristol in 1832 with Henry Habberley Price. With calls in *The Cambrian* for, '... we will have a railroad to London' from the 'voice of the people', a meeting to discuss the Welsh proposals took place at the Castle Inn at Merthyr, on 11 October 1833. This meeting was dominated by ironmasters. Indeed, Guest took the chair at this meeting and in terms of the proposal to support the Cambrian, Gloucester & London Railway, asked, '... whether this was the time it may be successfully attempted'.[57] As it turned out it was not to be the right time for William Wooddeson or indeed for Henry Habberley Price (1794–1839) who proposed a railway from Cardiff to Llanelly on 14 April 1834 as the 'Grand Cambrian & Western Railway'.[58] Price was an accomplished engineer who had worked under Thomas Telford and had worked with Brunton. In February 1837 he was behind a railway proposal from Swansea to Loughor with William Price Struve.[59] Brunton's 'Bath to Bristol Railway' proposal had been aired at a meeting in the Assembly Rooms in Bath on 4 January 1830.[60]

Price's Grand Cambrian & Western Railway could link with an alternative route proposed from London, an extension of the 'London & Windsor Railway'.[61] MacDermot refers to this as the, '… insignificant rival project calling itself "The London and Windsor Railway"… ' It would be, however, unfair to call the London & Windsor Railway Co. insignificant; it had sought approval at the highest level, King William IV accepting that such a line would have to cross Crown land. In the 1830s there was strong support for a London to Bristol railway going through Windsor, the line crossing the river from the east and to the north of the Home Park and between the castle and the river, with a station situated to the west of the town. There would need to be a further extension from the London & Windsor Railway if it was to provide a connection with proposals such as that put forward by H.H. Price. This could be the London & Severn Railway, which had commissioned Vignoles, and as one of three surveys he was engaged on in 1834, this:

> … on behalf of the Thames & Severn Railway Company (an extension of the London & Windsor), took him by gig, on horseback and on foot along the Thames valley, and over the Berkshire Downs, exploring an alternative line to I. K. Brunel's proposed Great Western. The route he chose was to run north of Brunel's line through the Vale of White Horse, and climb through the southern Cotswolds to reach the Severn at Sharpness. Here he envisaged an ambitious 20-arch viaduct to carry the line into South Wales, and branches to Gloucester and Bristol.[62]

The GWR, not having the required capital to proceed with the complete London to Bristol line, pushed ahead with a Bill for two sections of the total line first, i.e. Bristol to Bath and London to Reading, the latter including a branch to Windsor to try and negate support for the London & Windsor.[63] The GWR Bill passed through the House of Commons, receiving its second reading in March 1834 and shortly afterwards the London & Windsor Railway Co. withdrew their plans. The Bill for the 'truncated' GWR, as it became known, would fail in the House of Lords on 25 July 1834. Although Vignoles had surveyed an alternative line and supported the Commissioners of the Thames Navigation and the Thames & Severn Canal in their opposition and was called upon as an opposition witness during the reading of the unsuccessful 1834 GWR Bill, the following year Vignoles and Price would support Brunel when the second GWR Bill went to Parliament. Vignoles saw this as an opportunity to reconcile his differences with Brunel.

Two years later the Thames & Severn Canal put forward another scheme to turn themselves into a railway company. This time it was in opposition to the Cheltenham

& Great Western Union Railway (C&GWUR) who proposed to build a track running alongside the canal from Cirencester to Stroud. Also at this time the London & Birmingham Railway decided to put an alternative scheme forward known as the Cheltenham, Oxford & London & Birmingham Union Railway. The C&GWUR was successful in Parliament but at a cost.[64] The Thames & Severn had once again threatened, but failed in the act of converting itself into a railway.[65]

A Supplementary Prospectus for the second GWR Bill referred to the superiority of the line and the greatest facilities for junctions with, '... the manufacturing districts of Gloucestershire and Wiltshire, and through Gloucester with South Wales' whilst earlier versions saw south Wales being served by sea from Bristol.[66] Highlighting this as a potential trade route between south Wales would be an important incentive for attracting the support of Welsh businessmen for the GWR, and would no doubt be well practiced by Brunel and Charles Saunders, the first secretary of the GWR. The Earl of Kerry had seconded the second reading of the 1834 GWR Bill and Irish MPs like Daniel O'Connell supported both Bills, O'Connell seeing the GWR as, 'the means of conferring great advantages on Ireland, the great granary and feeding farm of this country'.[67] This comment assumed that a connecting railway would be built to complete the line of communications across south Wales but, sadly, before this link was completed Ireland's role as the 'great granary' was ravaged by the Great Famine. There was another upshot of the failure of the first GWR Bill, in that the Bill specified the gauge of the railway which was restricted to 4ft 8½in. When the second GWR Bill was presented, Brunel persuaded Lord Shaftesbury, the chairman of the examining House of Lords Committee, that a gauge clause was unnecessary, arguing as a precedent the London & Southampton Railway Act of 25 July 1834.[68] Thus, the way was left open for Brunel to present his proposals for a broad gauge.

Whilst the second GWR Bill was successful on 31 August 1835, a further proposal that would have taken forward such a link to Ireland, the 'Gloucester and South Wales Railway', was to fail due to a lack of financial support. The Gloucester & South Wales Railway (G&SWR) received public exposure in March 1836 with a meeting held in London for, '... the purpose of considering the expediency of extending the railway communication about to be established between London and Gloucester and Birmingham and Gloucester, into South Wales'.[69]

George Henry Gibbs recorded in his diary on that day, 'Getting up a new line from Gloucester to Swansea'.[70] At a further meeting in London on 16 April 1836, it was decided that a line extending from Gloucester to Milford Haven be considered and that no attempt to form a company should be considered until the engineer had reported on the best route. Brunel was appointed engineer on 23 April 1836 when a letter from him accepting the appointment of engineer was read at the meeting of the G&SWR committee on that day at the Thatched House Tavern, London.[71] The meeting at the Thatched House Tavern in London on 26 March 1836 had excited the attention of parties leading to a preliminary investigation on which Alderman Thompson MP, L.W. Dillwyn MP, Richard Blakemore MP, W. Crawshay Esq., R. Fothergill Esq., and Crawshay Bailey Esq., sat.[72] All were prominent ironmasters except for Lewis Weston

Dillwyn (1778–1855), a Swansea businessman with wide-ranging interests, who as an MP had voted for the Great Western Railway Bill during its first and unsuccessful attempt in Parliament in 1834.

Brunel did not waste any time and was in communication with James Kemp, the secretary of the G&SWR, at his office in Gloucester, relating to work on the report. In the July of 1836 he was surveying possible routes across south Wales from Gloucester.[73] Brunel was to complete and present his report but after this point the G&SWR appears to turn into the 'Gloucester and Cardiff Railway'. This was to come about following a resolution taken at a meeting at the office of Messrs Whitcombes & Helps in Gloucester, held to receive Mr. Brunel's report on the G&SWR on 22 September 1836.[74] A printed handbill describes the meeting's outcome in terms of resolutions taken:

1ST. That it is not expedient to construct at present, any Railway, west of Cardiff.

2ND. That the construction of a Railway from Gloucester to Cardiff, is calculated, to accomplish, National and Local advantages.

3RD. That the Line by Newnham and Chepstow is the best, and ought to be adopted.

4TH. That a sub-committee to be appointed...[75]

It went on to say that Brunel's report, based on the results of the survey between Gloucester and Milford, '... and the report of the Persons employed to take the Traffic on the different Lines of the probable amount of Income,' were submitted to the Meeting, which unanimously adopted the first, third and fourth Resolutions. The 'Severn' line was also favoured as opposed to a line running to the back of the Forest of Dean by Monmouth and Usk. Brunel reported that the line to Cardiff would be fifty-four miles long and he thought it; '... may be constructed for less (considerably as he thinks,) than a Million sterling'. However, the cost of the line to Swansea would cost another million even through it was only forty miles in length. Gloucester to Cardiff would cost less than half the cost of the whole line to Swansea, but the traffic between Cardiff, Newport and Gloucester would produce eight-tenths of the revenue that might be expected from the construction of the whole line, 'So there was no hesitation on the part of any Gentleman present at the Meeting, in adopting the Resolution that for the present the Railway ought to stop at Cardiff'.

Following on from these resolutions, a further meeting was arranged in Gloucester for Monday 10 October 1836, to be held at the Tolsey or Town Hall. This was a general meeting held for those interested in, 'forming a communications by Railroad between Gloucester and Cardiff'.[76] The persons nominated as directors included William Crawshay of Merthyr and Charles Williams of Cardiff, but everything depended on subscribers prepared to invest in the scheme, '... a preference be given in the allotment of Shares in the Company to those Gentlemen who have subscribed towards the expense of Surveys already made...' The time was not right, however, and subscriptions failed to materialise. In November 1840 *The Cambrian* reported on a meeting of subscribers to be held in Gloucester on 24 November 1840 to, '... consider the propriety of taking means for enforcing the recovery of unpaid subscription...'[77] The south Wales route would regain momentum in 1844 and is taken up in Chapter 3. It would not, however, be the only Irish route considered, even by the GWR camp. Brunel's position and recommendation for the south Wales route was clear, but there was still a demand for a direct London to Dublin route. A broad-gauge alternative would circumvent the piecemeal development that was the basis of the standard-gauge route, but it posed a considerable challenge for the supporters of the broad gauge and their engineer, in terms of time, resources and engineering innovation, in order to overcome the natural obstacles faced.[78]

NOTES

1 'Ceir gweld cledrffordd newydd,...' or 'We shall see the new railroad,...' part of a line from a poem by Evan James (1809–78) entitled *Can yr Adfywiad, Ar Agor y Gledrffordd newydd yng Nghymdogaeth y Bontnewydd a Mynwent y Crynwyr* or *The Revival or Renewal – that will come by the New Railroad in the vicinity of Newbridge and Quakers Yard*. This unpublished poem is a tribute to the improvement in the trade and commerce (and a revival in learning and culture) that will come about with the opening of the Llancaiach branch of the TVR, opened in November 1841 (see Jones, Stephen K. (2005), pp.193-194, *Brunel in South Wales vol.1 In Trevithick's Tracks*. Tempus Publishing: Stroud). I am grateful to Gwyn Griffiths, who is writing a biography of Evan James, for bringing this to my attention.

2 Blower, Alan (1964), pp.35-7, *British Railway Tunnels*, Ian Allan: London. The length is given as 1 mile 1,452 yards long.

3 Pudney, John (1974), pp.40-1, *Brunel and his World*, Thames and Hudson: London. Quote by Sir Harold Harding, p.41, from his chapter on Tunnels in Pugsley, Sir Alfred, ed, (1976), *The Works of Isambard Kingdom Brunel*, University of Bristol and ICE: London & Bristol. The first to attack Brunel's tunnel was the eccentric scientist Dr Dionysius Lardner (1793–1859) who made the claim that runaway trains entering the tunnel would emerge at the other end at 120mph, the consequence that all the passengers would suffocate! Brunel replied patiently that factors such as friction and air pressure would prevent the train from exceeding fifty-six miles an hour in such circumstances.

4 Rolt, L.T.C. (1959). p.138, *Isambard Kingdom Brunel*, Longmans, Green & Co.: London Pugsley, Sir Alfred, ed., (1976), p.48.

5 Jones, Stephen K. (2005), p.90.

6 Quote from *The Times* quoted in Matthews, James (1910), *Historic Newport*, Newport.

7 Letter dated 20 April 1841 and published in the *Glamorgan, Monmouth and Brecon Gazette* and *Merthyr Guardian,* 24 April 1841. See Jones, Stephen K. (2005), pp.166-7.

8 Barrie D.S.M. (1939, reprinted 1950, 1962 and 1969), pp.10-11, *The Taff Vale Railway*, Oakwood Press: Lingfield. See also Jones, Stephen K. (2005), pp.190-3, for details of the working of the incline.

9 MacDermot, E.T., revised by Clinker, C.R. (1964), p.68, *History of the Great Western Railway*, vol.1. Ian Allen: London. This was reported by Charles Alexander Saunders who also mentions the possible use of water power in working the incline.

10 Williams, Archibald (1925, reprinted 1972), p.11. *Brunel and After: The Romance of the Great Western Railway*, Patrick Stephens Ltd: London.

11 Rennison, R.W. (1981, second edition 1996), p.249, *Civil Engineering Heritage: Northern England*, Thomas Telford Publishing Ltd: London. The entry talks about it becoming quite a tourist attraction. This section of the L&MR also involved Vignoles.

12 Jones, Stephen K. (2005), pp.161 & 163.

13 MacDermot, E.T., revised by Clinker, C.R. (1964), p.67.

14 MacDermot, E.T., revised by Clinker, C.R. (1964), p.67-8.

15 Higgs, Edward (1989, third impression, 1991), p.8, *Making Sense of the Census, The Manuscript Returns for England and Wales, 1801-1901*, Public Record Office Handbooks No.23, HMSO: London.

16 Channon, Geoffrey (1985), pp.4-5, *Bristol and the Promotion of the Great Western Railway*, Bristol Branch of the Historical Association, Bristol University: Bristol. Jones, Stephen K. (2005), p.83.

17 Platt, Alan (1987), pp.31-32, *The Life and Times of Daniel Gooch*, Alan Sutton: Gloucester.

18 Martin, Sir Theodore (originally published 1892, Nonsuch edition 2006), pp.43-44, *Diaries of Sir Daniel Gooch*, Nonsuch Publishing Ltd: Stroud.

19 Martin, Sir Theodore (originally published 1892, Nonsuch edition 2006), p.44.

20 For this public insurrection, Richard Lewis (alias Dic Penderyn) was made an example of and was executed at Cardiff goal.

21 Platt, Alan (1987), p.13.

22 Strange, Keith (2005), p.83, *Merthyr Tydfil Iron Metropolis*, Tempus Publishing: Stroud. Merthyr was responsible for 14,710 signatures in the National Petition presented to Parliament in 1839, Merthyr's contribution to the Second Petition in 1842 was the fifth largest in the country.

23 Strange, Keith (2005), p.81. A Merthyr man was one of the Chartists shot dead outside the Westgate Hotel and two Dowlais men were imprisoned for their part in the insurrection.

24 Guest, Revel and John, Angela V. (1989), p.128, *Lady Charlotte: A Biography of the Nineteenth Century*, Weidenfeld and Nicolson: London.

25 Bessborough, The Earl of, ed. (1950), p.91, *Lady Charlotte Guest Extracts from her Journal 1833-1852*, John Murray: London. Diary extract 19 May 1839.

26 In 1856, following his transportation to Tasmania, John Frost was pardoned and greeted as a hero on his return to Newport.

27 Williams, David (1955), p.76, *The Rebecca Riots*, University of Wales Press: Cardiff. This occurred at the beginning of the lime-burning season, the gate having been erected to catch lime-carters evading the tolls.

28 1841 Census return. Llandaff schedule 136, entry 4. See Jones, Stephen K. (2005), p.117. A place of abode convenient for the TVR's Maindy works.

29 *The Glamorgan, Monmouth and Brecon Gazette* and *Merthyr Guardian*, 24 April 1841 commenting on Sir Frederic Smith's praise. George Bush died on 13 November 1841; he was thirty-one years of age and the cause of death was given as 'ulceration of the bowels'. See Jones, Stephen K. (2005), p.131.

30 Buchanan, Brenda, ed. (2005), *Bath History*, vol.X, Millstream Books: Bath. See article on; *Brunel in Bath* by R. Angus Buchanan, p.160.

31 Alfred Tennyson's poem 'Locksley Hall', see Jones, Stephen K. (2005), p.28 & 62 (Chapter 1 note No.4 and Chapter 4) and Warburg, Jeremy (1958), *The Industrial Muse*, p.23. Oxford University Press: London. Tennyson thought that the trains ran on tramplates not edgerails, 'When I went by the first train from Liverpool to Manchester (1830), I thought that the wheels ran in a groove. It was a black night and there was such a vast crowd around the train at the station that we could not see the wheels. Then I made this line.'

32 Higgs, Edward (1989, third impression, 1991), p.46. The railway passengers were waiting on a train at the station and enumerated as part of the entry for railway employees there.

33 Williams, Archibald (1925, reprinted 1972), p.10, *Brunel and After: The Romance of the Great Western Railway*, Patrick Stephens Ltd: London. Williams suggests that the Directors had the matter of a coal supply for the GWR in mind.

34 Jones, Stephen K. (2005), pp.127-8. Railways built on the 4ft 8½in gauge would be known as the narrow gauge until the ruling of the Gauge Commission in 1845 made it the standard gauge of Great Britain.

35 Jones, Stephen K. (2005), p.132. Such contracts were not unusual for newly constructed railways to enter into in those days and may have been thought a prudent move by the TVR following the death of Bush.

36 This was less than six months after the opening of the line, see Jones, Stephen K. (2005), p.201.

37 Jones, Stephen K. (2005), p.202. Coffin had told Howells and Evans, the contractors for the Goitre Coed Viaduct, that the company had no money and could not pay. 'Bush versus T.V.R.C.' would not be resolved until January 1848, see Jones, Stephen K. (2005), p.132.

38 Guest, Revel & John, Angela V. (1989). p.60, *Lady Charlotte: A Biography of the Nineteenth Century*, Weidenfeld and Nicolson: London.

39 Chappell, E.L. (1939), p.85, *History of the Port of Cardiff*, The Priory Press: Cardiff. Chappell cites John Nixon as the source of this story.

40 *Cardiff and Merthyr Guardian*, 23 August 1845, reproduced as a printed handbill in Bute V, 18, Cardiff Central Reference Library. Coffin was to become chairman following the resignation of Guest in 1847.

41 Jones, Gwyn Briwnant & Dunstone, Denis (1996), pp.22-23, *The Vale of Neath Line: from Neath to Pontypool Road*, Gomer: Llandysul.

42 Glamorgan Record Office (GRO), Q/D/P/94 & Q/D/P/101, Welsh Midland Railway deposited plans.

43 Jones, Stephen K. (2005), p.195.

44 *The Great Western Railway Magazine*, 1908, p.261, 'Some Reminiscences of Brunel' by R. Price Williams. Price Williams, an engineer who was related to Walter Coffin, also records that Brunel referred to Meyrick as the 'incorruptible guard, Meyrick.'

45 *The Great Western Railway Magazine*, 1908, p.261. Comments related to coke compression were made by Price Williams, coke was then still being used in locomotives.

46 *The Great Western Railway Magazine*, 1908, p.261. Price Williams reinforces this story by mentioning that rails were not fastened by fish-plates in those days.

47 Vignoles, Olinthus J. (1889), *Life of Charles Blacker Vignoles*, Longmans, Green & Co.: London. Diary extracts for 5–6 June 1843. Wurttemberg today forms part of the German region of

Baden-Wurttemberg with Stuttgart as its capital, the romantic valley of the river Neckar with its forests and castles, being a major tourist attraction of the region.

48 Bessborough, Earl of, ed. (1950), p.151, *Lady Charlotte Guest Extracts from her Journal 1833–1852.* London: John Murray.

49 Condor, F.R. Simmons, Jack ed. (1983), p.183, *The Men Who Built Railways*, Thomas Telford Ltd: London (published by Hodder and Stoughton in 1868 as *Personal Recollections of English Engineers*).

50 Rolt, L.T.C. (1971), p.103, *George & Robert Stephenson*, Longmans, Green & Co.: London 31 December 1824. Reynolds, P. 'The London & South Wales Railway Scheme of 1824/25', SWWIAS. This has been covered briefly in Jones, Stephen K. (2005), p.94.

51 Another view was that having Bristol in the title would put potential investors off.

52 Swift, Andrew (2006), p.25, *The Ringing Grooves of Change: Brunel and the Coming of the Railway to Bath*, Akeman Press: Bath.

53 *The Cambrian*, 31 August 1833.

54 *The Cambrian*, 7 September 1833.

55 Jones, Stephen K. (2005), pp.95-96.

56 *The Cambrian*, 5 April 1834.

57 Jones, Stephen K. (2005), p.94.

58 Jones, W. H. (1922), p.264. *History of the Port of Swansea*, W. Spurrell & Son: Carmarthen.

59 Glamorgan Record Office (GRO), Q/D/P/70.

60 Swift, Andrew (2006), p.12.

61 MacDermot, E.T., revised by Clinker, C.R. (1964), p.7, *History of the Great Western Railway*, vol.1., Ian Allan: London.

62 Vignoles, K.H. (1982), p.67, *Charles Blacker Vignoles: Romantic Engineer*, Cambridge University Press: Cambridge. Apart from the Vignoles' references, there appear to be no contemporary references to this railway scheme.

63 Philips, Daphne (1975), pp.5-6, *How the Great Western came to Berkshire: A Railway History 1833-1882*, Berkshire County Library: Reading. The Windsor branch was later dropped due to opposition from Eton College (MacDermot, E.T., revised by Clinker, C.R. (1964), p.6).

64 In 1836 the Cheltenham & Great Western Railway bought off the canal's opposition to their Bill with a payment of £7,500. See Gibbs, George Henry, Simmons, Jack ed. (1971). pp.19-20, *The Birth of the Great Western Railway, Extracts from the diary and correspondence of George Henry Gibbs*, Adams &Dart: Bath.

65 This also applied to later Thames & Severn Railway schemes of 1865/66 and 1881/82.

66 MacDermot, E.T., revised by Clinker, C.R. (1964), p.8.

67 MacDermot, E.T., revised by Clinker, C.R. (1964), p.6.

68 Awdry, Christopher (1992), pp.12-13, *Brunel's Broad Gauge Railway*, Oxford Publishing Co: Sparkford.

69 This meeting was held on 26 March 1836, although a preliminary meeting or agreement for this appears to have been made on 21 March. For the former see Chappell, E.L. (1939), pp.97-8.

70 Gibbs, George Henry, Simmons, Jack ed. (1971), p.20, *The Birth of the Great Western Railway, Extracts from the diary and correspondence of George Henry Gibbs*, Adams & Dart: Bath.

71 *The Cambrian*, 30 April 1836.

72 Petition for the South Wales Railway Bill, p.18, Misc. MSS 1674, Gwent Record Office, Cwmbran.

73 University of Bristol, Special Collections, IKB Letter Book, p.133, to J. Kemp, 29 July 1836. See Chapter 3 for his report in full.

74 Dowlias Iron Co. Letters 1836, 2, E-G, No.181. Glamorgan Record Office (GRO). Letter sent out 5 September 1836.

75 Dowlias Iron Co. Letters 1836, 2, E-G, No.182. Glamorgan Record Office (GRO).

76 Dowlias Iron Co. Letters 1836, 2, E-G, No.180. Glamorgan Record Office (GRO).

77 *The Cambrian*, 21 November 1840. I am grateful to Colin Chapman for pointing out what is probably the last action in relation to the Gloucester & South Wales Railway, the case of Brunel *v* Goodrich et al for recovery of unpaid fees at Bristol Assizes on 25 August 1843.

78 Such challenges would also apply to the narrow gauge camp in terms of their major natural obstacles, i.e. crossing the Conwy estuary and the Menai Straits.

2

CELTIC CROSSOVER

'PEDWAR LLEW TEW'[1]

Vignoles had already undertaken surveys, and was acting as consulting engineer to a number of proposed railways in Ireland including the Dublin & Drogheda, the Cork & Passage and the Cork & Limerick. In May 1836 he was appointed chief engineer of the Great Central Irish Railway; such a high profile of private work, however, does not appear to have been in conflict with his role on the Irish Railway Commission. In looking at the best trunk route from London, Vignoles, in conjunction with John Urpeth Rastrick, surveyed a route from Shrewsbury to Porthdinllaen, projecting a route that went across mid-Wales by way of Llangollen, Bala and Dolgelly, then along the coast through Barmouth and Porthmadoc, terminating on the north coast of the Lleyn peninsula.[2] By the necessity of the route, going as it did through Snowdonia, heavy gradients were inevitable but it offered a more direct route than the nearest railway port open at that time (Liverpool) and it offered a much shorter sea crossing. A major harbour was planned at Porthdinllaen, but this was not the first time that Porthdinllaen had been selected as the ideal Irish traffic port. In 1806 the industrialist and radical politician William Alexander Madocks (1773–1828), obtained an Act of Parliament for the construction of '… a Pier and other Works for the improvement of the Harbour of Porthdinllaen…'[3] Despite his efforts he failed to get Porthdinllaen accepted as the Dublin packet station by the London coach traffic in preference to Holyhead, but he established the port of Portmadoc (to be named after him) as an outlet for slate traffic and planned the railway that served it.[4] Following the death of Madocks, delays meant that the railway would not be completed until 1836, the year the TVR was incorporated. The railway was the Festiniog, the first to be built to the narrow gauge (1ft 11½in). Its new promoter was the Dublin-born Henry Archer (1799–1863), who would also pick up and champion the cause of Porthdinllaen.[5] Porthdinllaen may have been overlooked by coaching interests, but it now had a second chance to compete with Holyhead – as a port served by railways, the latest mode of communications. In 1836 Archer published a pamphlet entitled 'A New Line of Communication between Dublin and London via Portdynllaen, Worcester and Oxford… by means of Steam Packet and Railway'.[6]

He was putting his ideas forward for a railway from London to Porthdinllaen where a steam packet station would serve Ireland, ideas he had first voiced at a public meeting in Dublin in August 1835.[7] Elis-Williams, the author of *Packet to Ireland*, wrote that Archer had been assisted by a 'local engineer' in his proposals and speculated that this could be James Spooner, the engineer then engaged on the Festiniog Railway, or William George Owen (1810–85) who in January 1836 was appointed to Brunel's staff (see Chapter 5).

The contest was not just confined to Holyhead and Porthdinllaen; there were alternative proposals such as the St George's Harbour & Railway which put forward the undeveloped Orme's Bay (Llandudno) as the site for a packet port. The Bill failed to receive sufficient backing in 1837, the promoters hoping to receive support from the Grand Junction Railway to run the proposed line from a junction with their railway through Chester to Orme's Bay. As the first trunk railway in Britain, the Grand Junction Railway was to open for passenger traffic between Birmingham and Warrington on 4 July 1837. However, it had different ideas about who to support and instead backed the Chester & Crewe and Chester & Birkenhead Railways. The St George's Harbour & Railway Bill was to fail in Parliament, but it reinvented itself as the St George's Harbour & Chester Railway, the promoters then aware that Chester was the best option for an Irish route. Both the Chester & Crewe and the Chester & Birkenhead Railways had been incorporated in 1837 and both opened in 1840, with the former being absorbed into the Grand Junction Railway three months before opening on 1 October 1840. Thus, in 1840, Chester represented the nearest railhead to Wales, a situation that would last until the mid-1940s when railways reached Shrewsbury and Gloucester. A Chester to Holyhead link was, therefore, one solution, although many saw it involving a bridge or even two bridges too far because of the necessity of having to cross the Conwy estuary and the Menai Straits. Although George Stephenson had considered such a route and, indeed, Chester to Porthdinllaen as possible routes emanating from Chester, he came down on the side of Holyhead as the preferred railhead. The problem of bridging the Menai, however, remained. In late 1838 Francis Giles (1787–1847) put forward a plan at a public meeting at Bangor, proposing to cross the Conwy by a new bridge but using Telford's suspension bridge to cross the Menai Straits. Carriages would be uncoupled from locomotives at each end of the bridge and dragged across by rope, recoupled to a locomotive on the other side to resume their journey. Stephenson was, however, aware of the problems of using a suspension bridge for railway traffic because of his experience with the suspension bridge built by Capt. Sir Samuel Brown RN (1774–1851) for the Stockton & Darlington Railway. This had been built for the S&DR's Middlesborough branch. It opened in 1830 and suffered from the concentration of weight and the excessive vibration of locomotives. Even when full wagons were uncoupled and pulled across they could not handle more than four wagons at a time with a chain spacing them 27ft apart.[8] No doubt the supporters of Porthdinllaen felt that this greatly strengthened their case and a variety of schemes favouring Porthdinllaen or Holyhead that followed in this first period from 1835 to the beginning of the 1840s can be broken down into three groups:[9]

1. Proposals dating from the mid-1830s based on Archer's proposals '... Dublin and London via Portdynllaen, Worcester and Oxford...' to be taken up by Vignoles and then Brunel as the Worcester & Porthdinlleyn Railway.

2. Stephenson's proposed line to Holyhead known as the Chester & Holyhead Railway but also promoted by other interested parties from March 1839 as the Great Holyhead Railway.

3. The line rejected by Stephenson, from Bangor to Porthdinllaen, to be taken up by Archer as the North Wales Railway (a line that succeeded in receiving the Royal Assent in 1845, but was never built).[10]

With regard to the first, which supported the aspirations of Archer and Vignoles, Brunel was looking at a more direct London to Ireland route running from a junction with the GWR through Oxfordshire, Worcester and mid-Wales to arrive at Porthdinllaen. The course through mid-Wales proposed by Brunel in 1839 was different, however, to that put forward by Vignoles, in that it ran through Worcester, Ludlow, Craven Arms, Montgomery (crossing the Severn on a 170ft-high viaduct at Newtown) and on through Talerddig to Dinas Mawddwy and under Cader Idris to reach the coast.[11] Whilst only one of the three would ultimately succeed, it was not until 1846 that the 'contest' was effectively resolved although the winning route still had to be validated by technical achievement, i.e. the crossing of the Menai Straits.

The engineer Vignoles championed the potential of Porthdinllaen as an alternative to Holyhead, and despite the broad range of his engineering talents and achievements, he is overshadowed by his Victorian contemporaries today.[12] In view of these Welsh connections and his links with both of the Brunels, a brief résumé of his engineering career, lasting over sixty years and culminating in his election as president of the Institution of Civil Engineers in 1869, is attempted. Although his background was of French Huguenot extraction, he could claim a Celtic connection, having been born in Ireland on 31 May 1793, at Woodbrook, near Enniscorthy in County Wexford.[13] The family had a long tradition of military service, his father being sent to the Caribbean during the French Revolutionary Wars and accompanied by both mother and child. Sadly he was orphaned when just over a year old and had to be rescued from this situation and brought to London by his uncle. Here Vignoles was to receive an education from his grandfather, the famous Dr Charles Hutton (1737–1823), Professor of mathematics at the Woolwich Academy. Reaching manhood, Vignoles had intended to train as a lawyer in Doctors Commons, but financial constraints, following a rift with his grandfather, led to him enter military service. With the Royal Scots Guards he took part in the disastrous night attack against the French at Bergen op Zoom in the Netherlands on 8 March 1814. Taken prisoner, he and other prisoners were allowed under the surrender terms to return home but were soon ordered to embark for Canada to take part in the war with the United States. His return to Britain at the end of the war was followed by half-pay and the lack of financial prospects. He had, however, attempted to become a staff engineer while on military service, drawing on what he had learned from Dr Hutton and now decided to pursue engineering as his career and, despite getting married in July 1817, he returned alone to North America to work in this profession. In this respect there are similarities to those steps taken by Marc Isambard Brunel some years earlier in the pursuit of his engineering career.[14] Vignoles obtained his first appointment with the State of South Carolina as assistant state surveyor, commanding an annual salary of $1,000. In December 1817, he sent for his wife Mary and their expected child to join him from England. He was then occupied on a survey of the Charleston District, work that was followed by other surveys and the mapping of the Florida peninsular, but the irregularities of his earnings and the death of his grandfather persuaded Vignoles to return home in 1823.

There were now more engineering opportunities in Britain, particularly for those with practical experience and surveying skills, and he was to find a position with James Walker (1781–1862) in 1824. Walker was well versed across a wide range of civil engineering matters and had played a significant role in the development of railways. In 1829 Walker and a fellow engineer, John Urpeth Rastrick (1780–1856), were commissioned by the Liverpool & Manchester Railway Co. to report upon the 'Comparative Merits of Locomotive and Fixed Engines as a Moving Power' and had visited all the principal railways in the north of England.[15] Walker and Rastrick gave their findings to the L&MR in two separate reports, but their conclusions were similar, in essence favouring fixed engines based on the economics of running costs. Walker praised Stephenson's Royal George locomotive as '… undoubtedly the most powerful that has yet been made…'[16] but this was not enough for George Stephenson who felt inclined to write his 'observations' to the L&MR board. No doubt this prompted the board to adopt an idea in Walker's report about offering a prize '…for a Locomotive Engine which shall be a decided improvement on those now in use…' – the result was the Rainhill Trials of 1829.[17]

The work undertaken by Vignoles' was related to Walker's role as chief engineer to the London Commercial Docks, one aspect of which was improving access between St Katherine's Dock and the proposed South London Docks in Bermondsey.[18] A suspension bridge was the solution put forward, designed by Capt. Brown. Walker entrusted Vignoles to complete the final drawings of the bridge and he assisted in a presentation led by Brown, to the Duke of Wellington, for his approval on 23 February 1824. Possibly through the recommendation of Walker, or more likely Brown, as a pioneer of suspension bridge design, Vignoles undertook drawing work for William Tierney Clarke (1783–1852), then engaged on the Hammersmith suspension bridge, the suspension chains for which were supplied by Brown. This was followed by temporary engineering partnerships with other engineers or work on projects connected with canals, docks or bridges under Walker's direction. In 1825 he was asked by John, later Sir John, Rennie (1794–1874), working with his brother George Rennie (1791–1866), to work on surveys for a railway from London to Brighton. Before he could complete these, however, the Rennie brothers sent him to Liverpool to re-examine the route of the Liverpool & Manchester Railway. George Stephenson's Liverpool & Manchester

Railway Bill had failed in Parliament, the Rennies being brought in by the promoters to pilot the Bill through the next session. Vignoles was to play an important role in resurveying the route and making changes, particularly with regard to the approach of the line towards Liverpool. He also assisted the passage of the Bill which gained its Act of Parliament by forty-five votes on 5 May 1826. After some negotiation the directors of the L&MR turned down the terms put forward by the Rennies for their continued association and they withdrew. George Stephenson was now re-engaged and Vignoles, who had been responsible for the main 'improvements' between Stephenson's route and the line now being built, was well aware that his presence was resented. Retained as chief assistant, Vignoles was in charge of the eastern end of the line but during the construction of the Edge Hill tunnel he was blamed for the misalignment of the tunnel, which was corrected.[19] It blew up into a major row and Vignoles resigned on 2 February 1827.[20]

This did not mark the end of Vignoles' involvement with the L&MR as he supported the *Novelty* locomotive, entered in the Rainhill trials by John Braithwaite and John Ericsson.[21] Vignoles also took part in, and reported on, the actual trials, becoming a regular commentator to the *Mechanics Magazine* on the L&MR. John Braithwaite was associated with the Cyfarthfa Ironworks of Merthyr Tydfil and went on to engineer a 5ft gauge railway, the Eastern Counties Railway, in which Vignoles had an involvement.[22] This work was in the future, however, and Vignoles needed to find full-time employment. In November 1827 Brunel met with Vignoles and Stephenson at Liverpool;[23] the twenty-one-year old Brunel was taking some time off from his role as resident engineer on the Thames Tunnel following an injury on 23 October and was in Liverpool acting on his father's behalf in connection with an engineering commission for Liverpool Docks. Marc Brunel had designed a floating landing stage which would enable foot passengers to embark and disembark from vessels in the Mersey at low water. At Liverpool Brunel was shown over the railway works by the two engineers and Brunel returned to report back to his father. According to K.H. Vignoles (in his 1982 biography of Vignoles) an offer was made to Vignoles by Marc in connection with the Thames Tunnel which was subsequently withdrawn.[24] Another offer, assisting Marc in work being carried out on the Oxford Canal, was accepted and when he came down to London to discuss it in further detail with Marc he was given a conducted tour of the Thames Tunnel by Brunel.

Vignoles was to establish an office in Liverpool for the L&MR surveys, a facility he would maintain for a number of years. No doubt it was useful in picking up work opportunities in north Wales as in March 1828 when he submitted a proposal for the construction of a tramroad from the port of Amlwch to the Mona Mines on Parys Mountain in Anglesey. Parys Mountain had been mined for copper ore since the Bronze Age but operations up to 1768 had been small-scale and piecemeal in production. With the discovery of a rich deposit of copper ore at Parys, a series of shallow mines became a vast opencast quarry by the end of the eighteenth century and the two opencast mines of Parys and Mona the largest producers of copper in the world. Over 3,000 tons (3,048 tonnes) were extracted annually between 1773 and 1785, worked by 1,500 using 15,000 tons of gunpowder each year to extract the ore. Such a scale of production caused the hamlet and port of Amlwch to expand rapidly, shipping copper ore to Liverpool, Swansea and Holywell, its harbour undergoing improvement and enlargement in 1793. By the early part of the nineteenth century the best lodes were being worked out and the price of copper was falling. In an attempt to reverse the fortunes of the industry, outside expertise was brought in. The neighbouring Mona Mine had been established in 1785 and was still operated as a mine but in 1811 the Vivians of Swansea took over the lease and brought in the Cornish mine manager James Treweek (d.1851), to oversee its operation.[25] Treweek had worked for Vivian since 1804 at Swansea, and like Richard Trevithick before him, was spreading Cornish expertise in engineering and mining management around the country. Moving away from the shallow mine workings then in use, Treweek brought in men who were experienced in Cornish deep-shaft techniques, sinking new shafts such as 'Tiddys', 'Beers' and 'Treeweek's'.[26] By 1819 9,000 tons of ore were being mined compared to 1,000 tons in 1809.[27] The Cornish miners also knew how to deal with the problem of water in the mines, constructing the Pearl pumping engine house to house an 18in Cornish Beam Engine to help keep the mine dry. This engine was installed and commissioned over the period 27–30 March 1819 and was seen in operation that year by Michael Faraday.[28]

Transport was controlled by a carting monopoly and led to ever-increasing costs which forced the Plas Newydd agent, John Sanderson, to look at the possibility of building a railway from the mountain to the smelting works at the port. He first did this in November 1825 and obtained estimates, for which James Treweek reckoned that such a railway would cost in the region of £3,000 and take around three years to pay for itself.[29] It was not until February 1828 that real progress was made with the arrival of Vignoles to survey the route from the Mona mine to the smelting works. A month later Vignoles reported to Sanderson and recommended:

> … the formation of an edge railroad on the most approved modern principle laid down on Self Acting Incline Planes and intermediate level, transport of copper, ore, coal thereon in proper wagons. This would reduce costs of transport… such that railway would pay for itself in three years.

A direct line from the mountain to the port was proposed with a branch line to the Parys and Mona kilns and to the yards of the smelting houses. The railway would continue along the quay and enable two vessels to be loaded or unloaded at a time. Vignoles put the cost of building his 'modern edge railroad' from mountain to port at £6,350. At the time the mines were fairly quiet and Treweek tried to persuade the owners to build the railway while labour was cheap and plentiful. Progress, however, was slow and with no sign of a decision being made, Vignoles gave up on this opportunity in August 1830.

In the meantime, Vignoles became chief engineer to the Oxford Canal in May 1828, which Marc Brunel was happy to agree to because of his heavy commitment on the tunnel, although this was to come, rather abruptly, to an end.[30] On 12 January 1828 a second major inundation of the Thames into the tunnel occurred. It was to take until the beginning of April to plug and pump dry the tunnel, a process that exhausted the funds of the company. All tunnelling work now ceased and debris was cleared from the tunnel to enable visitors to view it and pay for the privilege.[31] Since work had begun on the tunnel it had attracted a great deal of interest, particularly in the engineering press, but now the floodgates, in terms of suggestions and discussion by engineers, and others not so well informed, were well and truly opened. The pages of the *Mechanics Magazine* were full of such solutions as how to remedy the problem and a number of engineers volunteered their services. One of these was Vignoles, who in March 1829, or possibly earlier, claimed he could complete the tunnel at a cost of £250 a yard using a system which he at first refused to disclose.[32] Although the board of directors was to vote in favour of retaining the services of Marc Brunel and to persevere in obtaining a loan from the Government to meet his estimates to complete the tunnel, Vignoles's involvement continued as an active proposal until June 1830. The shareholders, supported by the chairman and some of the directors, sought to pursue any scheme that had a chance of completing the tunnel and a panel consisting of William Tierney Clarke, James Walker and Professor Peter Barlow were tasked with assessing Vignoles's proposal. After two months of deliberation the panel decided, on 22 June 1830, that his proposals would be a waste of time and money. Such a move on Vignoles's part had reflected no credit whatsoever on him and one would have thought he would become *persona non grata* to the Brunels, but the younger Brunel does not appear to have held a grudge.

Under such circumstances Vignoles was no doubt relived to return to railway work through his appointment to survey the St Helens & Runcorn Gap Railway and the Wigan Branch Railway, both of which connected with the L&MR. Incorporated by Parliament in 1830, such schemes were instrumental in pushing forward railway development, in which Vignoles played a prominent role.[33] Vignoles also found time in August 1829 to go to Wexford, returning to his birthplace where he advised on improvements to the Enniscorthy Canal. Here he cultivated and built up his contacts for further work and in 1832 was appointed as engineer to the Dublin & Kingstown Railway (D&KR) following the death of Alexander Nimmo (1783–1832). George Bush, the resident engineer of the Taff Vale Railway, had also worked under Nimmo, and Charles Bourns, one of Brunel's assistant engineers on the TVR, had also worked on the D&KR.[34] The railway designed by Vignoles was notable for the artistic pretensions in the design of its works. The contractor was William Dargan and the resident engineer Thomas Jackson Woodhouse (1793–1855), who would work under Vignoles on the Midland Counties Railway. The line opened on 17 December 1834 and continues in use today as part of the Dublin Area Rapid Transit (DART) system. Vignoles commented about his appointment as engineer that he was, in the light of George Stephenson's involvement in the D&KR following the death of Nimmo, '… thus superseding my old friend Stephenson…'[35] With the successful opening of the D&KR on 7 December 1834 his skills as an engineer became in demand for a number of schemes in Ireland. During this time work was well advanced on the Midland Counties Railway (MCR), a line linking Derby to Rugby via Leicester. Regularly employed in Parliamentary Committees as a witness for his own schemes and those of others, Vignoles appeared six times before the Select Committee for the MCR Bill in 1836. He was particularly busy during the railway mania years of the 1840s but fell short of Brunel's record of appearing 220 times for the GWR and other companies that he was engineer to.[36] It was on the MCR that Vignoles made determined efforts to get his flat-bottomed rail adopted, however, despite his efforts, which saw the rail being taken up on the continent, British railway companies preferred to use bull-headed rail, a situation that lasted until after the Second World War.

Vignoles also looked wider than Great Britain in promoting railways, visiting France in 1833 to attempt to interest the French government in a line from Paris to Dieppe that would link with a London to Brighton line, thus returning to one of his earlier surveying contracts. This was the first of many such visits involving much of his time and expense and usually without reward. In 1834 he was in Germany promoting a line from Hamburg to Brunswick. While surveying the Irish schemes a select committee of Parliament recommended the establishment of a Royal Commission in October 1836 to enquire into the best system of Railway Communications through Ireland, through a:

> … survey of the harbours on the line of coast best calculated for a direct communication between London and Dublin, with a view of ascertaining whether the existing ports of Holyhead and Liverpool, or any other ports on that part of the coast of Great Britain, would, in the judgement of experienced naval surveyors, furnish the greatest facilities for steam communication by packet across the Channel.[37]

Vignoles was appointed by the Commissioners to survey possible lines to the south and south-west. One of the first reports, by the Admiralty hydrographer, Admiral Sir Francis Beaufort (1774–1857), confirmed that as far as road traffic was concerned, the present point of embarkation (Holyhead) was the best; however, in terms of railway traffic, another port might be better suited. This was because of the problems crossing the Menai Straits and that it would be unlikely that… a steam carriage with a loaded train would be allowed to traverse the present chain bridge at Bangor…'[38] Despite this pronouncement the Menai bridge would continue to put forward for a railway crossing although Beaufort also went on to say that a new bridge suited to railway traffic would be enormously expensive and that there would be considerable objections if it obstructed the navigation of the Menai Straits. The Commission's final report, published in July 1838, made a strong case for state involvement in developing railways in Ireland. One of the proposals suggested by Vignoles included an overhead railway through Dublin, linking lines from Kingstown and the south to a proposed route to the west. In the same year that Brunel made his views known regarding the best south Wales route, a Royal Commission was established in October 1836 the Under-Secretary of State for Ireland, Captain Thomas Drummond, R.E., as chairman. The other two Commissioners were Professor Peter Barlow (1776–1862) and the Irish engineer Richard Griffith, who was also to act as a Commissioner for the Improvement of Navigation on the Shannon River. It was charged with the consideration of a national system of Irish railways and Vignoles was appointed to look at the south and south-west of Ireland along with John

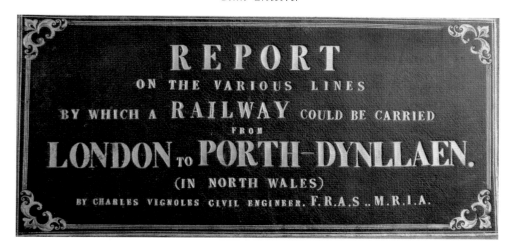

Coverplate of Vignoles' Report. (Courtesy of the Archives of the University of Wales, Bangor)

Macneill, who would undertake the north and north-west portion of the country.[39] The Commission also looked at the wider issues in terms of access to Ireland from other ports, and the connections thereof to London. Improving the North American traffic by steam packet boats was another consideration. For the latter, Vignoles envisaged that Ireland would play an important role as a through route from London to New York and as part of his work beginning in November of that year, he reported on the proposed packet station at Berehaven on Bantry Bay. This aspect of his work was to be circumvented, however, by Brunel with the launch of the PS *Great Western* in Bristol on 19 July 1837. In the following year, on her maiden voyage, the PS *Great Western* proved that it was possible for a steamship to cross the Atlantic without recourse to fuelling stops along the way.

By 1839 Vignoles was resigned to the fact that the Irish Railway Commission's proposals would not be enacted, and his aspirations of being appointed engineer for a large portion of the network there were to be dashed. He would continue his association with the D&KR and was appointed engineer for the Dalkey extension. He had become a keen supporter of the atmospheric system developed by Clegg and the Samuda brothers, who patented the first practical application for applying the system of atmospheric propulsion to railways in 1839.[40]

Vignoles persuaded the D&KR to adopt this system on the single-track line of the Dalkey extension. On this short section it was to prove to be more reliable than on other railways and it was to remain in use for ten years. This line was built by Dargan who was also the contractor on Vignoles' last Irish line, the Waterford & Limerick Railway.[41] Other railway work in the second half of the 1830s included the Sheffield & Manchester Railway, which Vignoles began work on in 1835. The longest railway tunnel built up to that date was to be built on this important trans-Pennine route at Woodhead and would have been Vignoles' greatest work to date but, unfortunately, the timing coincided with a financial crisis and Vignoles overreached himself in his share subscription to the company. This resulted in him being forced out at the end of 1839 and replaced by Joseph Locke (1805–60). Vignoles confided to his diary on 29 May 1841 his fears for his own future and his regrets for the situation he had placed his friends and associates in: '… such a mass of misery and distress [is] thrown on my friends that I think I shall go mad.'[42] Shortly afterwards he entered the teaching profession becoming Professor of Civil Engineering at University College, London, in June 1841. As such, it followed on from the first chair in engineering made to John Millington in 1827.[43] Other academic institutions also responded to demands for civil engineering instruction; Trinity College, Dublin, made a similar appointment in 1842 appointing John, later Sir John, Macneill (1793–1880) who had worked under Nimmo. He had also worked under Telford on the London to Shrewsbury section of the London to Holyhead road and in 1838 surveyed the northern part of Ireland for the Railway Commissioners.[44] In 1846 Trinity appointed the ex-TVR assistant engineer, Samuel Downing (1811–82) as Assistant Professor to Macneill. Downing was to succeed Macneill and become Professor of Practical Engineering in 1852, a post he occupied for the next thirty years.[45] Vignoles' academic career was much shorter as his contract failed to be renewed in 1843 due to a lack of pupils. His teaching style was very much a practical one, involving field visits to engineering sites and organising demonstrations using models and drawings as far as possible. When questioned on what he thought were suitable subjects for the syllabus, Vignoles wrote that he thought they should be '… strictly confined to pure Civil Engineering or the Art of Construction as distinguished from Decorative Architecture or more operative Mechanisms – of course avoiding all mathematics.'[46]

A question that Vignoles had become involved with a few years earlier, the best crossing point for London to Dublin communications, remained unanswered. There were other interested parties, however, who were convinced of the best route, favouring a route along the north Wales coast from Chester to the port of Holyhead. Prominent amongst these interests were the Chester & Crewe Railway who brought in George Stephenson to report on the Holyhead route as well as the alternative of Porthdinllaen. Stephenson's report, which came out in 1839, was very critical of the Porthdinllaen route on account of the gradients, earthworks and tunnelling envisaged. The only advantage he could see was that it would avoid a crossing of the Menai Straits.[47] The Irish Railway Commissioners were not so dismissive of the Porthdinllaen route even if the Admiralty could not recommend the Lleyn peninsula as a site for major port, arguing that it would be prone to silting up. Others continued to support Porthdinllaen, and it was reported in March 1840 that, 'The Worcester Chamber of Commerce have authorised Mr. Varden the engineer, to continue the sectionional surveys for the projected line of railway from Worcester to Porth Dinlleyn in North Wales…'[48]

In 1840 the Treasury appointed Commissioners to look at the relative merits of the north Wales ports and potential ports, and two years later the House of Commons set up a Select Committee to look at Post Office communications with Ireland.[49] In the same month and year, June 1842, James Walker was appointed by the Admiralty to report on the merits of Dublin and Porthdinllaen, his brief being:

a) to examine the capability and position of each place and to ascertain which is the '… most eligible to be established as the packet station and port of communication with Dublin.'

b) to ascertain which of the two there may exist '… the greatest facility for railway communication with London', and,

c) to make plans with estimates of the cost of constructing a harbour and works necessary for a packet station '… for vessels of the class now running between Liverpool and Kingstown; namely, of 900 tons, and drawing 10 feet 10 inches water, and for a refuge harbour for the Channel trade'.[50]

Walker, who had been the first to employ Vignoles when he returned from America, was sent all the papers on this subject then before the Admiralty, including plans of various projected railways and the comments of the Commissioners, Sir Frederic Smith and Professor Peter Barlow on their 1840 Report on London to Dublin Communication by the Treasury. Naturally, Walker examined the various documents and Stephenson's and Giles's lines of railway from Chester to Holyhead. He then surveyed the harbour of Holyhead and proceeded to Porthdinllaen in a naval steamer put at his disposal. There he took evidence from appropriate individuals, examined the facilities of the harbour and also looked at the proposed source of building stone if a new harbour was to be built there. He then returned to Holyhead and on 3 July 1843 was met there by Commander Tudor, RN, who had been sent down to meet him by Henry Archer, who, as we have already seen in Chapter 1, was a keen supporter of the Porthdinllaen cause.[51] Walker agreed to return to Porthdinllaen the following day with Commander Tudor to, 'have the advantage of his observations.'[52] He continued to look at the various proposals for railways proposed by coastal routes to Holyhead, surveying these and the projected line along the coast to near Caernarvon and on to Porthdinllaen. This line would be connected to London via the Chester & Bangor or coast line and was the only plan for railway communication to Porthdinllaen he had seen. He was critical of the lack of plans for railway communications through the interior of Wales that commenced '… at Porth-dyn-llaen or at Holyhead, and terminates at an existing railway to London.' Walker was to state to the parties principally interested:

> … the desirableness of having a connected plan of a line through the interior of North Wales, if this was intended to be offered as a rival to the coast line; and after considerable delay, the survey for this is now in progress, chiefly under the auspices of the Great Western Railway Company, and some of the principal proprietors in the inland counties of North Wales.[53]

His statement certainly motivated another round of alternative London to Dublin routes and before he embarked on yet another European project[54] Vignoles responded to a request for some urgent surveying work, relating once more to London to Dublin routes through north Wales. The initiative for this had come through James Pim, Jnr, a member of a prominent Dublin banking family and treasurer of the Dublin & Kingstown Railway.[55] Pim had wider interests in Ireland and Wales and sought to promote an alternative route before Stephenson's Chester to Holyhead line could be sanctioned by Parliament. Vignoles sought the support of Brunel and the GWR in undertaking this survey, to which Brunel was enthusiastic and agreed that the GWR would meet the costs. Leaving his Liverpool office at Harrington Chambers, South John Street, Vignoles set out with six assistants, headed by Wellington Purdon and John Collister, by steamer to Caernarvon. From there they were conveyed in a four-horse omnibus to Tremadoc, their base for frenetic activity through the month of August. Vignoles and his team reviewed both the coastal and inland routes and at the beginning of September he sent his report to Brunel and Pim. In addition to the Porthdinllaen line, Vignoles also prepared two alternative plans for a crossing of the Menai Straits, one for a four-arched bridge, the other for a seven-arched bridge of timber on stone piers.[56] Despite the pronouncements little action was taken and by the summer of 1843, Brunel joined forces with Vignoles in revising their respective routes to present a joint scheme. When the GWR started to back this scheme there was a reaction with the London & Birmingham and Grand Junction Railways combining to block any broad-gauge move for the Irish traffic.

Walker reported to the Admiralty on 6 October 1843, responding to his brief, already outlined, in addressing the three main points with reference to Holyhead and Porthdinllaen. It is inappropriate to repeat and analyse all the detail given here as Walker's position for Porthdinllaen as a harbour connected by railway is clear cut:

> In its present state there is nothing to recommend Porth-dyn-llaen as a station for packets. Everything would have to be done; and it cannot be denied that the elevation of the surrounding sand-hills, which is 80 to 100 feet above high water, close to the sea, would cause considerable labour and expense to make convenient buildings, approaches and communications. An example of this is given at the level at which Mr, Vignoles and Mr, Purdon, the engineers, have proposed to terminate the Porth-dyn-llaen railway near the point, being 70 to 80 feet above the level of the sea at high water. This may be lowered, but the inclination would be increased.[57]

Although the estimates of the cost of constructing a harbour and works necessary for a packet station and a refuge harbour at both sites work out in Porthdinllaen's favour by a considerable margin, i.e. £210,000 to £400,000, this is, as Walker points out, exclusive of all other buildings and accommodation, the expense of which would raise the total cost above that for all the works designed for Holyhead and then, '…Porth-dyn-llaen would be more contracted in quay room, and inferior in other conveniences, but would have a larger deep-water harbour'.[58]

In discussing Stephenson's and Giles' proposals for crossing the Menai Straits, Walker believed that, '… neither the Holyhead road, nor the Menai Bridge, should be injuriously interfered with'. In their respective routes from Chester to Holyhead he refers to that proposed by Vignoles in his 1837 report to the Irish Railway Commissioners as being nearly the same line. Walker had still not received any plans for an inland or southerly line, 'As the survey for the inland line of railway is unfinished, I have not enquired into the working of the Great Western Railway…' Despite the negative pronouncements on Porthdinllaen as a harbour, the GWR felt that with the advantage of the broad gauge, and a more direct route, although with considerable engineering works, it could therefore offer a faster route and reduce the overall travelling time from London to the packet port. Walker's final paragraph also expresses interest in an inland line to Holyhead and raises queries on the coastal route, '... which has some heavy work in parts, and which, in some places upon the coast, will be much exposed to storms'. Narrow-gauge opposition was goaded into action with the incorporation of the Chester & Holyhead Railway on 4 July 1844. There were also narrow-gauge threats to Porthdinllaen itself with schemes such as that proposed by Sir John Rennie's Great Welsh Junction Railway.[59]

Despite the South Wales Railway gaining its Act in 1845, the GWR was to make a final attempt to make Porthdinllaen part of an Irish communications chain. In that year the GWR supported Brunel's Worcester to Porthdinllaen line and succeeded in getting it through its first and second readings. Brunel was to be severely criticised by railway and engineering journals for the gradients he proposed on the line:

> It is to be lamented that Brunel has no more consideration for the credit of the profession to which he belongs, and of which, with reasonable care, he might have made a distinguished ornament. Should any of his professional rivals lay hold of this section, get it lithographed, and print in large letters over it; 'BRUNEL'S RAILWAY', it would be a standing joke against him to the end of his life.[60]

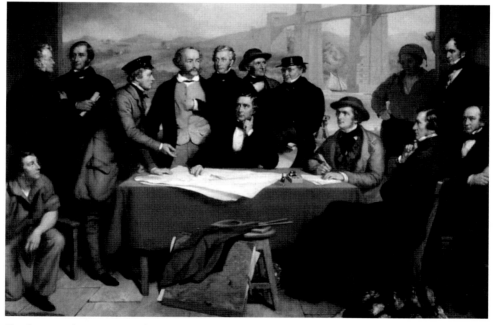

Conference of Engineers at the Menai Straits Preparatory to Floating one of the Tubes of the Britannia Bridge, *an imaginary scene by the Victorian portrait painter John Lucas (1807–1874). It shows Robert Stephenson centre stage against the backdrop of the unfinished bridge. Brunel is seated to the far right with Captain Christopher Claxton standing behind Stephenson on the right.*

Contemporary view of the Britannia Bridge. The bridge consisted of two main spans, 460ft (140m)-long wrought-iron rectangular tubes, each weighing 1,800 tonnes, supported on masonry piers. The centre pier was built on the Britannia Rock from which the bridge was to take its name. (SKJ collection)

Britannia Bridge postcard. Two additional spans of 230ft (70m) length completed the Britannia Bridge to make a 1,511ft (461m)-long continuous girder. (SKJ collection)

Section of the original tube from the Britannia Bridge. Note the use of bridge rail on longditudinal sleepers inside the tube. (SKJ photograph)

One of the four magnificent limestone lions that guarded the entrances to the Britannia Bridge tubes, carved by John Thomas. (SKJ photograph)

Luckily, as far as critics like this were concerned, Brunel's reputation would not be put to the test and the Bill was effectively killed with the publication of the Gauge Commissioners' report in 1846 restricting the spread of the broad gauge.[61] The GWR lost interest and the last chance of Porthdinllaen becoming an Irish railway port was withdrawn. The GWR and Brunel now concentrated their efforts, as far as Irish communications were concerned, in completing the South Wales Railway. The paths of Vignoles and Brunel would cross again but the scale of co-operation between the two engineers, as witnessed by the drive for Porthdinllaen, would not be repeated.[62] Holyhead may have won but the story of the construction of the Britannia Bridge cannot be given justice here, suffice to say Brunel supported his friend Robert Stephenson by attending the floating out of the tubes at Menai and had offered the services of Christopher Claxton in this process. When the mammoth task was completed some adornment was put in place, notably the four magnificent limestone lions that guard the entrances to the bridge. The sculptor responsible, John Thomas (1813–62), was no stranger to railway work, carrying out work for Philip Hardwick at Euston and on the pediment of the Great Western Hotel fronting Paddington Station.[63] His Britannia Bridge lions are almost 4m high and sit on plinths of equal height.[64] The bridge opened on 5 March 1850; but sadly the bridge today is no longer

Stephenson's tubular bridge due to the catastrophic fire in 1970 which distorted the great iron tubes. Major rebuilding took place and the bridge reopened for rail traffic in 1972 with a road deck added in 1980. The lions are out of the public gaze as they are still in their original position below the new road. It is because of Thomas's work that local people used to refer to the Britannia Bridge with less reverence as '*pedwar llew tew*' or the 'four fat lions'! This was a name invented or adapted by the Cockle Bard, John Evans (d.1888) of Menai Bridge, whose greatest stanza was:

Pedwar llew tew	Four fat lions,
Heb ddim blew,	Quite devoid of fur,
Dau'r ochor yma	Two on this side here,
A dau'r ochor drew.	And two on that side thur.

NOTES

1   Welsh for 'four fat lions', the local name for the Britannia railway bridge. Heulwen & Hedydd Isambard Owen (1963), p.10., *Sir Isambard Owen, a Biography*, privately published: Caernarvon.

2   Vignoles, K.H. (1982), p.63.

3   Jones, T.I. Jeffreys ed. (1966), p.181, *Acts of Parliament Concerning Wales 1714-1901*, University of Wales Press: Cardiff. 46 Geo. III (1806) 34 (L. & P.) entry 1363.

4   Dictionary of Welsh Biography Down to 1940 (1959), Honourable Society of Cymmrodorian: London.

5   In railway circles, Henry Archer is known mostly for the Ffestiniog Railway, but to philatelists he is known as the inventor of the perforating machine that made the perforations that separate postage stamps on a sheet selling the patent to the Postmaster General for £4,000 in 1848. http://www.greatorme.org.uk/Snowdonia.htm

6   Elis-Williams, Myrvin (1984), pp.61-2, *Packet to Ireland Porthdinllaen's Challenge to Holyhead*, Gwynedd Archives Service: Caernarfon.

7   Elis-Williams, Myrvin (1984), pp.61.

8   Hoole, K. (1975), p.54, *The Stockton & Darlington Railway*, David & Charles: Newton Abbot. The bridge was replaced in 1841.

9   Elis-Williams, Myrvin (1984), p.65. The author suggests four groups to include the Orme's Bay proposal.

10 Baughan, Peter E. (1980, second edition 1991), p.92. *North and Mid-Wales*, David St John Thomas: Nairn. The chairman of the NWR, William Chadwick, was found to have manipulated the finances of the company from which it never recovered.

11 Christiansen, Rex & Miller, R.W. (1971, revised edition), p.14, *The Cambrian Railways*, vol.1, David & Charles: Newton Abbot.

12 He gave his name to a rail profile: the flat-bottomed Vignoles rail. A rail form that, however, that had little application on domestic lines at the type of its introduction, but one that was to be used extensively in the rest of Europe.

13 Vignoles, Olinthus J. (1889), *Life of Charles Blacker Vignoles*, Longmans, Green & Co.: London. Chapter 1 extracts, pp.7, 14, 43 and 65.Vignoles, K.H. (1982). *Charles Blacker Vignoles: Romantic Engineer*, Cambridge University Press: Cambridge. Extract from Chapter 1.

14 Jones, Stephen K. (2005) pp.16-18.

15 Naturally the Stockton & Darlington Railway was to receive a great deal of the attention of these two engineers. Rastrick, was also well versed in the development of the railway locomotive having formed a partnership with John Hazeldine, at whose foundry he was engaged with Richard Trevithick on the construction of 'Catch-me-who-can', a locomotive which ran on a circular track in the area of what is now North Gower Street in central London.

16 Walker, James (1829 second edition), pp.20-21, *Report to the Directors of the Liverpool and Manchester Railway on the Comparative Merits of Locomotive and Fixed Engines as a Moving Power*.

17 McGowan, Christopher (2004), p.6, *The Rainhill Trials: The Greatest Contest of Industrial Britain and the Birth of Commercial Rail*, Little, Brown: London. *James Walker (1781–1862): Civil Engineer*, Denis Smith MSc, PhD, DIC, CEng (president), Newcomen Society Transactions, vol.69 A (1997) pp.23-56.

18 Vignoles, K.H. (1982), p.24. See also Jones, Stephen K. (2005), p.27.

19 Vignoles, K.H. (1982), p.32. Vignoles argued that Stephenson never been satisfied with the course of the tunnel, wanting to shift the line some 40ft to the north.

20 Vignoles, K.H. (1982), p.31.

21 McGowan, Christopher (2004), *The Rainhill Trials*, Little, Brown: London. This aspect has also been covered in vol.1, Jones, Stephen K. (2005), p.71.

22 Braithwaite's entry in the Dictionary of National Biography states: 'In 1834 the Eastern Counties railway was projected and laid out by him in conjunction with Mr. Charles Blacker Vignoles.' It also states that the works were made wide enough for a 7ft gauge. This aspect has also been covered in vol.1, Jones, Stephen K. (2005), p.29.

23 Vignoles, K.H. (1982), p.34. K.H. Vignoles indicates that this was George Stephenson, so some form of relationship must have continued after his resignation from the L&MR.

24 Vignoles, K.H. (1982) p.34. The author states that Marc offered Vignoles the post of Resident Engineer on the Thames Tunnel in November 1827, but Brunel had started work for his father on the Thames Tunnel on 2 March 1825 and assumed the position of Resident Engineer in August 1826 when George Armstrong resigned (a position that he continued in until work on the tunnel came to an end in 1828). I am indebted to Mike Chrimes, the Librarian of the Institution of Civil Engineers for checking Marc Brunel's diary, which unfortunately is blank from 5 November until the end of 1827, and also for checking the Directors' correspondence for the Thames Tunnel which does not shed any light on this.

25 See Chapter 9 for further details on the Vivian family.

26 References to Amlwch in University of Bangor archives: http://www.amlwchdata.co.uk/ amlwch_at_bangor_university.htm

27 Tomos, Dafydd (1972), p.136, *Michael Faraday in Wales including Faraday's Journal of his Tour through Wales in 1819*, Gwasg Gee: Denbigh.

28 Pearl survives as the oldest surviving example of a Cornish beam engine house in Wales It is now a Grade II listed monument; Record No.24458, date listed 12/12/2000, OS Grid Ref SH 447 907. I am grateful to Kaye Moxon at CADW for this information.

29 University of Bangor archives (MMS3180).

30 Vignoles, K.H. (1982), p.35.

31 Lampe, David (1963), p.132, *The Tunnel*, George G. Harrap: London.

32 Lampe, David (1963), p.140-141. Note that Vignoles, K.H. (1982) p.36-37, states that Vignoles' first communication on the subject was in secret to the Thames Tunnel Board, and Marc did not find out that Vignoles was behind the proposition until 14 April 1829.

33 The continuation of the Wigan Branch north to Preston, the North Union Railway, also occupied his attention but setbacks delayed the opening until October 1838.

34 Jones, Stephen K. (2005), pp.111, 118.

35 Vignoles, K.H. (1982), p.49, and Webster, N.W. (1970), p.106, *Joseph Locke: Railway Revolutionary*, George Allen & Unwin Ltd: London. Thomas Telford had first been invited to review the plans, he declined and Stephenson, was next to be invited. He, with Joseph Locke, examined the route a third engineer was invited: John Killaly, who died before he could carry out the report.

36 Gren, Andre (2003), p.71, *The Foundation of Brunel's Great Western Railway*, Silver Link Publishing Ltd: Kettering. This attendance record amounts to him making an appearance almost once a month for twenty-five years.

37 Dempsey, G. Drysdale (1864, reprinted 1970), p.54, *Tubular and other Iron Girder Bridges*, Virtue Brothers & Co: London, reprinted 1970 by Kingsmead Reprints: Bath.

38 Dempsey, G. Drysdale (1864, reprinted 1970), p.54, quoted from Beaufort's Report of 4 November 1836. In addition to his naval career and surveying expeditions, Beaufort had worked on shore telegraphs in Ireland.

39 Vignoles, K.H. (1982), pp.62-63. Macneill would later become Professor Sir John Macneill, of Trinity College, Dublin.

40 Jones, Stephen K. (2005), p.149.

41 Work began in 1845, but Vignoles resigned in 1847 through pressure of work as he was unable to devote the time the Directors saw fit to its supervision. It was completed by Richard Osbome, the American-born resident engineer.

42 Vignoles, K.H. (1982), p.95.

43 Cox, R.C. (1993), p.8, *Engineering at Trinity* (incorporating a Record of the School of Engineering), School of Engineering, Trinity College Dublin: Dublin. Although Millington was appointed it is not known if he actually took up.the chair as he went off to Mexico to work as an engineer in the silver mines. Formal engineering courses had also been established at the University of Durham, Kings College, London (1838) and Glasgow University (1840).

44 Cox, R.C. (1993), p.17.

45 Jones, Stephen K. (2005), p.132.

46 Rapley, John (2003), p.16, *The Britannia & Other Tubular Bridges and the men who built them*, Tempus Publishing: Stroud.

47 Christiansen, Rex & Miller R.W. (1971, revised edition), p.14, *The Cambrian Railways*, vol.1.

48 *The Surveyor, Engineer and Architect*, 1 March 1840.

49 Elis-Williams, Myrvin (1984), p.69.

50 ICE Record Acc No.1843 WALMWR, Mr.Walker's Report and Plans on Communication with Ireland. See also Elis-Williams, Myrvin, (1984), p.71.

51 In 1836 Archer published a pamphlet entitled: *A New Line of Communication between Dublin and London via Portdynllaen, Worcester and Oxford... by means of Steam Packet and Railway.* See Elis-Williams, Myrvin (1984), pp.61-2, *Packet to Ireland Porthdinllaen's Challenge to Holyhead,* Gwynedd Archives Service: Caernarfon.

52 ICE Record Acc No.1843 WALMWR, p.1.

53 ICE Record Acc No.1843 WALMWR, p.1.

54 This was in connection with plans for railways in Wurttemberg for which he had received an offer from the King of Wurttemberg in April 1843.

55 Vignoles, K.H. (1982), p.101.

56 Vignoles, K.H. (1982), p.101.

57 ICE Record Acc No.1843 WALMWR, p.4.

58 ICE Record Acc No.1843 WALMWR, pp.3-5. A major element of the Holyhead costs (£177,000) was for the construction of a breakwater to provide an enclosed harbour, which was not proposed for Porthdinllaen.

59 Baughan, Peter. E. (1972), p.63, *The Chester and Holyhead Railway,* vol.1, David & Charles: Newton Abbot.

60 Herepath's Journal, December 1845.

61 Baughan, Peter E. (1972), p.63.

62 Brunel wrote to Vignoles on 7 October 1858 to give a reference for Fredk M. Weedon, an ex-pupil who had worked in Swindon (p.193, PLB 11). See Chapter 11 for a continuation of Vignoles' career.

63 Brindle, Steven (2004), pp.124-5, *Paddington Station, Its History and Architecture,* English Heritage: Swindon.

64 He exhibited at the Royal Academy from 1842 to 1861, and his final works were shown at the Great Exhibition of 1862, which, it seems, was at least partly the cause of his early death. As recounted at the time he appears to have been disappointed that his Shakespeare Monument had been refused space, '... he went home after his last interview with the authorities at Kensington, took to his bed, and died within a very few days'. Among many portrait busts by John Thomas, a particularly characterful example is that of G.P. Watkins in the National Museum of Wales, Cardiff. http://myweb.tiscali.co.uk/speel/sculpt/thomasjn.htm

3

A LINE OF COMMUNICATIONS

'... THE REQUISITES AND CHARACTER OF A GOOD LINE.'[1]

Whilst Brunel was frustrated in 1846 with his endeavour to create an improved passage to Ireland using the natural harbour of Porthdinllaen, there was another opportunity in the south that presented by the south Wales coastal route. Such an opportunity, and indeed the route, was well known to Brunel and overlapped his first engineering commission in Wales, the Taff Vale Railway. The story of the South Wales Railway (SWR) however, was, not a straightforward one, especially at the beginning and the end of the route itself. Indeed, SWR was more of a saga than a story, with much deliberation about how the railway would physically enter Wales and where it would end or terminate. Throughout the building of the SWR there were challenges and setbacks caused by what appeared to be almost all of nature's elements ranged against it. The first of these was the barrier presented by the river Severn and the official rejection of Brunel's crossings; water was followed by fire, with a conflagration reducing the timber viaduct over the Usk at Newport to charred fragments followed by earth slippages threatening the progress of the line towards Swansea. These kinds of problems could be addressed by alternative routes and innovative engineering solutions but there was little that could be done in the aftermath of the one of the greatest natural disasters of modern times, the Irish Potato Famine or 'Great Hunger'. The central agent of the famine was the disease affecting potatoes called *Phytophthora infestans* spread by wind borne spores. Striking in September 1845, the fungus-like organism infected the potatoes as they grew in fields across Ireland causing the leaves to wither and the tubers to rot. Whilst the partial loss of the harvest of 1845 may not have spelled immediate disaster, it was the almost complete loss of the harvest the following year that led to the first starvations. Although there was an improvement in the 1847 harvest, the situation worsened the following year and the year after that, compounding the misery which together with the outbreak of diseases such as cholera, led to a second period of famine. Such a climate led to a slow down and eventually a complete stop of payments for railway shares from Irish subscribers, not only for the SWR, but for connecting lines on the other side of

Part of the Over Junction Bridge over the river Severn at Gloucester during reconstruction. The photograph, showing a cut through wrought-iron girder, is of a balloon flange shape dating from 1848. (Courtesy of the late P.S.A. Berridge)

the Irish sea, such as the Waterford, Wexford, Wicklow & Dublin Railway. Trying to resolve the financial shortcoming this presented led the SWR to consider truncating the line at Swansea or Carmarthen, and thus put them in conflict with the GWR over leasing agreements. A change of the company chairman, and Brunel acting as conciliator between both sides, eventually led to an agreement, but even Brunel was not able to stop the secretary of the SWR, Captain Nenon Armstrong, embezzling and absconding with £5,000 of the SWR's money.

South Wales Railway seal. (Courtesy of GWR Museum, Swindon)

Such a scenario could not have been anticipated when the line was first mooted in the 1830s. As we have seen in Chapter 1, it emerged from a background of competing schemes, such as that proposed in 1833 by William Wooddeson for the 'Cambrian, Gloucester and London Railway', a line intended to join with that proposed from London to Bristol, Brunel's Great Western Railway. As it was succinctly put at the time, the reason for it and other proposals such as the 'Grand Cambrian and Western Railway' failing to make any progress was in '… raising the "sinews of war", money, money, money was the only difficulty'.[2] Such proposals were being put forward at this time because of the opportunity presented by the proposed line of the GWR in extending communications to south Wales. In turn, the GWR and its supporters were prompted to move and ensure that any proposals extending or linked to it were under its influence, hence the 'Gloucester and South Wales', a proposal put forward as part of the GWR grand plan and one in which, Brunel, as GWR engineer, would also be engineer to. When the Gloucester & South Wales Railway was being actively pursued, Brunel was doing the pursuing, writing to his surveyor Morris in May 1836:

> … Press on the survey at Chepstow, Newport and Purton at the places indicated in order that I may mark a line there and have sections taken… I should wish to hear from you shortly as to your progress and to receive as soon as possible a tracing of the survey at Chepstow and Newport. Mr Bush and I will be with you very shortly.[3]

However, the Gloucester & South Wales Railway proposal did not move forward, largely due to the depressed financial climate of 1837 even though a truncated scheme was mooted (see Chapter 1), or as the petitioners for the 1845 South Wales Railway Bill, put it, '... it remained in abeyance from the closure of 1836 to the autumn of 1843'.[4] However, it is not quite the same as saying that the G&SWR now had a second chance, as it was now some eight years later and the Gloucester element was dropped from the title, for reasons that Brunel would reveal. In February 1844 a circular was sent to leading landowners and businessmen and MPs in Wales and Ireland to revive the plan. Brunel's views in 1844 were largely unchanged as far as the best route was concerned from views he had expressed in a letter of September 1836 to the Committee of the Gloucester & South Wales Railway and, indeed, the petitioners for the 1845 South Wales Railway Bill include a copy of this report.[5] In this report he sets out his views on possible routes, prefacing his letter with the resolution passed by the committee on 16 April:[6]

> That is the opinion of this meeting, that the different lines radiating from Gloucester passing through Monmouthshire and terminating at Milford Haven, should be surveyed, with a view of ascertaining which may most practicable, and that Estimates be taken of the expected Traffic upon each, for the purpose of enabling the comparative accounts of each line, as regards Engineering facilities, advantage to the Public, and amount of Traffic to be fairly estimated, before any one of the lines be recommended for adoption. But that the Engineer, who maybe employed, should be empowered to recommend any other Termaines in South Wales, short of Milford Haven.

Brunel proceeded to examine possible routes throughout the lines of the country and direct such levels to be taken as should enable him to ascertain at as early a stage as possible of the survey those lines which offered any probability of being ultimately adopted:

> It is of course quite unnecessary to attempt any description of those lines which from the difficulties of the Country or the absence of any compensating advantages were abandoned at the outset but it may be satisfactory to the members of the Committee to know that every line which could by probability be taken with any rational prospect of success has been examined more or less according to the nature of the Country most of them have been actually levelled and now ['some' crossed out] now have been abandoned until by comparison with the other lines under survey it became evidently waste of time and money to pursue them further.

The report was accompanied by an ordnance map showing these lines of which continuous sections had been taken, stating that partial sections of other lines '... in numerous other directions both distinct from these lines and branching from them have been examined. These sections led to the abandonment of possible routes such as that from Gloucester by Abergavenny, up the Clydach Valley and by Dowlais, with the view of communicating by the Taff Vale Railway through Merthyr to Cardiff, and then by Pant Sychbant and the Vale of Neath to Neath & Swansea. A second commencing at Quakers Yard in the Taff Valley and proceeding up the Cynon Valley:

> … and from the summit of this Valley descending by Pont Walby & by the Neath [valley] to Neath & Swansea which would have formed a continuation of various lines leading both direct to Quakers Yard and by Cardiff and thence by the Taff Vale Railway to the mouth of the Aberdare Valley. The former line by Dowlais was found impracticable on account of the immense height of the first summit level to be attained immediately on leaving Abergavenny several parts of the Valley or hollow north of Dowlais being upwards of 1200 feet above the sea and the nature of the Country generally being of a difficult and impracticable description, and besides which a second summit must be passed of nearly equal height and attended with difficulties fully as great to enable the line to be carried to Neath.

Brunel goes on to say that a line was levelled by the Cynon Valley route, with the view of reaching Neath, but the engineering difficulties between Quakers Yard and Neath, compared with the lines ultimately selected between Cardiff and north of Llanharan, added to the difficulty of reaching Quakers Yard, except by way of Cardiff, and the abandonment of the Cynon line:

> A line proceeding from Gloucester coastwise and their running into the interior by Caerphilly by Nant Garw and across the Taff and under the Garth mountains somewhat in the direction of a line which I was informed had been once suggested for a Turnpike Road was examined but the difficulty of crossing the Valley of the Taff after attaining the level necessary to run up the Nant Garw and the disadvantage of avoiding Cardiff together with the irregularity the Ground generally compared with that upon the lower line passing through Cardiff left no doubt as to the ineligibility of the former.
>
> Of those lines which may be considered practicable the principal ones may be clasped under two heads, the Northern or interior lines and the Southern or Coasting lines.

As he states, Brunel had decided there were, logically, two options: the first he referred to as the 'Northern' route, i.e. from Gloucester passing near Ross, through Monmouth, Raglan, Abergavenny, Brecon, Llandovey, Llandeilo, Carmarthen, Eglwysilan to Pater;[7] the second was the 'Southern or Coasting' route:

> The latter might follow either of two lines to Newport thence to Cardiff, by Llanharen, Bridgend with a choice of three lines near this place to Neath, with an extensive or Branch to Swansea beyond which place the survey has indeed extended, but I think with little chance of any line of Railway being formed, of the two lines to Newport, the one would pass by Monmouth, Usk, Caerleon, and the other by the Coast passing through Newnham and Chepstow.

He eliminates the 'Northern' option as being a difficult and costly route, which would also be detrimental to the existing carriers such as canals and tramroads that operated in the upland valleys, such as the Monmouthshire Canal, Rumney Railway and so on. He goes on to say that it would be an unprofitable route:

> Between these two principal lines the northern and the Southern the destination is obvious, their characters are totally different and the comparison consequently is simple and does not require any very detailed or accurate estimates of cost on either side the northern line passes over a difficult Country, would be costly in its construction and the gradients would unavoidably be such as almost to preclude the possibility of attaining either great speed for passengers travelling in great economy for the transport of Goods. In addition to these national difficulties there appears to be existing Traffic which could in any way compensate for the outlay required and such traffic as might be calculated upon eventually and in prospect would in a great measure be taken from the sources of the numerous railways and canals which now lead from the interior to the Coast and consequently would be obtained only at their expense and probably therefore the attempt would be not with their determined opposition of the Parties interested.

This northern route would meet the proposal for complete communication between Gloucester and Milford Haven, or rather Pater, an objective that, he thought, could hardly be attained by the coastal line. The coastal line, however, could be built with considerably less engineering difficulties and '...offers much greater, more immediate & palpable advantages'. The route and the benefits by the coastal line was summed up by Brunel:

> A line from Gloucester by way of Newnham and Chepstow to Newport and thence to Cardiff would really be an easy line – the expense of would be moderate and when constructed the character of the line would be such as to admit of the greatest profitable economy of Newport? And the full speed of travelling. For the whole of this distance about 56 miles of the line would be nearly level, it would intercept nearly at their lower extremities the various existing channels through which the produce of country rich in essentials and Manufactures is now carried to the sea and consequently while it would derive its revenue from these sources it would confer a corresponding benefit upon them by increasing the demand for the produce the immediate capital already embarked in these works would by thereby materially benefited and the support of everybody interested might consequently be safely calculated upon Beyond Cardiff, the line mightn be ascending the Valley of the Ely to Llanharan and thence descending the estuary either to its mouth and then passing through the sands and proceeding coastwise, on by Bridgend or by a shorter but more hilly Country by Coity – by either of these directions Neath may be reached without greater difficulties of Country even on this portion of the line beyond Cardiff, and rather beyond Llanharran than must be encountered on the greater part of the distance from Gloucester by the Northern line. From Neath of course a branch of extension be formed to Swansea the nature of which must depend materially upon the manner in which the Neath

river may be ultimately crossed – beyond Swansea the line may be extended to Llanelly, Pembrey, Kidwelly, and to the mouth of the Towy but such an extension would be attended with great difficulties and expense and I think without any corresponding commercial advantages, the navigation of the River Towy would impede any further progress in a direct line and although a line might be carried thence along the coast and up the Valley of the River to Caermarthen and the total distance from Gloucester by this route to Carmarthen and thence to Pater would only be increased 20 miles upon about 140 with far superior levels to the direct line yet it must be admitted that neath or Swansea must be considered as the natural terminus of the Southern line, on account of the difficulty of crossing the different navigable Rivers which would be intercepted between these places and Pater.

In comparing this with the northern line, which would be '… comparatively useless and unprofitable unless continued to Pater and considered as part of communication with the South of Ireland', Brunel estimates the cost of such a line, some 140 miles in length, at not less than £3,500,000 and, furthermore, '… there is no present prospect of any traffic that would produce a revenue to repay the advance of such a capital'. As a national work the northern or interior line might be considered preferable to the southern because it would effect a line of communication:

> … not likely to be attempted by a private company at least not in the present state of railway speculations, but as a work for a Company formed with the view of obtaining what is now considered a fair recompense for the first advance of Capital, the Southern line I think alone of the two purposes in any degree- the requisites and character of a good line.[8]

The following comment at this stage of his report relates to the cost of the construction of the southern route in two separate stages; from Gloucester to Cardiff as one stage and then on to Swansea about cost, albeit an estimate because of insufficient data, is that the first stage would not exceed £1 million, whereas continuing on to Swansea would be £2 million (this is the rationale for the decision to proceed with a Gloucester & Cardiff Railway covered in Chapter 1). He also states that how the returns of traffic revenue might repay the capital expended, '… is a matter of calculation which I have not entered into…', a situation that is very quickly entered into, the next day in fact at a meeting in Gloucester, where it is stated that; '… the traffic between Cardiff, Newport and Gloucester would produce eight-tenths of the revenue that might be expected from the construction of the whole line.'[9] Brunel would continue to labour the point but it was obvious what his preference was:

> … I believe before the Committee I have only to report in the words of your resolution that having surveyed 'the different lines radiating from Gloucester through Monmouthshire and terminating at Milford Haven' I find a line passing by Newport and Cardiff to Swansea is far the greatest part of the distance by far more practicable, than a line passing by Monmouth to Abergavenny, Brecon and Carmarthen, and that considering the comparative merits of the

two lines in an 'Engineering point of view, Advantages to the Public, and amount of Traffic', I should recommend adopting Swansea or Neath as the present Terminus, and following the Newport & Cardiff line.

In the consideration of the main question of the Northern or Southern lines I have expressly avoided embarrassing the subject with the question of the best mode of reaching Newport. Two lines offer themselves, in their distinguishing Character, very similar to the two mainlines which I have before described.

That by Newnham and Chepstow is the shortest measuring from the River at Gloster being about 43 miles in length, the easiest of construction, and would be nearly level, that by Monmouth and down the Valley of Usk measuring from the same point would be about 48 Miles, would pass over a very difficult country, and consequently be more expressive in its construction, would have two rather considerable inclined planes, and be generally very inferior in the Levels and other qualities of a good line – the increased distance would be about 5 Miles, the increased expense at least £200,000 and as I before observed the gradient very inferior and consequently the cost of transport would be materially increased. I think it probable that the length of the monmouth line may be somewhat reduced by a careful survey, as the nature of the Country is difficult and consequently requires very close examination but I do not think this would lead to a diminution of expenses and in other respects I feel that I have correctly described its character. On the other hand the communication with Ross and Monmouth and by branch to Hereford, and probably Abergavenny would be important advantages, although I am disposed to think they might be dearly bought:

Considering the economy of transport to and from Cardiff and Swansea and the greater importance of these two places and the extent of their trade combined with the facility of Construction and the great superiority of the levels independently of the difference in the distance I should be disposed to give a decided preference to the line by Chepstow but at the same time I think the other line is worthy of consideration and that there maybe advantages which I have not foreseen in favour of it I should wish therefore that this point should be further considered by the Committee.

Signed I K Brunel[10]

Two years before he submitted this report Brunel took the opportunity to push forward his ideas for a new railway gauge. No doubt this had occupied his thoughts for some time in his quest to develop the steam locomotive railway as a high-speed line of communications. To accomplish this he put aside the accepted standard for a railway gauge, that is the 'Stephenson' gauge of 4ft 8½in, in order to arrive at what he believed was the optimum gauge for railways. The origin of the gauge adopted by Stephenson, it has been argued, can be traced to archaeological excavations at Pompeii and elsewhere, which reveal it as the approximate gauge of Roman road vehicles.[11] This gauge was exported to the rest of Europe, including Britain, during the expansion of the Roman Empire, and many centuries later it was to be carried over onto early railways. The reason for that particular size of gauge is simply based on the motive power used by road vehicles, namely the horse, as it probably represents the optimal size of a road vehicle relative to the indivisible size of a horse. Anything less would have underutilised the horse, and anything greater would have put excessive strain on the animal. Of course, early tramroads also relied on horse power and although a variety of different gauges were in use on tramroads up and down the country, the gauge consistently revolved around the figure of 4ft 8½in. At industrial locations like Merthyr, where there was a need for interconnectivity between the various ironworks' tramroads, there was a logical progression to a common gauge; elsewhere there it was not critical for one tramroad to connect with another as the majority were built as feeders to canals and did not connect to other tramroads.

The way forward for Brunel to promote such a gauge had, it has already been seen, come about by the failure of the first GWR Bill, in which the gauge was specifically restricted to 4ft 8½in, with Brunel persuading Lord Shaftesbury, the chairman of the examining House of Lords Committee, that a gauge clause was unnecessary.[12] Thus the way was left open for Brunel to present his proposals for a broad gauge. His objectives were straightforward; he wanted such a gauge to be capable of allowing more spacious trains, greater stability and higher speeds. In evidence to the Gauge Commission, Brunel stated:

> Looking to the speeds which I contemplated would be adopted on railways and the masses to be moved, it seemed to me that the whole machine was too small for the work to be done, and that it required that the parts should be on a scale more commensurate with the mass and the velocity to be attained.[13]

Brunel had to convince the GWR directors of the advantage of the wider gauge, and he says of his own thoughts, 'I think the impression grew upon me gradually, so that it is difficult to fix the time when I first thought a wide gauge desirable'. At any rate, it was sometime between the rejection of the first Bill in July 1834 and a letter to the directors in September 1835, in which he set out the advantages of the wide gauge. For the GWR, Brunel chose a gauge of 7ft (the gauge would be eventually fixed at 7ft ¼in in order to allow more play to the wheels on curves) which was to be a characteristic feature of all his British railways, with the sole exception of the TVR. Brunel arrived at this gauge on the grounds that it was technically superior to the 4ft 8½in gauge, allowing the running of trains with a lower centre of gravity and larger wheels, all of which Brunel argued, would help to reduce friction. Although he believed that a gauge broader than 4ft 8½in was desirable, there is little evidence that Brunel used any mathematical formula to calculate the ideal gauge and the gauge specifically of 7ft had actually been used on a horse-drawn railway built by his father at his Battersea sawmill. Presumably, Marc Brunel's railway got around Charles E. Lee's rule for horse power by the fact that it was built to a high standard with well-machined running surfaces presenting a low friction operation and probably just involved the drawing of a single truck. When Brunel was asked whether he had any regrets about the broad gauge, he replied that, if anything, he would have preferred to have adopted an even broader gauge.

The broad gauge offered constructional advantages to the locomotive builder by allowing an improved locomotive layout with a lower centre of gravity. Although these advantages were never fully exploited, the broad gauge represented a challenge of speed to narrow-gauge railways and was a general stimulus to high-speed railway operation. As designed by Brunel, the GWR was a line of communications built for speed and, despite some early setbacks in the construction of the permanent way, Brunel's promise that the broad gauge offered high speed and safety was one that would be delivered. In December 1839 a test run from Paddington to Maidenhead achieved a top speed of 45mph and Brunel was confident enough to wager £100 that he would be able to travel from Bristol to London in two hours.[14] The choice of gauge for his first railway in Wales has already been covered and the 'ordinary gauge' was more suitable for the TVR.[15] Under George Bush, the TVR had favoured passenger locomotives built by Sharp, Roberts & Co., of Manchester, with 5ft 6in driving wheels and capable of pulling trains of 25 to 35 tons. One of the partners of that company, Richard Roberts (1789–1864), had advocated the gauge Bush tried to adopt on the TVR – the 5ft gauge. Roberts had written to the *Railway Times* on the subject in 1838 and was to give evidence to the Gauge Commissioners in 1845. When asked by the Gauge Commissioners why he supported a wider gauge, he replied that it was in order:

> ... to get a good-sized boiler to attach to the fire-box and keep it within the wheels. With the present gauge of 4 feet 8½, a sufficient width of fire-box cannot be got between the wheels to admit of a good-sized boiler being attached to it readily; and the cylinders are necessarily so close together as to make the works much cramped for room, and consequently difficult to put together, or to take asunder for repairs; my object was to remedy these defects.[16]

To accommodate such a 'good-sized boiler', he stated in his letter to the *Railway Times*, it was necessary to adopt a gauge of '... between 5 feet and 5 feet 4 inches'.[17] Roberts believed that the Irish Railway Commission had made their choice of 5ft 3in, as the national standard for Ireland, on his arguments. As a partner in Sharp, Roberts & Co. he had supplied locomotives to Vignoles's Dublin & Kingstown Railway (4ft 8½in) and the Ulster Railway (6ft 2in). The latter was the gauge recommended in 1838 for Ireland, but one which was changed in 1841 when the 5ft 3in gauge was adopted, a gauge that has remained the Irish standard to this day.[18] Roberts had also supplied some locomotives to the GWR and when questioned by the Commissioners about GWR locomotive design he replied that he thought that they had not taken advantage of the greater space between the frames to enlarge the cylinders in proportion although he did admit that he was not conversant with their latest designs.[19] This was because he had left the Sharp, Roberts partnership in 1843 and had little to do with locomotive design after this date.

Roberts was also questioned by the Commissioners about the ideal gauge, and thought that both George and Robert Stephenson would prefer a gauge wider than 4ft 8½in; in his view this would probably be 5ft. This is a similar story to that recalled by Professor Babbage about a conversation he had with George Stephenson when he asked him what gauge he would choose if he was able to start completely from scratch. Would it be 4ft 8½in? Stephenson is supposed to have replied, 'Not exactly that gauge, I would take a few inches more, but a very few'. Roberts told the Commissioners that in 1831 he had written to Members of Parliament to urge them to consult engineers about the rail gauge, putting his view forward that the gauge should be 5ft and the space between the lines as 6ft. He also recommended to the Government that they should appoint a Commission in order, '... to superintend a national survey of all mail lines' and thus follow the best routes.[20]

Bush appears to have been influenced by Roberts's views, and these might have been reinforced when he went around the north of England on a railway fact-finding tour in 1838, following which he recommended that the TVR should be built to the 5ft gauge. The TVR ordered two locomotives from Sharp, Roberts & Co. in August 1840, which were delivered the following month, complete with drivers.[21] The TVR were very pleased with the locomotives, named *Taff* and *Rhondda*, and wrote to the suppliers in May 1842, 'Taff & Rhonda [sic] have completed 26 Thousand miles & have not cost the Company five pounds in new Repairs. I have only put 4 new Tubes into the engs & I think I can challenge all the World'.[22]

Many engineers, like John Hawkshaw, recognised the dangers posed by not adopting a uniform gauge although at this time there were also arguments for having different gauges for main lines and feeder lines, a scenario that Brunel subscribed to saying that other gauges could feed into the broad gauge. The writer Charles Frederick Cliffe talks about the route of the South Wales Railway passing through Cardiff in 1847, '... where a feeder will be met in the shape of the Taff Vale Railway.'[23] Despite Roberts's comments about alerting MPs to the evils of break of gauge dating from 1831, the first attempt in which the Government moved to resolve the gauge question came about in 1845. Richard Cobden moved in the House of Commons that a Gauge Commission should be appointed. This was carried unopposed and the commissioners appointed were Sir Frederic Smith, George Airy, the Astronomer Royal, and Professor Peter Barlow. The final report was of considerable length and addressed three main lines of enquiry; firstly, the break of gauge was an inconvenience of so much importance as to demand the interference of the legislature; secondly, what means could be adopted for obviating or mitigating such inconvenience; and finally of the considerations that needed to be taken into account on the general policy of establishing a uniformity of gauge throughout the country.

Daniel Gooch, then twenty-nine years old, was given the responsibility of presenting the case for the Great Western. He wrote in his diary:

> Sir F. Smith had been for a time Inspector of Railways but knew nothing about them, and neither of the other Commissioners had any railway knowledge. They were certainly a most incompetent tribunal, yet when it is considered that the fight was to be between one railway Co on the broad gauge and the host of narrow-gauge companies, it would have been well to put some more practical men on the Commission. For one witness we could call, the narrow-gauge interests could call a dozen.[24]

Gooch went on to say the question before the commissioners was left to him alone, '... a responsibility I did not much like; but it was to be, so I undertook the task'. Gooch gave his evidence on 17 and 18 October 1845 which he felt disproved the evidence of the narrow-gauge witnesses (including Robert Stephenson and Joseph Locke) about the disadvantages of the broad gauge and that his tables and calculations showed that the '… broad gauge could carry traffic at a higher speed and at a far less cost than the narrow gauge.'[25] Despite all of the GWR's ablest men, including Brunel and Gooch, giving evidence and producing some outstanding results in terms of broad-gauge locomotive performance which demonstrated that the broad gauge, compared to the narrow gauge, offered greater capabilities for speed with equal loads and was capable of transporting greater loads with equal speed, it was clear that if a single main-line gauge had to be decided on, the broad gauge could not win based on the consideration that the broad-gauge mileage stood at only 274, compared to the narrow gauge's 1,901. Robert Stephenson had actually built a railway to the broad gauge, or rather laid down rails for special inclines, of which the outer rails were 7ft apart, to take wagons sideways down each side of Hownes Gill ravine on the Stanhope & Tyne Railway.[26] Stephenson also used bridge-pattern rail where there was a danger of the rail coming loose in confined spaces, such as in the iron tubes of his Menai and Conway tubular bridges. In these circumstances the bridge rail was superior and it was not until the application of the fishplate as a secure method of joining rails together did the situation change. Hence the story told by Brunel (related in Chapter 1) about the time he was asked by Walter Coffin about the safest seat in a railway carriage, the advice being 'not the window seat' if he wanted to avoid what had happened to a friend of his when the end of a rail ran up the tyre of the wheel of the railway carriage '… and spitted him like a trussed fowl.'[27]

The recommendation was that the broad gauge was an evil and that 4ft 8½in should be fixed by law as the standard gauge of the country. When 'An Act for regulating the Gauge of Railways' was passed on 18 August 1846, the GWR and its broad-gauge allies would be penalised as much as they thought all future gauges of railways in Great Britain would have to be 4ft 8½in, or 5ft 3in in Ireland, '… unless any present or future act contained a "special enactment defining the gauge."'[28] The expansion of the broad-gauge railway empire, such as those lines proposed for the West Country, Dorset and south Wales, would be exempt from restrictions. Any proposals the GWR had for new broad-gauge railways outside this territory would be subject to stiff opposition both inside and outside Parliament. Commercial considerations and narrow-gauge interests had, and continue to have, more impact in controlling the growth of the broad gauge than Government interference. Outside Parliament the GWR was outmanoeuvred by its opponents and the GWR itself was to commit a series of technical errors in failing to takeover or merge with companies that would assist its expansion. In 1861, the standard-gauge West Midlands Railway was amalgamated with the GWR, but the break of gauge within the GWR itself meant that many of the advantages of a single network were lost. The opposition was formidable: George Hudson controlled a railway network in 1846 that linked Newcastle and Bristol and covered in excess of 1,000 miles of track. In the same year the London & North Western Railway (L&NWR) was formed and was to present a significant rival to the GWR. In looking at the reasons for the failure of the broad gauge, some have argued that the main reason appears that the critical mass of the network was not large enough, '... the GWR never succeeded in dominating a large enough territory to make the gauge self-sufficient and for the amount of traffic with standard-gauge railways to remain relatively insignificant.'[29]

NOTES

1 University of Bristol, Special Collections, PLB, G&SWR, p.62, 21 September 1836.
2 *The Cambrian*, 19 October 1833, comment made by Mr Vivian. See also Jones, Stephen K. (2005), p.95.
3 University of Bristol, Special Collections, IKB Letter Book. May 1836. See also Jones, Stephen K. (2005), pp.119-120.
4 Petition for the South Wales Railway Bill, p.22, Misc. MSS 1674, Gwent Record Office, Cwmbran. The truncating of the proposal to just Gloucester and Cardiff (see Chapter 1) is not mentioned.
5 Petition for the South Wales Railway Bill, p.34, Misc. MSS 1674, Gwent Record Office, Cwmbran.
6 University of Bristol, Special Collections, PLB 2, G&SWR, p.56, 21 September 1836.
7 University of Bristol, Special Collections, PLB 2, G&SWR, p.59, 21 September 1836.
8 University of Bristol, Special Collections, PLB 2, G&SWR, p.62, 21 September 1836.
9 Dowlias Iron Co. Letters 1836, 2, E-G, No.182, Glamorgan Record Office (GRO).
10 University of Bristol, Special Collections, PLB 2, G&SWR, pp.56-64, 21 September 1836. On 5 December 1835 *The Cambrian* had reported that: 'Mr Brunel, the celebrated engineer, who has surveyed the several proposed lines of communication between Merthyr and Neath, has declared his decided opinion in favour of the Sychpant line by way of Cwmffrwd and Penmallwg. That proposed by Mr Hallett would have been preferred had not the expense of the undertaking amounted to a prohibition.'
11 The American engineer, Walton W. Evans, sought to test this hypothesis by measuring with a metric rule, to avoid bias, the ruts made by carts and chariots at Pompeii. He converted his measurements to inches and found that the ruts, centre to centre, were about 4ft 9in wide and thus consistent with a gauge of slightly less than that. Archaeological research has confirmed that this was the Romans' common gauge.
12 See Chapter 1.
13 Sidney, Samuel (1846, reprinted 1971), *Gauge Evidence: 1845*, originally published Edmondes & Vacher: London, reprinted SR Publishers/Turntable Enterprises: Wakefield. See also Vaughan, Adrian (1991, reprinted 1992), p.23, *Isambard Kingdom Brunel, Engineering Knight-Errant*, John Murray: London.
14 Jones, Stephen K. (2005), p.125, 127. MacDermot, E.T., revised by Clinker, C.R. (1964). p.45, *History of the Great Western Railway*, vol.1. Ian Allen: London. *The Cambrian*, 22 August 1841 (Sat.) Experimental Trip on the Great Western Railway.
15 Jones, Stephen K. (2005), p.127. In August 1838 he reported to the directors:

As regards the gauge or width of the rails I see no reason in our case for deviating materially from the ordinary width of 4ft 8½in. The general gradients, the inclined planes and still more the nature and the immediate extent of the peculiar class of traffic to which the line must always be devoted not only render high speeds unnecessary but must almost prevent their being attempted, while the same causes operate to diminish any advantage that may be gained in reducing friction by increased diameter of carriage wheels. The curves also which the nature of the ground render unavoidable would be unfit for a wider gauge, but are not objectionable for moderate speeds with the ordinary gauge.

16 Hills, Revd Dr Richard L. (2002), p.204, *Life and Inventions of Richard Roberts 1789 – 1864*, Landmark Publishing Ltd: Ashbourne. Quoted from Par. Papers, 1845, Q. 5356.

17 Hills, Revd Dr Richard L. (2002), p.204. Quoted from *Railway Times*, No.46, No.35 New Series, 8 September 1838, p.507.

18 Jones, Stephen K. (2005), pp.129-30.

19 Hills, Revd Dr Richard L. (2002), p.205. Quoted from Par. Papers, 1845, Q. 5376 & 5389.

20 Hills, Revd Dr Richard L. (2002), p.205. Quoted from Par. Papers, 1845, Q. 5433.

21 Jones, Stephen K. (2005), p.183.

22 Hills, Revd Dr Richard L. (2002), p.211. Quoted from Sharp, Roberts & Co., Order Book 1, No.32, letter written 12 May 1842.

23 Jones, Stephen K. (2005), p.130. Cliffe, Charles Frederick. (1847 1st ed.) p.63, *The Book of South Wales*, Hamilton Adams & Co.: London.

24 Wilson, Roger Burdett ed. (1972), pp.48–49, *Sir Daniel Gooch: Memoirs and Diary*, David & Charles: Newton Abbot.

25 Wilson, Roger Burdett, ed. (1972), p.49.

26 Rolt, L.T.C. (1959), *George & Robert Stephenson*, Longmans, Green & Co.: London. The Taff Vale Works supplied the Stanhope and Tyne Railway with 3,000 tons of rail in 1837 (Bernard *v.* Harford, Printed Report of Case), see John, A. H. (1950), *The Industrial Development of South Wales 1750–1850*, University of Wales Press: Cardiff.

27 *The Great Western Railway Magazine*, 1908, p.261.

28 Day, Lance (1985), p.26, *Broad Gauge*, Science Museum: London.

29 Miller, Robert C.B. (2005), p.84, *railway.com: Parallels between the early British railways and the ICT revolution*, IEA: London.

4

WESTWARD TO WALES

'... IS 1,100FT PRACTICABLE'[1]

Eight years would elapse from Brunel's report of 1836 to the proposals of 1844, a year when it was felt that the conditions for taking forward such a scheme were right. A prospectus for its successor, the South Wales Railway, was issued in the summer of 1844. As the first broad-gauge line to be built in south Wales, the SWR, supported by the GWR, promoted and gave active support to a raft of railway proposals in order to establish a coherent broad-gauge network throughout the length and breadth of the SWR. The SWR was to form the main communications spine of this network with other railways extending the network and tapping into the mineral wealth of the districts that the SWR passed through. There would be, however, numerous setbacks and changes from beginning to end as far as building the SWR was concerned, and the following is an attempt to tell that story in legal terms. Covering the first Act from 1845 up to 1863, the year that marked the end of the SWR as an independent undertaking, it will attempt to address the changes that it and fellow broad-gauge companies chose or were forced to make in order to complete their railways. Even this is not straight-forward because of the schismatic events of 1849 that divided the SWR and GWR. A contemporary view is taken of those companies up to 1849 by drawing on the statement made by John Duncan, a SWR shareholder who admitted that he only held a nominal shareholding, but that, '... proprietors holding a very large stake in the undertaking have entrusted their interests to him, and practically, therefore, he is the representative of several thousand shares'.[2]

In his statement Duncan is concerned with the financial position of the SWR and the companies connected to it, particularly with regard to any subscribing by the SWR to these companies and powers to sell or lease. A greater exploration of what was behind some of these changes will be covered in the following chapters dealing with the route and its works from east to west. The promoters of the SWR first went to Parliament in 1845, a year that marked the beginning of the 'large' railway mania of 1845–48.[3] Even in these mania-fuelled times the SWR was no ordinary line as it was the longest railway authorised by Parliament up to that date and that was without the connecting elements that Brunel would have to return to Parliament for. This, 'An Act for making a Railway to be called "The South Wales Railway"', was granted on 4 August 1845 (8 & 9 Vic., cap. 190, 1845).[4] The line of railway authorised ran from Fishguard and Pembroke Dock to Chepstow (i.e. to the west bank of the Wye), with a branch to Monmouth. The share capital of the company was to be set at £2,800,000, to be raised by 56,000 shares of £50 with powers to raise loans up to £933,333.[5] As the said railway would be '… beneficial to the Interests of the Great Western Railway Company…',[6] the GWR was to subscribe £600,000 (12,000 shares) to the undertaking and by return the SWR could lease or sell its railway to the GWR. The Act gave powers to the SWR to lease the railway and works to GWR, empowering the company to accept a lease and enter into contracts and so on. The GWR was allowed to appoint six of the eighteen directors, the remaining twelve to be shareholders of fifty shares of the South Wales Co., and to be elected according to the Consolidation Act. Powers were given to pay 4 per cent interest on calls, until the railway was completed. Voting by the shareholders at general meetings was regulated by the Consolidation Act, but the GWR were to have one vote for each two shares, (or 6,000 votes at each meeting).

Amongst the individual subscribers in this original Act are men such as Frederick Pratt Barlow, William Chambers, junior, Rowland Fothergill, Thomas Powell and Nicholas Roch. Sir Josiah John Guest and John Henry Vivian are named as two of the SWR's eighteen directors. The Act outlines, in reverse order, that the main line would commence at or near Fishguard Bay and at or near to Pembroke Dock (otherwise known as Pater). It then passed through the four counties of Pembroke, Carmarthen, Glamorgan and Monmouth to '… terminate at the West Bank of the River Wye in the Parish of Chepstow'.[7] There were numerous conditions placed on the SWR and its 194½ miles of line, for example, on the Monmouth branch the railway had to keep its distance from the church and rectory of Mitcheltroy and that the company could not divert from the line shown on the plans. Vested interests were also protected at Llanelly and Pembrey, where the line skirted the foreshore and the construction of works had to be approved by the Commissioners of Her Majesty's Woods, Forests, Land Revenues, Works and Buildings. The Rights of the Marquis of Bute for the Bute Dock would also be protected. There were also navigational rights: at the river Towey bridge, the stream above and below were to be straightened and secured and the navigation of the river could not be interrupted during the construction of the railway. Specifically, the drawbridge to be erected here by the SWR was to be:

> … constructed in such Manner as the Commissioners for executing the Office of Lord High Admiral may, in Writing under the Hand of the Secretary of the Admiralty approve of; and in a suitable and proper part of the Said Bridge the Said Company shall construct a Drawbridge, with a clear opening of not less than Fifty Feet, for the passage of Vessels through the same, the piers of which Bridge are to be made parallel to the Stream, and the Span of the Arches, and the Dimensions, Construction, and site of the Said Bridge, shall be such as the Said Commissioners shall approve of as aforesaid…[8]

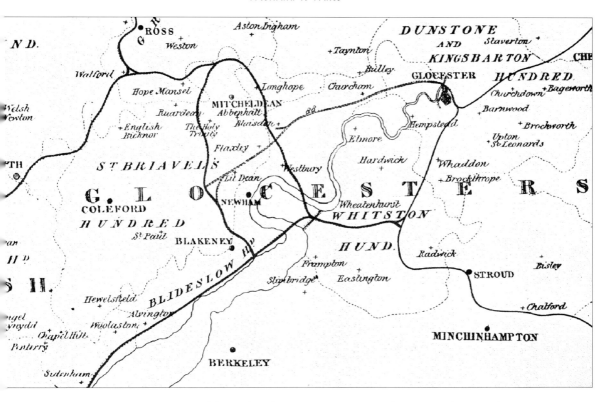

Section of the Parliamentary map of the South Wales Division, Session 1845, showing Brunel's proposed crossings of the Severn. (SKJ collection)

A swingbridge or drawbridge was to be constructed across the river Lougher '… not less than the Width or Opening of the present Swingbridge, across the Said River, on the Road from Lougher to Llanelly, and on the same Side…' whilst the height of the bridge across the river Tawe at Swansea was to be not less than 75ft from the ordinary high-water mark.[9] The Act also covered the amount of land to be taken, details of compulsory purchase powers, tolls, charges and rates, but so far powers did not specifically allow the railway to be connected to the broad-gauge system or indeed to any other railways.[10] How the SWR was to be linked to the GWR system was yet to be determined, as was the question of how two major towns along the route, Swansea and Haverfordwest, not on the main line of the railway as proposed, would be served. In a similar vein to that followed by the Chester & Holyhead Railway, whose primary legislation did not cover the means of crossing its major obstacle, i.e. the Menai Straits, it had to return to Parliament to obtain this authority.

The second Act granted to the SWR on 27 July 1846 (9 & 10 Vic., cap. 239, 1846) gave some of these answers.[11] The Act allowed the line to be extended from Chepstow to Hagloe Farm, in the Parish of Awre, County of Gloucestershire, to join the proposed Gloucester & Dean Forest Railway. Branch railways were also proposed to Swansea, leaving the SWR main line and proceeding from Landore (given as the sixty-seven and a quarter mile mark) to terminate for passenger services on the south side of Pottery Lane and for minerals and goods at or near a point on the Oystermouth tramroad. Another branch line, fourteen miles long, would connect the town of Haverfordwest to the main line. Powers were also granted to alter the Monmouth Branch (and other portions of the line), connect with the Monmouth & Hereford Railway and gain access to collieries in the Forest of Dean. Section xiii related to the building of a Depot at Baglan Bay on land belonging to the Earl of Jersey. There were further fundraising powers, allowing the raising by share issue up to £200,000 and by loans £66,666. A third Act in 1847 might have been considered the final defining Act of the SWR, but for future events beyond the company's control. In this Act, the South Wales Amendment Act of 2 July 1847 (10 & 11 July Vic., cap. 109),[12] powers were given to purchase the Forest of Dean (formerly called Bullo Pill) Railway, as agreed, or as may be agreed, and also power to the SWR to sell or lease to GWR, and for the latter company to purchase or rent said railway and branches, neither purchase or lease to be made without certificate of the Commissioners of Railways, upon proof that half the whole capital had been paid up and expended of each of the companies. The Act also allowed for the diversion of the river Taff at Cardiff.

The following Acts were related to the SWR in the sense of completing or extending the broad-gauge network, the first being the Bristol & South Wales Junction Railway (B&SWJR) of 26 June 1846.[13] What is interesting about the B&SWJR, and the similar railway ferry schemes across the river Severn that followed, is that Brunel was not initially the engineer. These railway ferries can be seen as an attempt to address the setback Brunel had incurred in trying to bridge the river Severn in order to avoid the long way round through Gloucester. The B&SWJR allowed the construction of a railway, with ferries, from Bristol to join the SWR. Its share capital was set at £250,000, with power to borrow £83,333. No subscription by the SWR was authorised to this line. Difficulties in raising share capital and arguments over legal title to property and ferry rights, however, were to end in the abandonment of the company in 1853.[14] A year later the Bristol South Wales & Southampton Union Railway was the subject of meetings and prospectus.[15] In 1857 this was to give way to the Bristol & South Wales Union Railway with Brunel as engineer, but it would not be completed until after Brunel's death.

Returning to 1846, an Act of 16 July of that year authorised the first of the connecting lines in Ireland with the construction of the Waterford, Wexford, Wicklow & Dublin Railway.[16] Despite the strategic importance of this link, no authority was given to the SWR to subscribe and the events of 1848–49 were to cause major changes and delays to the construction of this line. Back in Wales the Tenby, Saundersfoot & South Wales Railway was authorised on the 27 July 1846.[17] Capital was set at £140,000 and, as with the previous line, it had no powers to allow the SWR to subscribe, but powers to that company to purchase or lease the line, which in any event was not proceeded with. Rail connections with Tenby and Saundersfoot would have to wait until 1863 and then the railway would be a standard-gauge one.[18]

Contemporary lithograph of Grange Court Junction station. (SKJ collection)

Grange Court, the scene in the 1970s, no longer a junction or even a station. (SKJ photograph)

Aftermath of a collision on the main line near Bullo Pill, in which a mail train from New Milford (Neyland) ran into the back of the up cattle train from Carmarthen. This occurred at about ten o'clock on the night of 5 November 1868 with the guard and five drivers being killed. The 4-4-0 locomotive, Rob Roy, is one of the Waverley class of engines built by Robert Stephenson & Co of Newcastle in 1855. Following repairs the engine continued in use until 1872. (From The Railway Magazine, *vol.III, 1898)*

Derailment of an up broad gauge express at Lydney. (From The Railway Magazine, *vol.III, 1898)*

'Steropes' a six coupled engine derailed near Llanwern. (From The Railway Magazine, *vol.III, 1898)*

The position in Gloucestershire and the Forest of Dean was relatively straightforward in terms of connecting the SWR to the broad-gauge network, but in the serving of an important mineral district, frequent recourse was made to Parliament. To provide the connection, a nominally independent line, the Gloucester & Dean Forest Railway, was authorised on 27 July 1846.[19] It had powers to raise £320,000 by shares and £105,000 by loans. It allowed the SWR and the GWR to subscribe the sums of £100,000 and £50,000 respectively. Of the nine directors, two always had to be GWR directors. The scale of voting at general meetings gave to the SWR and GWR companies, one vote for each three shares. Interest was to be paid at 4 per cent on calls. The time it had to take lands expired on 27 July 1849. It had powers to sell or lease to the GWR or SWR. The line provided the link between Gloucester and Hagloe Farm, as well as a connection to the Monmouth & Hereford Railway which had been authorised on 4 August 1845. As the latter was part of Brunel's original branch network, based on a railway crossing of the Severn, it was soon abandoned, although some work was carried out relating to tunnel shafts and headings.[20] Hereford was to be served by the later Hereford, Ross & Gloucester Railway from a junction of the SWR at Grange Court. Brunel claimed that he had been extremely active in promoting this line, writing on 26 May 1855, 'I look on [it] as peculiarly my own child, I made great personal exertion originally to promote this line, from motives which I feel rather proud of...'[21]

A railway seen as an important part of this broad-gauge 'communications and coal' network was the Vale of Neath Railway, which was incorporated on 3 August 1846.[22] The Act authorised the construction of the main line of the Vale of Neath Railway from the SWR at Neath to Merthyr Tydfil with four branches, one of which was to meet with the standard-gauge Aberdare Railway.[23] It had powers to raise £550,000 and £183,333 by loans and could sell or lease its lines to the SWR. Another mineral line incorporated four days later on 7 August 1846 was the Llynvi Valley Railway (LVR).[24] Originally promoted as the Llynvi Valley & South Wales Junction Railway, it was authorised to construct a steam railway, but it did little beyond purchasing (under a further Act) the Duffryn Llynvi & Porthcawl Railway, a horse-drawn tramroad that had opened in 1828. Share raising powers amounted to £200,000 and £66,000 by loans. No power was given to the SWR to subscribe but the LVR could lease or sell their railway to the SWR. The LVR was to return to Parliament twice in July 1847, on 2 July to seek extension[25] and on 22 July for authority to purchase the Duffryn Llynvi & Porthcawl Railway.[26] It was not empowered to the raise further capital and nothing is said about the SWR in those two Acts. It was not until a further Act in 1855 that the LVR was moved to complete this line, prompted by the threat of another railway 'muscling' in on its territory, when it converted the tramroad into a broad-gauge railway connected to the SWR at Bridgend.[27] Another Irish railway, the Cork & Waterford Railway, was authorised on the 26 August 1846,[28] and under its Act no powers were given to allow the SWR to subscribe. Staying with Irish branches, the Waterford, Wexford, Wicklow & Dublin Railway was authorised to carry out alterations in a further Act of 25 June 1847.[29]

The Swansea Valley Railway was authorised on 2 July 1847.[30] It had powers to form a railway from Swansea into the Swansea Valley towards Ystradgwynlais and to acquire a railway or, more accurately, a collection of tramroads, also known as the Swansea Valley Railway. This was the start of a complicated story which saw the Swansea Valley Railway going on to become the Swansea Vale Railway and eventually ending up in the ownership of the Midland Railway.[31] Under the 1847 Act the SVR could raise up to £220,000 by shares and £73,333 by loans. There were powers to sell or lease to the SWR or GWR, but, and this was to cause problems in the future, no powers given to the SWR to subscribe.[32] The Vale of Neath Railway Co. returned to Parliament in 1847. On 2 July 1847 it was authorised to construct additional branches and to lease or sale them to SWR, but gives no power to the SWR to subscribe.[33] The additional share capital of the VNR was set at £45,000 and by loans £15,000.

In 1848 the SWR took legal powers to subscribe to the Waterford, Wexford, Wicklow & Dublin Railway and the Vale of Neath Railway. For the former, an Act of 30 June 1848 authorised the SWR to subscribe £250,000 to the Waterford, Wexford, Wicklow & Dublin Railway and to raise the same, but not by guaranteed shares or preferential dividends.[34] The SWR could vote by an agent in respect of their shares and the Waterford, Wexford, Wicklow & Dublin Railway could have twelve directors in number with the SWR nominating seven that were also directors of the SWR. For each £25,700 sold off by the SWR of their investment of £250,000, they would lose the right of appointing one director. The SWR were restricted from paying interest on calls of any shares issued to raise the amount of their subscription of £250,000. The Act also allowed for the alteration of the gauge of the Dublin & Kingstown Railway to 5ft 3in. The Dublin & Kingstown Railway had been built to the Irish uniform standard gauge of 6ft 2in and the Act allowed for it to be reduced to the new Irish standard of 5ft 3in gauge, which remains the Irish standard. The Vale of Neath Railway Amendment Act of 30 June 1848 authorised the SWR to subscribe for £127,780 of the Vale of Neath Railway Co.'s capital and to nominate four directors of the latter company.[35]

So in the year 1849, and a difficult period for the SWR, the main constituents can be seen in place, legally if not physically, of a broad-gauge 'communications and coal' network, the SWR itself, the Gloucester & Dean Forest, Bristol & South Wales Junction, Tenby, Saundersfoot & South Wales, Vale of Neath, Swansea Valley & Lynvi Valley Railways together with the Irish lines, the Cork & Waterford and the Waterford, Wexford, Wicklow & Dublin Railways. Almost all of these lines would undergo setbacks and changes to plans with further Acts to follow. With the problems of defaulting subscribers and the financial depression generally, the SWR returned to Parliament to extend the time originally granted to acquire land on 17 May 1850 and further powers on 15 July 1850. The year 1850 marked the opening of the first section of the SWR and with the line now open, the GWR sought powers to purchase the SWR and the Gloucester & Dean Forest Railway by an Act of 3 July 1851.[36] On the same date the SWR obtained an Act giving powers to build a new railway in the Forest of Dean and new lines at Cardiff and Briton Ferry. It had powers to make mutual agreements over a dock at Baglan and to build a joint station at Neath for the VNR and SWR. There was also a clause to stop the SWR taking the property of the TVR without consent, a sign of the distrust existing between the two Brunel engineered lines. Since 1849 the SWR had been seeking to make changes regarding the western end of the line and by June 1852 it had overcome opposition to do so. By an Act of 17 June 1852 the SWR obtained powers to abandon portions of the line from Fishguard and at Haverfordwest and construct a new line to Milford Haven, specifically to construct a viaduct across the river Cleddau and a landing place at Neyland Point. It also allowed new lines at Newport and to address the position regarding the SWR and TVR regarding station accommodation – on the TVR's terms. Connections with another standard-gauge line, the Monmouthshire Railway & Canal Co., also featured in this Act. Three other Acts on 20 August 1853 dealt with the Forest of Dean, the sale to the GWR and powers to extend the Pembroke line to Pennar Mouth.

The first 'post crisis' broad-gauge railway was incorporated on 15 August 1853, the South Wales Mineral Railway (SWMR). This short railway, eleven and a half miles long, was to run from a connection with the SWR at Briton Ferry to the Glyncorrwg mineral district, with a short branch from Baglan to coal mines at Fordecwyn. The dock at Briton Ferry, of which Brunel was engineer, was the main destination for the trade of the line. Another railway in this period was the Carmarthen & Cardigan Railway which was incorporated to build a line from the SWR at Carmarthen to Newcastle Emlyn with the intention, hence the name, to eventually reach Cardigan town and harbour, an objective it never realised. The SWR continued to return to Parliament; on 10 July 1854 it was granted powers to acquire land at Swansea and the following year to build new works (26 June 1855). On 2 July 1855 the Aberdare Valley Railway was incorporated, essentially a short (one and a quarter miles) extension to the Aberdare branch of the

VNR. In 1856 the Milford Railway was promoted by interests aggrieved that Brunel had chosen Neyland instead of Milford Haven as his terminus. This three-and-a-half-mile line ran from a junction at Johnston on the Neyland extension of the SWR and was incorporated on 5 June 1856.

A new line was proposed and incorporated on 13 June 1857 which was to be the last broad-gauge railway company incorporated in south Wales. The Ely Valley Railway ran from Llantrisant on the SWR to Tonyrefail and Penygaig, with branches to Gellyrhaidd colliery and the iron ore mines at Brofiskin. Whilst some broad-gauge lines and extensions would continue to be authorised, for example the Portskewett branch of the Bristol & South Wales Union Railway (27 July 1857), the SWR and its allies were continually engaged in fighting standard-gauge incursions or conversions. Indeed, even the new Ely Valley Railway was threatening in 1860 to promote a Bill in Parliament to change its gauge from broad to standard.[37] On 2 August 1858 the SWR obtained an Act to take land at Newport and in connection with the Pembroke line, the final Act as far as the SWR came five years later. This finally allowed for the amalgamation of the SWR with GWR and was granted on 21 July 1863.

To return to the first broad-gauge railway in south Wales, the South Wales Railway, the change of the title from 'Gloucester & South Wales Railway' clearly indicated one thing: that Gloucester was no longer as important as first mooted in the route of the line. Brunel decided that a more direct crossing of the river Severn with regard to the line entering Wales, rather than passing through and around Gloucester, was warranted. The city was obviously not happy about the change of plan involving the potential loss of trade that a main railway trunk route might have brought. When Brunel's plans became known about the crossing of the river Severn, a petition by the Mayor and citizens against the possible constraints on navigation was raised, but the main objection would be raised by the Admiralty. In June 1845 James Walker reported on the proposed crossing of the river Severn. His report, 'River Severn and South Wales Railway',[38] dashed Brunel's plans for a railway crossing of the Severn, echoing what had been done to his aspirations for a railway packet port at Porthdinllaen two years earlier by another of Walker's reports. Walker was experienced in all matters maritime, having a long association with Trinity House for which he, or his partnership, had been responsible for some twenty-nine lighthouses.[39] His first lighthouse for Trinity House was the modest West Usk lighthouse, on the foreshore of the Usk estuary near Newport in Gwent, a small, squat circular tower lighthouse that was first lit on 1 December 1821.[40] As a light, West Usk served vessels proceeding from the Bristol Channel to the river Severn, the latter being a river of which Walker had a long association. In 1836 he accompanied Thomas Rhodes (1789–1868), the engineer to the proposed Severn Improvement Co., and William, later Sir William, Cubitt (1785–1861) on a view of the river which he to quote as '… in point of importance inferior to scarcely any river in the Kingdom'.[41]

As with the earlier report on communication with Ireland, this report had been commissioned by Sir John Barrow (1764–1848), who served as the second secretary to the Admiralty from 1804 to 1845. Barrow's skills as an administrator and able organiser were credited with much of the British Navy's supremacy and he was to become a founder member and key figure in the foundation of the Royal Geographical Society in 1830.[42] Barrow retired in 1845, and in 1850, two years after his death, a lighthouse-style monument, which took the shape of a former Eddystone Lighthouse, was erected in his honour on Hoad Hill high above the market town of Ulverston in Lancashire. The monument was erected by public subscription and included donations from Walker and Brunel.[43] Before Barrow retired, however, Walker reported to him on 3 June 1845, stating that he had been instructed on 28 March 1845 to inform the Lords of the Admiralty of his opinion of the effects upon the navigation of the river Severn by two bridges. From a junction at Standish on the eastern bank of the Severn with the Cheltenham & Great Western Union Railway, a line was to travel as far as Saul, within one mile of the Severn, and then form two branches, one going off in a southerly, and the other in a northerly, direction. Walker refers to these two railways forming one trunk from the C&GWUR.[44] The first and most important of the two railway bridges was, '... proposed to cross it at Frethern, half a mile above Hock Crib, three miles below Newnham, or twenty miles below Gloucester, for the purpose of carrying a Railway into South Wales'. The second was to cross at Priding, three miles above Newnham, where it would proceed towards the Forest of Dean, Monmouth and Hereford. As part of his report Walker briefly relates the importance of the Severn for navigation, stating that the annual tonnage of the river passing the site of the proposed bridges is 363,000, or about 1,000 tons a day.[45] The vast majority of vessels are barges or trows fitted with lowering masts; those vessels with fixed masts that would be unable to go beyond the bridges comprise five sloops that go to Newnham and a much greater number which go to Bullo Pill, '... one mile below Newnham, to which the place the coal, and other produce of the Forest of Dean is conveyed by a Railway'.[46] Walker discusses the merits in saving distance by crossing the river rather than going via Gloucester, 'The temptation to an improved lower crossing is great, as the distance from Bristol to Newport, round by Parliamentary line of Railway, is sixty miles, or double the distance by crossing the Severn at or near Chepstow.'

At this point a note is made of a proposed suspension bridge by Thomas Fulljames (1808–74) the County Surveyor of Gloucester, architect, and civil engineer. This bridge is proposed to cross at the Old Ferry or Upper Aust passage 120ft above high water. Having stated that the purpose of the crossings is in shortening distance, Walker now deals with the measure of how they might affect the free navigation of the river, '... and preserving it unharmed for the improvement of future skill and capital'. Walker goes on to describe the bridges as follows:

> ... of timber, the soffits level, the distance between the piers fifty-seven feet, and the piers themselves three feet, the clear navigation height above high water twenty-two feet, and above low water forty-two feet. Mr. Brunel states, that if fifty-seven feet be thought too little, the Railway Company would agree to extend the openings to even one hundred feet clear opening.

In anticipation of objection to the bridges interfering with the clear navigation, the SWR had also proposed a straight cut or canal across the horse-shoe bend of the river, from Hock Crib to Framilode, a one-and-a-half-mile cut that would save eight miles around the horse-shoe. The exact method of operation had not been settled; it could be a canal with locks or an open channel, by whatever way an additional bridge would be required to take the railway across the Arlingham horse-shoe. Walker then deals with the effect of the two bridges, without taking this cut or canal into account, and describes the nature of the river, the changing route of the navigational channel and the tidal rise and fall. He describes the natural weirs that cause the unusual feature of the river high-water mark being higher at Sharpness point than higher up the river (at any point below Gloucester) and the effect of the Severn Bore. The benefits of the tides for navigation are outlined by the statement that the Severn is of value as a navigation during spring tides only and for a very short time during each tide, for the return of the ebbing current is almost as rapid as that of the flood. Notwithstanding this, the business done upon the Severn '… by taking advantage of the sudden rise and rush of the spring flood tide, is very great'. All of which meant that the vessels using the river will rely on sail to steady them and keep them under command of the helm; if they had to lower their masts to go under the first of the bridges (the SWR main line) all control would be lost, 'Even supposing the openings to be 100 feet, as some of the trows are seventy-six feet long, there must be a risk of their being lifted up "broadside on" and striking the piers'.[47]

Walkers concludes his opinion, backed by that of a number of professionals connected with the trade of the river and trow-men, by stating that, 'Indeed this bridge is unfortunately in about the very worst place in the river for navigation.' The other bridge is considered not to be so dangerous but still has problems because of its position at the upper end of another shifting part of the navigation called 'the Lake'. The railway company had been negotiating with the two groups of vessels with fixed masts; they would compensate the Newnham wharfs for loss of trade and had offered to extend the Forest of Dean Tramroad to Brimspill below the proposed bridge. However, in light of the navigational difficulties that would be caused and unless a safe substitute for the present channel was found, Walker considered the objections to be quite decisive, 'in preventing the execution of the Railway bridges'. There was still the option of the cut or canal as a substitute, the feature of this being described by Brunel as having the qualities of a canal and open river:

> … a canal in so far as the navigable channel will have a lock near each end, with the water between the locks, kept up to a level, but each end, for about one quarter of a mile, to be outside the lock and open, that is, a canal with locks, but arranged to pass a large body of water so as to create an in-draught to vessels going into it out of the river at one end, and a current out of the other end, which would also keep the channel clear. It is also proposed to run out jetties from the end of the canal into deep water; that at Hock Crib being for the purpose of creating an eddy at flood tide, and for sheltering vessels before entering the canal.[48]

Brunel also proposed a back cut parallel to the canal, for the purpose of passing a large body of water, with sluices at each end to scour the entrance outside the gates. The locks were proposed to be 45ft wide and it was suggested that the flood tide could be used to accelerate the passage of vessels through the canal. Another option for a new channel for the river would be just a straight cut without lock gates and he (Brunel) had no objection to make it:

> … As an engineer, however, he thought there would be difficulties in managing the current, but that the principle of the back cut might be extended, so as to take the river through it.

Despite all this, Walker concludes that although Brunel is prepared to do whatever may be reasonably demanded to meet the objections of the trade, '… none of the plans I have seen give a reasonable probability of accomplishing this…' There were five objections to the proposed canal, ranging from problems of maintaining water depth of the approach channels, maintaining sufficient width through the build up of mud, tides and currents carrying vessels past the canal entrance and striking the piers of the bridge, vessels missing tides while in the canal and the fact that there would three or four opening bridges spanning the canal. Each bridge would necessitate the canal to be of a contracted width at that point and there would be delays to either railway or navigation. Walker felt that if such a proposal were effected it would be improper to charge for using the new channel and that the burden of maintaining the canal in terms of water depth, locks and bridges would have to be properly provided for. There was also the effect that would be created by the river now passing through the channel and tearing up the ground with great force. Problems of silting up would be caused and there was a danger that a higher head of water would be taken up to the quays of Gloucester and Worcester. If the locks and swing bridges were put in place, Walker believed they would be obstructions that would preclude any future improvements, '… the improvements of the Severn deserve the best attention, the facility of making these improvements should not be interfered with, without a much stronger necessity than the present'.[49]

There was an attempt not to be completely negative by Walker who concluded his report by referring to the possibility of tunnelling under the river, referring to the aborted Severn tunnel of 1810. This came about following the construction of the Haie Hill tunnel in September 1809 when various individual proprietors of the Bullo Pill Railway Co. (the railway having been built without an Act of Parliament up until June 1809) felt confident to engage in a more ambitious venture – a tunnel under the Severn.[50] This, the Severn Tunnel Co., was incorporated by Act of Parliament of 24 May 1810 to build a tunnel starting at a point midway between Newnham Church and Bullo Pill to a point in the parish of Arlingham. It was to be a road tunnel some 13ft high and 12ft wide, and although there was no reference to rails being laid in the tunnel, adapted rail or tramroad vehicles would be allowed to travel through. By 13 November 1812 the tunnel had progressed to roughly midway under the river when disaster struck; water broke in and flooded the workings. The miners escaped with their lives and although it was felt at the time to be a temporary setback, the tunnel was abandoned when the breech proved irreparable. Walker thought that such a proposal could be picked up:

> The rocky strata, particularly where the Bridge for the South Wales Railway is now proposed, the low level of the ground on one side, and the shallowness of the river at that

spot, all appear favourable for tunnelling; which, if done at proper levels, and in the proper directions, appears a comparatively unobjectionable substitute for the bridges.[51]

Brunel was to take this advice on board and is believed to have consulted Vignoles in examining the possibility of tunnelling under the river Severn. For the time being, at least, Brunel was to abandon his ideas here and go 'the long way round' through Gloucester, but he was to later consider an alternative to the timber viaducts with their 57ft spans and 3ft-wide piers, with sketches for the first designs for the Saltash crossing. Alongside these sketches Brunel writes the comments, 'Is 1,100ft practicable?'. That he did not proceed indicates that perhaps it was impracticable. Considering that his longest railway span was 455ft, the span of each of the two main spans of the Royal Albert Bridge over the river Tamar at Saltash, it is somewhat incredible to contemplate. Whilst the Royal Albert Bridge was to be Brunel's final form of his tubular suspension bridge, he would develop the idea with a work not too far removed from the Severn, the Chepstow Bridge over the river Wye.

As well as the two Severn bridges, the branch to Monmouth would also be abandoned, but not before some work had been carried out. In connection with the branch, Brunel entered into negotiation with local landowners; in Monmouth itself he agreed conditions put forward by the vicar of Dixton, through whose land the line would pass on its way from a proposed station at May Hill, to Ross. The line followed the river on an embankment passing through the vicarage field, and a letter from Brunel to the vicar of Dixton confirms the conditions, i.e. £500 and £50 costs for the strip of land, with the embankment facing the house to be 'ornamented' and the tunnel for the drive to be at least 10ft high.[52] It was also agreed that the works would be completed to the vicar's satisfaction. An embankment from the station to a bridge over the river Wye and a viaduct would take the line across the Troy meadows to a tunnel leading into the Trothy Valley. Some 170 tons of equipment was brought by the contractors in order to be close to the worksite, and workmen were reported to be at work on the tunnel in February 1847. The excavated spoil was dumped on the Troy meadows, but such activity was short lived and in May the same year the *Glamorgan, Monmouthshire and Brecon Gazette* remarked that the spoil remained as a '… memorial to the broken promises of the South Wales Railway Company'.[53] It was said that the Duke of Beaufort, for whom Brunel was to be called upon for advice on engineering matters at Swansea in 1846, had only agreed not to oppose the line of the SWR from Chepstow to Newport if the Monmouth branch was built. Finally, in 1849 an advertised sale of railway goods, wagons and tools brought closure to the episode.[54]

The Bullo Pill or Forest of Dean Railway has already been mentioned in connection with the harbour of Bullo Pill. Originally built as a 4ft-gauge tramroad, it was opened in 1809, with the harbour at Bullo Pill following shortly afterwards. The tramroad had been nearly completed when an Act of Parliament was obtained on 10 June 1809 by the proprietors who now sought powers to extend their line and make branches.[55] The line proceeded from the tramroad already built, at Cinderford Bridge, in a northerly direction to the summit of the hill above Churchway Engine, a three-mile-long line which would connect with a junction with the Severn & Wye Railroad. A branch also ran from a place

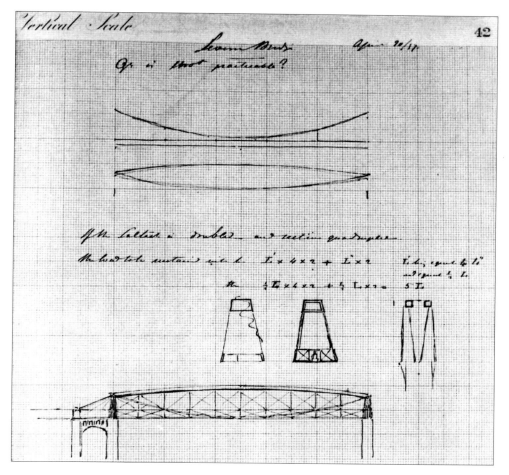

Sketch of Saltash bridge design but headed 'Severn Bridge. Q: is 1,100ft practicable?' From large sketchbook 11, f.42, 20 April 1857. (Courtesy of University of Bristol special collections)

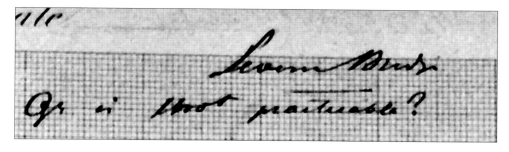

Close-up of comment, 'Is 1,100ft practicable?'. (Courtesy of University of Bristol special collections)

called the Dam, to the Upper and Lower Bilson Works; another from the same place to Kelmsley Green, with another branching off from Nofold Engine, to the Old Engine and Nofold Green. A number of short branches then extended from these to serve coal and other mines in the forest. On 5 May 1826, the royal assent was given to another Act, by which a company, consisting of eighteen persons, agreed to purchase the interest of the Bullo Pill Railway Co., and make the whole undertaking public, to be incorporated by the name of 'The Forest of Dean Railway Company'. Twenty-four years later the line was purchased by the SWR in 1850 and was converted to broad gauge in 1854. In his engineer's report to the half-yearly meeting of the SWR, dated 27 February 1854, Brunel reported that, 'The works of the Bullo Pill or Forest of Dean Branch have been proceeded with vigorously, under considerable difficulties, more particularly that of enlarging and lowering the bottom of the original small tunnel, without stopping the traffic'.[56]

Described by MacDermot as a very small tunnel, and quoting Brunel as saying it was a 'tedious and difficult work', this was Haie Hill tunnel which, '… seems to be the first on a public railway in the British Isles, probably the world. Its length is now 1,064 yards.'[57] Two other tunnels were constructed near Soudley as part of the task of improving and converting the line to the broad gauge and at Bullo Pill wharf Brunel designed a 30ft-span drawbridge of wrought iron on a timber framework, which crossed the lock entrance and has since been removed. As Bullo Pill became part of the SWR, the line at this point did not cause any interference to its operation as a harbour; other ports on the Severn would not escape so lightly. Purton in Gloucestershire was one of the places specifically mentioned by Brunel during his 1836 survey for the Gloucester & South Wales Railway. Writing in May 1836 to his surveyor, Mr Morris, in Newport, Brunel instructed him to, '… Press on the survey at Chepstow, Newport and Purton at the places indicated in order that I may mark a line there and have sections taken'.[58]

When Brunel returned with the SWR he would be responsible for changing the working way of life for Purton and the nearby hamlet of Gatcombe. Exporting the timber of the Forest of Dean through the ports that existed at both places, much of which was destined for the Royal Navy, would stop, and the salmon fishing trade was curtailed. With its quay and a large stone slipway, Purton also operated one of the earliest ferries, known as the Purton Passage Ferry, which continued until the late nineteenth century. Both ports would decline due to the construction of the SWR. The low embankment of the railway carved through Gatcombe's quay, stone and timber pier and slipway, but access to the quay, now on the wrong side, allowed salmon fishing to continue. A building very close to the line, a red house now known as Drake's House, was once the *Sloop Inn*, which served the busy port and was patronised by sailors such as Sir Francis Drake.[59] Purton also has some unusual railway connections, dating to before and after the opening of the SWR. A three-span viaduct crossing the Etloe to Purton road was built around 1832 for the Purton Steam Carriage Road, a railway that was never completed, but planned to include the first crossing of the river Severn by a moveable bridge.[60] The remains of a Severn bridge that was completed can be seen at Purton, not a movable bridge but the Severn Railway Bridge, constructed in 1879 and continuing in use until the tragic events of 1960.[61] One of the engineers on the Severn Railway Bridge was George Wells Owen (b.1839), the eldest son of William George Owen.

The Haie Hill tunnel on the Forest of Dean branch of the SWR. (SKJ photograph)

NOTES

1 University of Bristol, Special Collections. Comment made by Brunel in his large sketchbook 11, f.42, 20 April 1857.

2 *Statement of the position of the South Wales Railway Co., in reference to its relations with the Great Western Railway Co.* A pamphlet published by John Duncan of 72 Lombard Street, London, 12 July 1849. National Library of Wales, Cilciffeth 2 collection 794.

3 For an explanation of the 'little' and the 'large' railway manias, see Jones, Stephen K. (2005) p.103.

4 Examination of copy of SWR Act of 4 August 1845 in Newport Reference Library (qM000625 SOU). This is the 1845 Act, reprinted in 1858. The long title can be found in Jones, T.I. Jeffreys ed. (1966), p.87. *Acts of Parliament Concerning Wales 1714-1901.* University of Wales Press: Cardiff. cxc (L. and P.) (582).

5 The Act lists the Capital of the Co. at £2,800,000 but both E.T. MacDermot (in *History of the Great Western Railway,* vol 1. revised by Clinker, C.R. (1964)) and Barrie, D.S.M. (in *A Regional History of Great Britain,* vol.12, *South Wales,* revised by Baughan, Peter E. (1994)) give the capital as £2,500,000.

6 SWR Act of 4 August 1845 in Newport Reference Library (qM000625 SOU), section vi.

7 SWR Acts in Newport Reference Library (qM000625 SOU), section xxv.

8 SWR Act of 4 August 1845 in Newport Reference Library (qM000625 SOU), section xxviii to xxxi.

9 SWR Act of 4 August 1845 in Newport Reference Library (qM000625 SOU), sections xlii & xliii.

10 The Taff Vale Railway was built to the standard gauge and there would not be a connection for several years.

11 SWR Act of 27 July 1846, in Newport Reference Library (qM000625 SOU), section vii. Jones, T.I. Jeffreys ed. (1966), p.87, ccxxxix (L. and P.) (585).

12 Jones, T.I. Jeffreys ed. (1966), p.89. cix (L. and P.) (602).

13 9 & 10 Vic., cap.105, 1846. The first prospectus for the B&SWJR, in *The Times* for 9 April 1845, gives George and John Rennie as Engineers. Brunel had taken on this role by the time of the publication of the Monmouth Extension Prospectus in June 1845.

14 Norris, John (1985), p.7, *The Bristol and South Wales Union Railway*, Railway and Canal Historical Society: Oakham.

15 Colin Chapman informs me that J.E. Blackwell was appointed engineer of this scheme at the first meeting of the Provisional Committee on 3 November 1854. Plans were deposited in November 1854 but the scheme was abandoned. A revised proposal (along the lines of B&SWJR) was suggested by Brunel who succeeded Blackwell as engineer in 1855. This was enacted as the Bristol & South Wales Union Railway by Act of 27 July 1857.

16 9 & 10 Vic., cap.208, 1846.

17 9 & 10 Vic., cap.256, 1846.

18 The intention of the Pembroke & Tenby Railway, incorporated on 21 July 1859, was to lay mixed gauge but it opened on the standard gauge.

19 9 & 10 Vic., cap.240, 1846.

20 MacDermot, E.T. (revised by Clinker, C.R., (1964)), p.156, *History of the Great Western Railway*, vol.1, Ian Allen Ltd: London.

21 University of Bristol, Special Collections, PLB 26 May 1855.

22 9 & 10 Vic., cap.341, 1846.

23 The Aberdare Railway would become part of Brunel's only standard gauge, the Taff Vale Railway, see Jones, Stephen K. (2005), p.200–202.

24 9 & 10 Vic., cap.353, 1846.

25 10 & 11 Vic., cap.72, 1847.

26 10 & 11 Vic., cap.295, 1847.

27 MacDermot, E.T. (revised by Clinker, C.R., (1964)), vol.1, p.305. See Chapter 9 for further details.

28 9 and 10 Vict., cap.397, 1846.

29 10 & 11 Vict., cap.71, 1847. The Act is silent as to the SWR.

30 10 and 11 Vict. cap.101, 1847.

31 Barrie, D.S.M., revised by Baughan, Peter E. (1994), p.205–207, *A Regional History of Great Britain*, vol.12, *South Wales*, David St John Thomas Publisher: Nairn.

32 10 & 11 Vict., cap.101, 1847. A joint stock company would also become involved in the acquisition of the old SVR.

33 10 & 11 Vict., cap.74, 1847.

34 11 and 12 Vict., cap.29, 1848.

35 11 & 12 Vict., cap.27, 1848.

36 On the same date, 3 July 1851, the SWR was granted powers to ratify subscriptions.

37 For a full account of the Ely Valley Railway see Chapman, Colin, (2000), *Ely Valley Railway*, Oakwood Press: Usk, and MacDermot, E.T. (revised by Clinker, C.R. (1964)), vol.1, p.306.

38 ICE Record Acc No.1845 WALRSS River Severn and South Wales Railway, Walker, James. An associate of Thomas Telford, Walker succeeded him as president of the Institution of Civil Engineers, serving from 1834 to 1845.

39 Hague, Douglas B. (1994), p.18, *Lighthouses of Wales, Their Architecture and Archaeology*, Royal Commission on the Ancient and Historical Monuments in Wales: Aberystwyth.

40 Hague, Douglas B. (1994), pp.95-96, West Usk was a traditional light that went out of use by 1922 and is now a hotel.

41 Smith, Denis (1997), p.43, James Walker (1781–1862): Civil Engineer, in *Newcomen Society Transactions*, Volume 69A, Newcomen Society: London. Quoted from Walker's Report to the Glos. & Berkly Canal Co., March 1841, p.3.

42 Barrow also promoted British exploration, official and semi-official, most notably of West Africa and the North Polar Region with attempts to find a north-west passage from east to west through the Canadian Arctic.

43 Brunel, J.K. Esq. [sic], gave £5.5.0 (five guineas) and Walker, James, Esq., O.E. gave £3.3.0 (three guineas). See www.sirjohnbarrowmonument.co.uk/subscribers1850.htm. Another donor was Smyth, Captain W. H., R.N., F.R.S., the same Capt. Smyth, who had criticised Brunel and the TVR through his '*Nautical Observations…*' see Jones, Stephen K. (2005), pp.171-2, and another donor was John Brogden, a Lancashire entrepreneur who was to establish a family business based on mineral exploitation in the Llynvi and Ogmore valleys.

44 ICE Record Acc No.1845 WALRSS p.1.

45 This figure excludes 205,000 tons that pass through the Gloucester and Berkely Canal and leave the canal at Sharpness Point.

46 ICE Record Acc No.1845 WALRSS, p.2. This was the Bullo Pill Railway which had become part of the Forest of Dean Railway Co. in 1826.

47 ICE Record Acc No. 1845 WALRSS, p.10.

48 ICE Record Acc No. 1845 WALRSS, pp.11-12.

49 ICE Record Acc No. 1845 WALRSS, p.17.

50 Paar, H. W. (1965, second edition 1971), p.141, *The Great Western Railway in Dean, A History of the Railways of the Forest of Dean: Part Two*, David & Charles: Newton Abbot.

51 ICE Record Acc No.1845 WALRSS, p.17.

52 Kissack, Keith (1986), p.167, Victorian Monmouth, Monmouth Historical and Educational Trust: Monmouth.

53 *Glamorgan, Monmouthshire and Brecon Gazette*, 20 February and 15 May 1847.

54 Kissack, Keith (1986), p.167.

55 49 George III. Cap.158, Royal Assent 10 June, 1809.

56 *Cardiff and Merthyr Guardian*, 4 March 1854.

57 MacDermot, E.T. (revised by Clinker, C.R., (1964)), p.302.

58 See Jones Stephen K. (2005), pp.119-20.

59 Visits connected with naval business; the Vice Admiral Sir William Wintour, lived at Lydney. Purton House is also reputed to have associations with Sir Walter Raleigh. Mitchell, Jim, *Explore the Severn* in the Severn Tidings Newsletter, Issue 4, Autumn 2004, Severn Estuary Partnership, Cardiff University.

60 The viaduct is a Grade II listed structure.

61 On 25 October 1960 two spans of the bridge were brought down when fuel barges collided with one of the piers, killing five members of the barge crews.

5

CAPITAL CREATION
'WELL I'LL GO TO CARDIFF'[1]

William George Owen (1810–85) started work for Brunel shortly after the start of his professional career as an engineer, a career that was to see him eventually succeed to the position of GWR engineer. Owen has been briefly mentioned already in Chapter 2 as a possible collaborator of Henry Archer in promoting Porthdinllaen as a railway port. Owen had four sons, three of whom became engineers and it was the one son who chose medicine instead of engineering that Brunel was godfather to in 1850. Herbert, later Sir Herbert, Isambard Owen (1850–1927) was the subject of a biography by his daughters in 1963.[2] A statement in the book claims that his father was '... actively engaged on the famous "pedwar llew tew" [Britannia Bridge] carrying the Holyhead railway across the Straits, when the great Brunel made him a tentative offer to be his second-in-command in his lifework of the Great Western'.[3]

Although this information on Owen tends to be anecdotal, it is difficult to align it with the chronology of Owen's work with Brunel, and far from being his second-in-command, Owen was actually offered the post of 'sub-assistant engineer' in January 1836 and then not even by Brunel himself, in January 1836.[4] Owen was then employed by Brunel until his death, which obviously makes it difficult for him to have been engaged in any capacity on the Britannia Bridge.[5] Owen was the son of William Owen of Caernarvon, where William George Owen was born in 1810. He was educated at Malpas School, Cheshire, and on 27 May 1828 become an articled apprentice with George Hennet. Hennet is listed as a civil engineer of Guildford Street, London, although the indenture gives Great Ormond Street as the address. During his stay with Hennet, Owen was to carry out surveys on the route of the London to Birmingham Railway.[6] Before Owen joined Brunel he had supervised the building of the bridge over the River Seiont near Caernarvon which was completed in 1835.[7] Of the sons that went into engineering, William Lancaster Owen is better known as an engineer. At Chepstow Brunel had to cross the river Wye at a point where there were cliffs on the English bank and muddy flats on the Welsh side. Brunel originally considered taking the line, on the Gloucestershire side, closer to the Severn to cross near the mouth of the river

Wye. However, George Ormerod of Sudbury Park objected to Brunel taking the line through his estate.[8] There was also the consideration of river navigation in providing a clear headway of 50ft and a clear span of 300ft, leading to an alternative –the present route – being chosen. Vessels were to have uninterrupted passage up to Rastrick's iron road bridge less than half a mile away, where the customs house was situated and beyond to Brockweir, Redbrook and Monmouth. Chepstow provided the proving ground for his new bridge, crossing the river Wye where Brunel's first thoughts were for a trussed timber structure. Brunel had replied to Vignoles in November 1844 in answer to his request for his views on large timber works he was considering for what was to be his last Irish line, the Waterford & Limerick Railway. Brunel did not pass comment on Vignoles' design for these but makes a comment that appears to refer to his proposed use of timber at Chepstow, '… I have used timber a great deal in construction and see no difficulty in making arches for railways of 250 feet span – in fact I am projecting a larger one at the present.'[9] Brunel, however, rejected timber in order to solve the problems involving a total crossing of 600ft, and developed his tubular suspension design, in which a wrought-iron tubular arch takes the pull of the suspension chains from which a girder bridge deck is suspended. It was a design described as:

> … two independent and statically determinate Pratt-type trusses resulting in much reduced construction costs, compared with the contemporary tubular bridges of Stephenson at Conway and across the Menai Straits. Thus, the Chepstow Bridge should be considered as a prototype for major railway bridges for the hundred years rather than simply the proving ground for the design for the Saltash Bridge which has remained a unique structure.[10]

Brunel's tubular suspension bridge across the river Wye. In this Illustrated London News *engraving of 24 July 1852 the artist has shown the tube without any camber and the station with an all-over roof. (SKJ collection)*

Left: *William George Owen 1810–85.
(From* Heulwen & Hedydd Owen,
Sir Isambard Owen, A Biography,
Caernarvon, 1963*)*

Below: *Plaque to Sir Isambard Owen on
Bellevue House, later known as High Trees
and now Monmouthshire County Council
offices. (SKJ photograph)*

Bellevue House, the home of William George Owen in 1850. (SKJ photograph)

Contemporary lithograph of Chepstow station shortly after opening. (SKJ collection)

Although this was not the river Severn, with all the dangers and navigational interests that had worked against Brunel for his proposed crossing, the river Wye, like the Severn, still had the second highest tidal range in the world and the foundations for the cast-iron river piers had to be sunk far below the water level of the river until they found a solid foundation and then filled with concrete. Unusually for Brunel, the result was an non-symmetrical design although there was little he could do with the constraints of the landscape. The bridge consisted of a single high-level span of 300ft long and 100ft above high water with three approach spans 100ft long, the railway emerging from a cutting cut into the cliff, crossing the main span and then the low lying banks on the Welsh side, and then on a high embankment into Chepstow station. Brunel built his Chepstow tubes on the flat land behind the shore of the right bank of the river; they had to be raised more than 100ft and lifted clear of shipping within twelve hours. Brunel kept the weight as low as possible. The tubes were 9ft in diameter, 312ft long and weighed a mere 138 tons apiece, but were not self-supporting. Without the inward pull from the chains at each end, and the upward support of the posts or struts of the 'trusses', the tubes could not be expected to carry their own deadweight. Temporary trusses were, therefore, used and tested. The tube was built on low ground and floated by manoeuvring into launching position at right angles to the bank. A pontoon of six barges was brought under the overhanging tube. The tube was launched end-on across the river. On 8 April 1852 the launch began at 9 a.m. During the course of the day the tube was lifted well clear of ship masts. Shortly afterwards the tube reached the top level of the tower which was built of cast iron above the pier cylinders which Brunel had sunk by the pneumatic method, the upper end being sealed and compressed air introduced to keep water out. The down line was opened for single-line traffic on 14 July 1852. The up line was dealt with in the same way and was completed the following April.[11] The main line between Chepstow and Swansea had been open for two years before traffic could pass across the bridge.

No doubt returning from work on the SWR, Brunel was travelling in the direction of Gloucester when he was involved in a road accident, within a mile or two of Newnham, on Saturday 14 April 1849, stating that he '... was ascending a hill and near the top when we came into collision with a gig... I had very strong lights to the carriage and I was awake at the time...'[12]

Brunel was reporting on the accident in anticipation of a letter from Matthew & Son, prominent attorneys and solicitors of the City of Gloucester, representing their client, Mr Halford, who was involved in the accident.

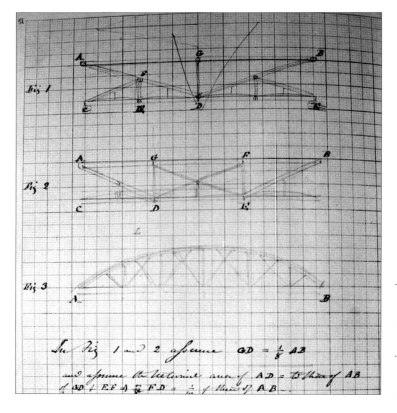

Sketch showing various ideas being worked out for large-span crossings, ideas for tubular suspension and bow string girders. From small sketchbook 25, f.21, February 1848. (Courtesy of University of Bristol special collections)

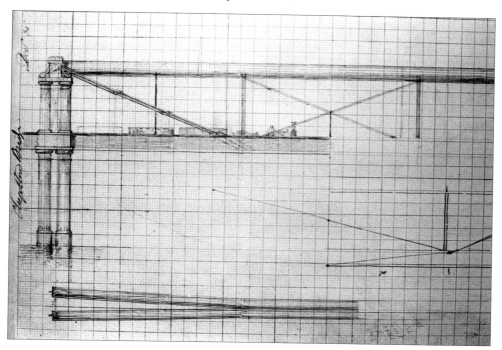

Above: *Brunel's development of the Wye Bridge at Chepstow. From small sketchbook 25, f.27, 30 December 1848. (Courtesy of University of Bristol special collections)*

Right: *Sketch from the same process of development; note the rail deck girdes being tried at an inclined angle. From small sketchbook 25, f.26, 30 December 1848. (Courtesy of University of Bristol special collections)*

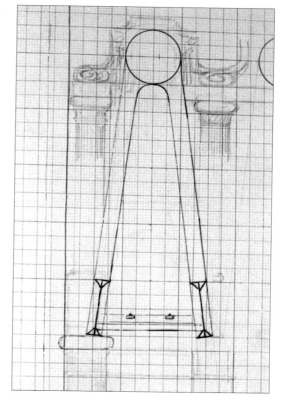

View of Chepstow station. A porter can be seen on the left with a pointsman next to him. The building seen behind is a steam mill built by Robert Sharpe, a SWR contractor, as a speculative venture. (From The Railway Magazine, *vol. II, 1898)*

The Wye Bridge, Chepstow, photographed on 11 June 1852 by John Dillwyn Llewelyn. (Courtesy of Richard Morris)

One of the three photographs taken by John Dillwyn Llewelyn, who wrote in his diary: 'The suspension bridge over the Wye at Chepstow in the course of construction, 11 June 1852. We crossed the bridge when returning from Cornwall 26 October of the same year.' (Courtesy of Richard Morris)

The Wye Bridge was being built by Edward French who came to Chepstow from Liverpool as the successful contractor (representing Finch & Willey). He stayed in Chepstow and established a bridge works as Finch & Heath. The company became Edward Finch & Co. Ltd in 1870. (Courtesy of Richard Morris)

Above: *View of the Chepstow Bridge. Note the slight bow to the iron tube; Brunel built each tube with an upward camber. (SKJ collection)*

View of the Chepstow Bridge. 'The present work of MR Brunel's is another mode, and shows, as might be expected, his peculiarly original and bold conception, accompanied by extraordinary economy...' (Courtesy of Fairfield-Mabey Ltd)

Opposite below: *View from a Victorian stereocard showing Chepstow Bridge with boats tied up at the wharf. See modern view in colour section. (SKJ collection)*

In the meantime the section of railway from Grange Court was opened on 19 September 1851 and to accommodate the traffic between the two railheads of Chepstow and the temporary Chepstow East station on the east bank of the river Wye, passengers were taken by omnibus 'over a rough country'. This involved crossing the cast-iron road bridge over the river Wye, the first major work by the engineer John Urpeth Rastrick (who had worked with Vignoles and Walker). Chepstow East passed into history on 19 July 1852 with the opening of the down-line 'half' of the bridge and one mile of broad-gauge track between the two points, the second 'half' doubling that mileage on 18 April 1853.

Early in 1850 a major part of the railway line was complete and it was decided to run the first train on 18 June from Chepstow to the terminus at Swansea. The great day arrived and at 10 a.m. many thousands of people gathered at Chepstow to witness the start of this historic journey. The directors of the company were presented with an address and speeches were made, after which, together with many important personages, they boarded the train for the journey to Swansea. The train left on its seventy-five-mile journey to tumultuous cheers. All along the track were well-wishers, many of them waving flags, who had come from far and wide for this great event. The expected arrival of the first train caused great anticipation and excitement in Newport where the station had been decorated with wreaths of flowers, evergreens and triumphal arches. Flags flew from every building and the ships in dock were decked overall. The whole town appeared to have turned out for this great occasion, every available vantage point being taken. At last the train, pulled by two engines and with a military band in the tender, hove into sight over the new bridge. A great roar of approval went up from the crowd as it was seen that the architect and chief engineer of this massive enterprise, Brunel himself, was on the footplate of the leading engine bringing the first train slowly to its first stop – Newport.

Newport was the first major town after Chepstow; indeed the only intermediate station was Portskewett until Marshfield was opened on 2 September 1850.[13] In the early part of the 1840s Newportonians had not forgiven Cardiff for overtaking their town in size and population, but the realisation that the town would, by geographical location, receive the first train gave it one over on Cardiffians. From that time on the expression 'Well I'll go to Cardiff' was born and it is still used, particularly by old Newportonians, to denote amazement or disbelief. Meanwhile music was played continuously while greetings were exchanged by the Mayor and Corporation with the officials of the South Wales Railway Co. Then the train was on its way again, through the tunnel and on to Cardiff, the second stop, and then on to Swansea, the end of the line, where a celebratory breakfast had been arranged for 4 p.m.

Newport was no stranger to the development of the railway; an important tramroad from the two ironworks of Tredegar and Sirhowy to the port at Newport had been built between 1802 and 1805. The Sirhowy Tramroad had originally been proposed by Samuel Homfray who, with his partners, obtained an Act of Parliament for its construction at an estimated cost of £50,000. The tramroad was the longest in Britain at the time, some twenty-three miles in length, and included a road alongside, wide enough to allow carts

Newport by H. Symes, note the shape of the main span of the Usk Bridge, possibly the artist's interpretation of the original timber superstructure. (Courtesy of Newport Museum and Art Gallery)

Another view showing the bow string arch of the completed Usk Bridge. (Courtesy of Newport Museum and Art Gallery)

to pass. The major work on the tramroad was the Long Bridge viaduct at Risca, a stone viaduct approximately 50ft high with thirty-three arches, the largest number built to date in Wales. It has the distinction of being one of the oldest established in Britain for public transportation. In 1828 the tramroad was extended northwards from the east end of the Long Bridge to Crosskeys and Crumlin. Because it included a road, it provided a better means of transport than the turnpike and parish roads, being metalled and well-maintained. It was used to get to market in Newport from the valleys and the Chartists used it to march on Newport in 1839. The town was an ancient borough that had gained borough status by *c.*1120.[14] The succeeding centuries saw the market town on the river Usk flourish, despite the occasional Welsh raid or bridge collapse in the twelfth and thirteenth centuries.[15] The stone castle of Newport was to fall into decay after Owain Glyndwr's raid in 1402, but much of the east range, rising from the tidal mud banks of the Usk, was still in existence when Brunel arrived. It is still an impressive and dramatic sight today, '… in spite of the cruel pinching of the railway bridge on the N and the road bridge to the S'.[16] The local newspaper, *The Merlin*, did not support the merits of the railway:

> The proposed railway is uncalled for and unnecessary, there being for its maintenance merely the travelling and carrying which is barely sufficient to support on the road two mail coaches, two stage coaches, and four stage waggons.[17]

The opening of the SWR was to coincide with the Borough of Newport adopting far-reaching powers under the Public Health Act to deal with the increasing problems caused by a rapid growth in population in a town with hopelessly inadequate sanitation arrangements and a shortage of clean water. The small market town on the river Usk was well on the way to becoming an industrial town and port. There were also radical changes illustrated by the social unrest that culminated in the Chartist conflict led by John Frost against the establishment in 1839. Lady Charlotte Guest (1812–95) had narrowly avoided the flashpoint of this conflict, the Westgate Hotel, in November 1839. In 1848, when the SWR was being constructed through Newport, cholera was making its presence felt as part of a wider outbreak throughout industrial south Wales. In response to a petition George Thomas Clark (1809–98) reported on the aftermath of this outbreak and the general sanitary state of Newport in August 1849. Clark was an engineer who had trained under Brunel and his work as a superintending inspector was contemporary with the building of the SWR along the south Wales coast.[18] In his report Clark recommended that only the adoption of wider powers under the Public Health Act, giving it the authority to install efficient main sewerage, house drainage and the provision of clean drinking water throughout the whole town of Newport, would avoid future problems of this magnitude.[19] Consequently driven by these recommendations, the Borough of Newport decided to adopt the provisions of the Public Health Act, extending its power to the whole Borough, and constituted the Corporation as the Local Board of Health. The passing of the necessary Act of Parliament was confirmed by the Town Clerk, Thomas Woollett, a year later on 6 August 1850.

Brunel crossed the river Usk at what has already been pointed out was a congested site; it was close to the present, and ancient, crossing of the river Usk within the Borough. The present road bridge dates from 1927, having replaced a bridge built in 1800 by David Edwards, the son of the builder of the famous bridge at Pontypridd, William Edwards (1719–89).[20] Brunel's first attempt at crossing the river Usk was by a timber viaduct 1,200ft long, consisting of eleven spans ranging from 40 to 52ft, with a main span of 100ft for river navigation. When the viaduct was almost complete, disaster struck on 31 May 1848 and fire destroyed almost two years of work. The viaduct had been constructed of some 80,000 cu. ft of timber subjected to the creosoting process, in which every beam of timber had been immersed under pressure in a tank of creosote for over twelve hours at 120lb to the square inch. Its cost had exceeded £20,000 and, according to local legend, was pronounced by engineers to be the finest structure ever put together.[21] But it took less than six minutes from the ignition of the first beam of timber for the whole bridge to become a leaping, living line of flame, all caused, so it is said, through the carelessness of one of the workmen, who in using a heated iron rymer to clean out a bolt hole before driving in a bolt, neglected to keep a supply of water close at hand according to instructions. The result was that the red-hot rymer ignited the timber, which could not be put out in time. Brunel was faced with a dilemma; starting from scratch would have meant that the opening of the line would be considerably delayed. He quickly decided to design wrought-iron bow-string girders to replace the central timber truss, girders that could be fabricated whilst the rest of the viaduct was being reconstructed in timber. Designed, it is said, 'out of his own head', the new span consisted of three polygonal girders of bow-string design to form an arch of triangular section, from which is suspended a horizontal girder supporting the rail deck. Because the bridge carries two lines, the centre girder is designed to have twice the strength of the others by being built up of thicker wrought-iron plates.[22] Timber in the rebuilt sections of the viaduct was prepared by a method known as the chyanizing process, which would not readily take fire.[23] The timber spans were replaced in the mid-1880s by iron girders on masonry piers. Brunel's bow-string girders gave over seventy years of service but by 1925 were replaced as part of the work to double the viaduct to accommodate four tracks.

In driving his railways forward, Brunel usually tried to avoid destroying any significant archaeological remains on route, and his treatment of Newport Castle was not considered unacceptable bearing in mind that part of the castle was then being used as a brewery. Remains of the castle's three ranges and enclosing moat survived as late as 1970, only to be swept away by the building of a twentieth-century transport solution, the inner ring road.[24] Brunel's railway had, however, obliterated what was Newport's first castle, an earthwork motte and bailey castle erected some distance away in the late eleventh or early twelfth centuries, on high ground close to St Woolos church. The railway did not actually go through this site but spoil from excavation of its railway tunnel nearby was to bury the motte.[25] Travelling through Newport, the railway crossed Thomas Street on the level, the SWR paying the sum of £150 to the Borough of Newport for the

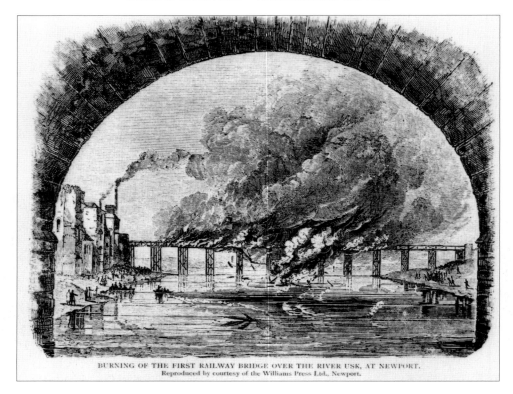

BURNING OF THE FIRST RAILWAY BRIDGE OVER THE RIVER USK, AT NEWPORT.
Reproduced by courtesy of the Williams Press Ltd., Newport.

The destruction of the timber bridge over the Usk at Newport on 31 May 1848. The main span of 100 feet and much of the timberwork, almost two years of work, going up in smoke. (SKJ collection)

Usk Bridge at Newport, here the bowstring girders supported on masonry piers can be seen as can the wrought-iron spans that replaced the timber trusses in the mid 1880's, but still supported on Brunel's timber piers. (SKJ collection)

Looking from the Usk Bridge at Newport, part of the bowstring girders can just be seen on the right and it is doubtful that the bridge was ever used by pedestrians! (Courtesy of Newport Museum and Art Gallery)

privilege of laying a double line of railway across it.[26] The Thomas Street level crossing provided the only means of access between High Street and Mill Street and the marches district. Due to its close proximity to the station, there were frequent complaints about the gates being closed against road traffic to allow for the shunting of trains. Although the problem for pedestrians was eased by the erection of a footbridge in 1854, the demands for shunting across Thomas Street increased. In 1857 the SWR attempted to double the number of lines running across Thomas Street by covert means, but they had not reckoned on the alertness of the Town Clerk, Thomas Woollett, who on 16 August noticed something going on; the SWR '... without the knowledge or permission of the plaintiffs have lately commenced laying down near the said level crossing an additional line of rails across Thomas Street...'[27] Woollett surmised that they '... intend to use such two additional lines as parts of their railway and thus to cross Thomas Street by four lines of rails instead of two lines and they intend therefore to obtain additional facilities for shunting trains along their railway at the said level crossing'.[28] Woollett wrote to the SWR the same day but there was no response and so he followed it up with a second letter on 8 August, a Bill of Complaint being lodged with the Court of Chancery on 15 August. It was clear to him that the SWR were trying to hide what they were doing as a single rail, which had been laid down on the south side of the crossing, was then hidden by earth and rubbish with the wall forming the SWR's boundary at this point being partially dismantled and then reinstated '... so as to avoid observation until the whole work should be ready for use'.[29] Further rails, fixed on timber sleepers, were ready to be moved into position. The SWR had informed Woollett that if they were to taken to be court, Her Majesty's Attorney-General was a necessary party to this suit, the SWR's solicitors W.O. & W. Hunt appearing for the defence.[30] The Borough of Newport appear to have successfully restrained the SWR in their attempts, and almost a year later SWR obtained an Act of Parliament, which amongst other powers allowed it to, '... acquire certain additional lands and buildings near their station at Newport...'[31] The gates figured in a later incident in 1874 when the down express crashed through them '... at this very dangerous level crossing...'[32] The *Star of Gwent*, the Newport newspaper, reported that it was very fortunate that no person was crossing the iron road at that time. The iron road was now standard gauge, the broad gauge having been narrowed in 1872 by the Great Western Railway, who had absorbed the SWR in 1863. In the year before the accident, the GWR entered into an agreement with the Corporation to create a new entrance to the town through the precincts of the old castle, eroding even further the ancient remnants. The GWR met two thirds of the cost for this and a subway was constructed to allow foot traffic from High Street to Mill Street.[33]

Further changes affected the station in 1878 with the rebuilding by the GWR under Lancaster Owen and J.E. Danks of the station buildings. The result of this can be seen on the island platform today, buildings with round-headed windows using rock-faced stone with ashlar for bands and dressings.[34] Nearby, the round-arched portal of the railway tunnel is formed of huge rock-faced blocks, in a rock-faced retaining wall.[35] David Morgan (1799–1875), the draper who was to establish a shop in Cardiff that was to grow into a large department store, recalled the construction of the SWR through Newport, stating that when the tunnel was completed but before the rails were laid, it was a popular Sunday 'constitutional'.[36] He and others would walk through the tunnel and marvel at the undertaking of this new form of transportation. Morgan also went to Cardiff on one of the first excursions run by the SWR on the first day after the opening, i.e. 19 June 1850, and to visit the Great Exhibition of 1851 by the railway. Today there is a second bore alongside Brunel's original tunnel. The great increase in traffic, following the opening of the Severn tunnel, was to lead to the driving of a second tunnel in 1912.[37]

The last mail coach left Cardiff on 2 August 1850 with the mail bags being conveyed by train the following day.[38] The SWR inaugural train arrived at Cardiff had arrived a decade after the first steam locomotive operated out of Glamorgan's country town on Brunel's Taff Vale Railway. The TVR had encountered considerable delays and disputes in their dealing with Lord Bute (1793–1848) to gain access to his dock, and there was much opposition to his political grip on Cardiff, but his role as the maker of modern Cardiff cannot be denied.[39] His investment in projects such as the building of the first dock was to establish Cardiff as the chief coaling port of the world and the port with

An early photograph of Newport station, note the Thomas Street crossing and beyond it the three triangular-shaped arches carrying the line accross the canal. (Courtesy of Newport Museum and Art Gallery)

In what appears to be a later photograph of the crossing, mixed-gauge rails can be seen as well as a railway policeman but the most important figure seems to be the bearded gentleman with a rolled-up umbrella almost in the centre of the photograph. Looking south with the King's Head Hotel on the High Street in the background. (Courtesy of Newport Museum and Art Gallery)

Looking west at Newport station. The goods shed is on the left beyond the station and on the right, in the background, are the carriage sheds. (Courtesy of Newport Museum and Art Gallery)

Opposite below: Firefly class 2-2-2 locomotive Argus, *at Newport. Built in 1842 by Fenton, Murray & Jackson of Leeds, the locomotive is seen here at Newport with the carriage sheds behind. (Courtesy of National Museum and Galleries of Wales, WI&MM collection)*

Above: *Another broad-gauge locomotive at Newport, Victoria class 2-4-0 locomotive,* Victor Emanuel, *built in Swindon in 1856. The carriage sheds, although no longer as carriage sheds or with glazed screens, remain in railway use today. See colour photograph. (SKJ collection)*

Looking east towards Newport station. The goods shed can be seen on the right before the station, the engine shed out of view on the left. (SKJ collection)

The subway or low tunnel access from High Street to Mill Street. Note the man on the horse having trouble and the bearded gentleman with the umbrella! (Courtesy of Newport Museum and Art Gallery)

The work of renewing the bowstring girders and doubling the viaduct to take four tracks was carried out in the mid-1920s. (From Archibald Williams' Brunel and After *(1925), GWR: London)*

the largest export trade.[40] Cardiff's position as the administrative centre of Glamorgan had never been threatened despite the rapid growth of other towns such as Merthyr Tydfil and Swansea. Cardiff was also home to many industrial concerns operating in the hinterland and exporting through Cardiff docks. A number of buildings associated with the growing importance of the town begin to appear from the 1820s, such as the building of the County Goal in 1826 (completed in 1832), the first theatre in 1827, a market building in 1835 and the Infirmary in 1837. Hospital provision was one of the numerous charitable causes that Bute supported, and included education and the restoration of churches. As early as 1815 he chaired a meeting at the Cardiff Guildhall that sought to do something about the education of the poor. The second resolution passed at this meeting called for a school to be established for the education of the children of the poor.[41] The foundation stone for 'The Cardiff School', later to be known as St John's School, was laid on 6 April 1818.[42] Opened on 3 January 1819 by the Marquis of Bute and at a cost of £700, it was, by 1824, providing accommodation for 115 boys and seventy girls.[43] In all, Bute provided sites and endowments for seventeen schools in Glamorgan. Bute's reputation among the poor was also enhanced by personal acts of kindness – '£10.00 a year to Mrs Roderick for her idiot son, £1.00 a month to the post boy who broke his leg'. Yet the Marquis had little patience with the idle poor and showed scant sympathy towards the Irish immigrants who arrived in Cardiff, 'with pestilence on their backs and famine in their stomachs',[44] even though he had been responsible, in the breaking of a strike on the building of his dock in the late 1830s, for the bringing over of over 200 Irish workers.[45]

The 'importation' of Irish navvies was to keep this new world turning and even women and children were pressed into the harshest of environments, and whilst moral standards were seen as the bedrock of society, illegitimacy was rife. To address

Newport tunnel, with work on the new tunnel alongside underway. (Courtesy of Newport Museum and Art Gallery)

this 'unacceptable face of business', some of the privileged middle and upper classes involved themselves in charitable acts to help the poor and the children who lived on the streets. As the major landowner in Cardiff facing a clamour for liberal reforms, Bute was certainly held up as representing the reactionary face of Tory interests. In a traditional sense, however, he was regarded with some affection by the lower classes of society. In this patriarchal role he objected to the misuse of power some of the Merthyr ironmasters wielded in the exploitation of workers. He criticised the lack of safety regulations in their mines and that unruly workers could be incarcerated by the ironmasters. Most of all, he objected to the truck system whereby wages were partly paid in tokens valid only at the company shop. In this respect he was showing a humanitarian interest. Merthyr had the third highest fatality rate in the UK, behind Manchester and Liverpool, and three fifths of its population could expect to die before the age of five. Cholera was rampant throughout south Wales, but in Merthyr it was responsible for 1,467 deaths in 1849 alone; other diseases, such as Typhus, causing one in every nine deaths in Merthyr.[46] Politically against anything the Merthyr ironmasters, such as Guest, stood for, Bute supported the construction of the TVR insofar as it would provide trade for his first dock, the Bute West Dock.[47] The TVR and the Bute Docks were to provide an enormous boost to the growth of Cardiff. Merthyr Tydfil, twenty-five miles away at the head of the Taff Valley, was to become one of the most important ironmaking centres and the dominant force in the first phase of the industrial development of Wales. Cardiff grew as the centre for exporting the produce of Merthyr and, from the 1830s onwards, steam coal from the Taff Valley and its tributaries brought down on the Glamorganshire and Aberdare canals.[48] Extensive industrial facilities such as ship repairing and engineering grew alongside the development of the docks, Merthyr's role as an iron and steel centre was usurped in 1891 when a new steelworks for the Guest concern was opened alongside the docks at Cardiff, where the imported steel ores could be unloaded directly into the works.[49] Lady Charlotte Guest, who had taken took control of the Dowlais works when Sir John died in 1852, would direct the works until the spring of 1855 when responsibility was passed to trustees, including George Thomas Clark. One of the last major changes overseen by Clark took place in 1891 when the company opened steelworks, known officially as 'Dowlais by the Sea' but more commonly as 'East Moors', in Cardiff.[50] Shifting steel production from Dowlais to a new works at Cardiff beside the Roath and East Bute Docks closed the transport loop that had been initiated in shipping iron products to market at one end of the valley and supplying the process of ironmaking at the other. Unlike Merthyr, whose prosperity had been linked to the fortunes of iron production, Cardiff's position was more broadly based and adaptable, particularly when it later faced the decline of coal exports in the mid-twentieth century.

There was one thing in common, however, between Cardiff and Merthyr and, indeed with all the other industrial towns – overcrowding and a poor quality of life for the working population. Slum housing meant bad health, severe poverty led to crime and working conditions produced their own hazards. Villages grew rapidly without any planning or basic sanitary provision into towns, and where there were streams and rivers there were now open sewers. Grey 'satanic mills' covered green fields, parish roads became thoroughfares and slum housing filled in the spaces between factories. There were options for those who could afford it but the working class had to make the best of it. An example of the rapid urbanisation taking place during industrialisation can be seen by the fact that in 1750 only two cities in Britain had populations over 50,000. In 1850, there were twenty-nine. At that date nearly one person in three lived in a city with more than 50,000 inhabitants.

Such appalling conditions and radical fervour following economic recession in the summer of 1831 erupted into the Merthyr riots. For a time, the ironworkers were in control of the town and raised the red flag for the first time on British soil. One extreme group of industrial agitators in Monmouthshire, known as 'Scotch Cattle', intimidated fellow workers. Even rural areas were not free from disorder, the Turnpike Trusts hitting farmers in the west of Wales, where the disturbances known as the 'Rebecca Riots' occurred in 1839 and again in 1842–43.[51] On 19 June 1843 'Rebecca' marched into Carmarthen, and what began as a protest against turnpikes and tolls turned into an attack on the workhouse and ended with the last cavalry charge in Britain. The 4th Light Dragoon Guards, being ordered from Cardiff to Carmarthen as a result of magistrates' demands, rode into the town scattering hundreds of demonstrators in all directions. The placards proclaimed, '*Cyfiawnder a charwyr cyfiawnder ydym ni oll*' ('Justice, and lovers of justice are we all') but were to be trodden underfoot by the

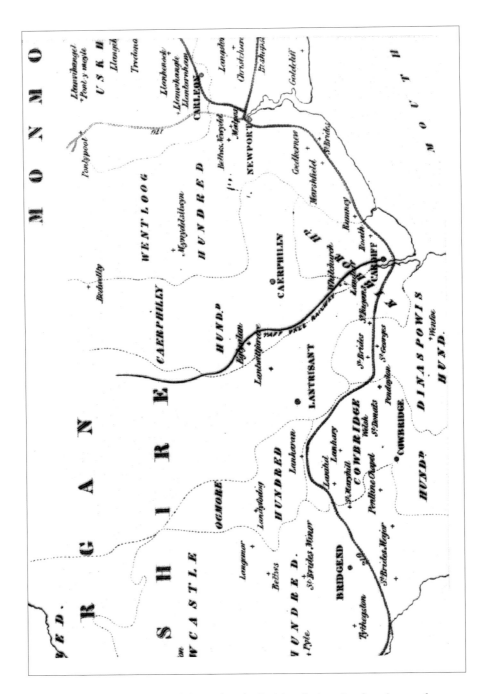

Section of the Parliamentary map of the South Wales Division, Session 1845, from the east of Newport to the west of Bridgend; note the line of the Taff Vale Railway with no branches shown. (SKJ collection)

dragoons.[52] It was a scene reminiscent of what happened in 1819 at St Peter's Field in Manchester, but thankfully without the scale of violence that occurred at Peterloo.[53] The Cardiff-born novelist Howard Spring (1889–1965) worked as a reporter on the *Manchester Guardian*, giving him the opportunity to research, at first hand, material for his political book *Fame is the Spur*, which takes the Peterloo incident as the starting point.[54]

By the 1850s consolidation of Cardiff's position in the coal trade was much in evidence; in 1851 work on the East Bute Dock and Basin began in Cardiff and it was opened in 1855, considerably expanding the capacity of the existing West Bute Dock. The new dock covered 46¾ acres. In 1855 the first consignment of Rhondda steam coal was sent from Treherbert to Cardiff and marked the start of the prosperity of the Rhondda Valley as a major producer of quality coal. In the year the Taff Vale Railway began operating from the Rhondda Valley to Cardiff there was also a revival of the National Eisteddfod.[55] Whilst Brunel's SWR may not have had the industrial impact that the TVR had brought to Cardiff, it connected the town by a line of communications linked eastwards to the Great Western Railway and continued west to Carmarthenshire and Pembrokeshire. What did make a considerable physical impact in Cardiff was the turning of the Taff. The river Taff had long caused structural problems to the fabric of the town of Cardiff. The church of St Mary had suffered the eroding effects of the river Taff for hundreds of years and finally collapsed following the great flood of 1607. Today, it is possible to see an outline representation of the church on the old Prince of Wales theatre, looking at the rear of that building from the Great Western Lane or Wood Street.[56] Flooding was a common occurrence that would continue to cause problems for buildings in St Mary Street for another 143 years, until Brunel came along and changed the course of the river in 1850. However, that did not remove all the problems and before it was built Bute had sought an opinion on it, and following a request by John Plews responded on 7 May 1846:

> It appeared to me that the proposed New Channel was not sufficiently wide: it will therefore be necessary to give a little additional width or to force the side slopes very strongly with rubble stone well secured with stakes & binders; or the Floods will wash away the side slopes...

Plews goes on to give his opinion on the need for a warping sluice to enable the old channel to fill up with mud and that a small permanent sluice would be needed to take the water which passes out of the feeder behind the castle. He would form, '... a more decisive opinion' when the detailed plans and sections are prepared, stating in the meantime:

> I am of the opinion that the change of the River by cutting the Strait Channel will not damage the Land either above or below the New Cut; and that it will be a very great improvement particularly considered with reference to the Town of Cardiff...

Despite this view, the Cardiff Board of Health saw the new cut as one of the new 'nuisances' caused by the railway itself, such as on 27 November 1850 when the clerk

The rear of houses on St Mary Street and the old bed of the Taff. (Courtesy of Cardiff Central Library)

View of the culvet draining in the old bed of the Taff under the SWR, now GWR, station in 1866. Note the timber station building and the wrought-iron water tank. Compare this with the water cooler looking from the station in the colour section. (Courtesy of Cardiff Central Library)

The river Taff at Cardiff, taken in 1866 and showing the side view of the Royal Hotel which opened that year. (Courtesy of Cardiff Central Library)

was instructed to write to Mr Owen, '... the engineer of the SWR Co., to prevent the leakage of the bridge crossing Bute St.' Growing concerns over the condition of the old river bed led to the clerk being ordered on 28 April 1851:

> ... to write to Mr. Brunel pointing out the nuisance and injurious effects to the Public Health, arising from the old bed of the river Taff in consequence of the diversion of the river by the SWR, and urging him to take such measures as may abate the nuisance.[57]

On 16 May 1851 the board were concerned with a new problem and the clerk was ordered to serve the SWR with notice to clean the open ditches adjoining the railway in Newtown. However, the letter to Brunel had not been answered and on that same day it was resolved that the clerk call Mr Brunel's attention to the letter sent relating to the, '... nuisance caused by the diversion of the river Taff and request an early reply to the same'. Clearly, the board did not have legal grounds to resolve matters as they had on 8 March 1853 when they requested Jeremiah Box Stockdale, of the Cardiff Borough Police, to remove the obstruction caused by parties landing iron between the canal and the SWR. Incidentally, Stockdale had, in 1839, been responsible for the capture of the Newport Chartist leader, Zephaniah Williams, who was hiding out in Cardiff waiting passage to France. What appears to be the final attempt by the board to persuade the

SWR to rectify the problem of the old channel was on 28 August 1857 when the clerk was ordered to, '… ascertain whether the SWR Co., can be compelled to renew the bank of the old riverbed, so as to remedy the nuisance created by the insufficiency of water'.

At Cardiff a wooden bridge crossed the old bed of the Taff and the new cut was to be crossed by a seven-arch stone bridge,[58] but examination of a photograph taken around 1865 shows a timber bridge over the new cut. The diversion of the Taff also caused a disruption of business for John Batchelor (1820–83) who with his brother, James Sydney Batchelor, had bought the Cardiff yard off William Jones in 1843 and developed a number of timber yards.[59] W.J. Tounce, writing about *Cardiff in the 50's*, talks about the great undertaking involved in diverting the broad expanse of the river, '… closing Messers Batchelor's Timber Yard and other industries was occasioned by the South Wales Railways engineers completing their line through Cardiff'.[60] Another writer on old Cardiff, John Winstone, was to write in the Cardiff Naturalists Society on *Old Cardiff*, about this impact, particularly in the reclamation of land:

> The SWR brought other advantages to Cardiff; instead of building a bridge over the river where the station now is, they made one farther west, and put the river to run under the bridge, thus cutting off a piece of land from that which was called the 'Little Park' the property of Col. Wood, Stout Hall, Swansea. This piece of land had no right of way to it, freshets and ordinary spring tides flowed over it. It was at all times a silt subway of little value, and of unsightly appearance. 'Who would have thought it?' Mr. Jacob Mathews, our remarkable old townsman, took it on a long building lease at £150 per annum. He made a road from it to St. Mary Street, drew plans of streets and ballasted the streets up to a level of the town, then drained them and built a temperance Music Hall at one end. He laid out £6,000 and he would not allow any intoxicating liquors, by clause in leases, to be sold in Temperance Town.[61]

The reformed Borough of Cardiff came into existence on 1 January 1836, the year the TVR gained its Act of Parliament, and comprised an area of 1,191 acres with a population of about 8,000. The main hotels in Cardiff at this time were the Angel Inn and the Cardiff Arms; the Angel had provided the venue for the first General Meeting of the TVR proprietors following the Act of Incorporation on 16 September 1836.[62] Charles Richardson (1814–96), an engineer employed by Brunel in checking the quality of rails at Ebbw Vale and Merthyr, stayed at the Cardiff Arms on a number of occasions. Richardson had originally been employed by Brunel on the Cheltenham & Great Western Union Railway but this had been suspended due to a shortage of funds, so Brunel found him work as part of a group of engineers on this task.[63] At the end of November 1837 he records in his diary that he returned to the Cardiff Arms in the evening and had a long talk with George Bush in his room.[64] It would be interesting to know if Bush shared any comments with Richardson about his relationship with Brunel on the TVR! Two years later, in December 1839, the Wiltshire polymath and photographic pioneer William Henry Fox Talbot (1800–77) was on his way through Cardiff, to Margam, to visit his cousin Christopher Rice Mansel Talbot, and on

View from Cardiff Castle clock tower looking towards Temperance Town with the tidal fields of the old river Taff in the foreground. (Courtesy of Cardiff Central Library)

Enlargement of view from Cardiff Castle clock tower of Temperance Town with the SWR line, station and other buildings. The timber bridge over Brunel's new cut can be seen on the extreme right. (Courtesy of Cardiff Central Library)

reaching there wrote about his travelling ordeal, to his wife Constance. The letter gives an insight into coach travel and crossing the river Severn in these pre-railway days:

> I had a tedious & troublesome journey. I was obliged to post all the way, as the few coaches there were, were quite full – I left Bath at 9 o'clock & when I got to the Old Passage I found it low water and the Steamer aground, & likely to continue to so for the next hour & a half, so I crossed in a sailing boat with the passengers of a coach which drove up at the same time. We got across well enough and proceeded to Chepstow, when I found a coach, but already were 21 passengers wanting to go by it – so I proceeded to Newport & Cardiff, at the latter place there was not a single horse to be had in the town, so I was compelled to stop the night at the Cardiff Arms – I left the place next morning soon after nine and got to Margam at ½ past one in very stormy rainy weather, which has continued almost without intermission ever since…[65]

By 1841, the year the TVR opened throughout between Cardiff and Merthyr, the population of the town had risen to over 10,000, but there were only 240 burgesses, those able to vote through being eligible and able to pay rates.[66] In just over a decade Cardiff had seen three major developments, the opening of the Bute Dock, the TVR and the SWR, and in 1854 the Borough of Cardiff opened the 'new' Town Hall in St Mary Street (the first public meeting to promote the SWR had been held in the 'old' Town Hall in September 1844). The year 1855 marked the consolidation of much change and laid the foundations of future growth, as on 21 December 1855 when the first train of Rhondda steam coal was sent down to Cardiff docks on the recently completed Rhondda Fawr Valley branch of the TVR, which was extended to Gelligaled in that month.[67] This, the first rail consignment of Rhondda steam coal, marked the start of the Rhondda Valley's 'prominence as a major producer of quality coal. Within ten years, the Rhondda was established in the premier position as regards the existing coalfields of south Wales, with the shallower coal seams, then being exploited in the Cynon Valley, being played out, and by 1875 the Rhondda's output exceeded that of the Cynon Valley. In 1855 the new East Bute Dock and Basin opened at Cardiff after four years of construction, and covered 46¾ acres. Not only was dock provision in Cardiff being expanded, but earlier proposals on the river Ely were being revived. In 1856 the Ely Tidal Harbour & Railway gained its Act of Parliament, followed a year later by the Penarth Harbour Dock & Railway (PHDR).[68] On 4 January 1857 Cardiff witnessed the last public execution at Cardiff.[69] In 1858 the Rhymney Railway was opened and extended to Cardiff, the same year that the SWR's locomotive shed for Cardiff was opened, being situated to the east of Cardiff station at Newtown and comprised of a two-road shed; one of Brunel's sketches also shows a number of layouts for goods sidings at Newtown. The shed was converted for standard gauge in 1872, only to be closed ten years later when the Canton depot was opened.[70]

As a town of 50,000 inhabitants, Cardiff was designated a County Borough on 1 April 1889. As early as 1897 the town petitioned for city status; it was rejected by the Government, as was a similar petition in 1902.[71] In 1897 the County Borough also set out a case for recognition of Cardiff as the capital of Wales. Cardiff's petition for city status was finally accepted in 1905 but it was not recognised as the capital of Wales until 1955.[72] As part of

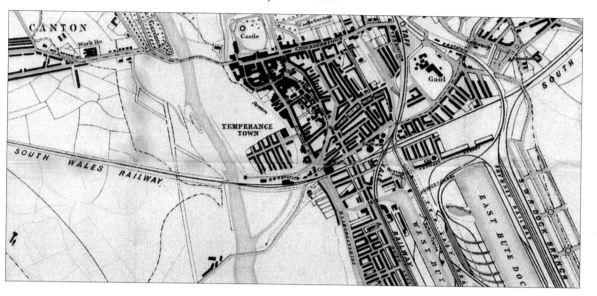

Development of Cardiff in the 1860s. (SKJ collection)

Cardiff's petition for County Borough status prepared in 1888 (when it was thought such status was dependent on a population of 150,000 or over), its case based on a 123,000 population was boosted with information showing that Cardiff was the premier port of Great Britain based on registered tonnage.[73] In this, Cardiff, for the year ending 1887, was registered at 4,677,301 tons, ahead of Liverpool at 4,622,014 and London at 4,320,304 tons. Those three ports were considerably ahead, by some four times, of the next ranked port, Glasgow, at 1,062,394 tons. Not only was Cardiff the premier British port, but in the world rankings it was second only to New York (5,549,928 tons). In 1887 7,516,894 tons of coal were exported from Cardiff, which together with coastwise shipments, bunker stocks and coke exports, added up to almost 10 million tons.[74]

In the commercial centre of Cardiff, Butetown and the dockland area, trading on exports went from strength to strength, one example going down in Cardiff folklore as the world's first million pound deal – struck on the trading floor at the Coal Exchange in 1904.[75] Back in the old town, 'another' new town hall was being built to replace the 1854 Town Hall. It was not destined, however, to serve as a town hall for long, for as already mentioned, Cardiff's position was acknowledged with the granting of city status in 1905. Howard Spring sums up the mood of the citizens of the premier port of Great Britain:

> No longer were we mere townsfolk: we were citizens, whose Mayor had become a Lord Mayor and had been knighted to boot, and we built for ourselves goodly white palaces, dragon-straddled domes and slender campaniles whence the mellow bells called the hours of that golden and prosperous day.[76]

Cardiff Arms Hotel, demolished to make way for the widening of Castle Street in 1878, with part of the site being used for the new Angel Hotel. Part of the castle wall can be seen on the right. (Courtesy of Cardiff Central Library)

Thanks Brunel! One of the many inscribed paviours on the Millennium Stadium walkway. (SKJ photograph)

NOTES

1 Vaughan, Derrick Cyril (1990), *Newport first stop. 1800-1900*, DC Vaughan: Newport. The expression comes from the time of the first train running through Newport, because of the fact, it is said, that Newport would receive the first train and thus irk Cardiffians. From that time the ying; 'Well I'll go to Cardiff' came about and is still used, particularly by old Newportonians, to denote amazement or disbelief. See www.newportpast.com/nfs/contents.htm

2 Owen, Heulwen & Hedydd (1963), *Sir Isambard Owen, A Biography*, privately published: Caernarvon.

3 Owen, Heulwen & Hedydd (1963), p.11.

4 Bell to Owen, PLB 16 January 1836.

5 If there is any truth in the story according to the biography – his mother completed the job on the Britannia Bridge!

6 Another biographer, Jones, Gwilym Arthur Jones, *The life and work of Sir Isambard Owen (1850–1927): with particular reference to his contribution to education in Wales* (1967), MA Thesis, University of Wales (U.C.N.W., Bangor: Education. UWB (Normal Thesis, 67:12), also states that in 1834 [changed on the typescript from 1844 to 1834] he was employed on [*added above to the typescript in pen;* preliminary plans] the construction of the Britannia Tubular Bridge over the Menai Straits.

7 There is also reference to his offering to the public of a map of Caernarvonshire, which appears never to have been produced (the intention to produce such a map was based on a family document but Gwilym Arthur Jones could not find any evidence that it had actually appeared, consulting the National Library of Wales and other bodies).

8 I am indebted to Henry Llewellyn Warren of Fairfield-Mabey Ltd for this information.

9 See Chapter 2, Vignoles was to resign from this post in 1847.

10 University of Bristol, Special Collections, PLB, 22 November 1844. Dr L.G. Booth makes this assumption in his chapter on *Timber Works*, p.135, in Pugsley, Sir Alfred ed. (1976). *The Works of Isambard Kingdom Brunel An Enineering Appreciation*, Institution of Civil Engineers/University of Bristol: London.

11 I am grateful to Barry Mawson and Professor Ben Barr for allowing me to see a pre-publication draft of their paper (as Lark, R.J., Mawson, B and Barr, B.) *Brunel's Bridges in Wales: A Re-assessment of his Contribution to Bridges Engineering.*

12 Completed on target for £77,000.

13 University of Bristol, Special Collections, PLB 6, p.274, 7 May 1849, letter to W. Hunt.

14 Smith, David: *Marshfield* (*Welsh Railways Archive*, Supp. to vol.1), March 1994.

15 Newman, John (2002), *The Buildings of Wales; Gwent/Monmouthshire*, p.421, Yale University Press: New Haven and London.

16 Brynmor, Pierce Jones indicates that the first charter was granted in 1385. Jones, Brynmor Pierce (1957), *From Elizabeth I to Victoria*, p.1, Newport Corporation: Newport.

17 Newman, John (2002), p.436.

18 *Cooperative Congress Newport* (1908), p.115, CWS: Manchester. Extract from *The Merlin* newspaper.

19 Clark's relationship with Brunel is examined by the author in Chapter 11, Jones, Stephen K. (2005), *Brunel in South Wales vol.1, In Trevithick's Tracks*, Tempus Publishing: Stroud. For background on

G.T. Clark as a superintending inspector under the Public Health Act, see 'G.T. Clark, Slums and Sanitary Reform' by Andy Croll in James, Brian Ll. ed. (1998), *G. T. Clark, Scholar Ironmaster in the Victorian Age*, University of Wales Press: Cardiff.

20 Jones, Brynmor Pierce (1957), pp.186-8.

21 David Edwards was assisted by his two sons, William and Thomas, see Jervoise, E. (1936, reprinted 1976), p.108. *The Ancient Bridges of Wales and Western England*, EP. Publishing Ltd: Wakefield and Jones, Stephen K. (2005), Chapter 8. For information on the current bridge by Mott, Hay & Anderson see Newman, John (2002), p.454.

22 *Cooperative Congress Newport* (1908), p.115.

23 Williams, Archibald (1925, reprinted 1972), pp.70–71, *Brunel and After: The Romance of the Great Western Railway*, Patrick Stephens Ltd: London.

24 *Cooperative Congress Newport* (1908), p.115.

25 Newman, John (2002), p.436.

26 Newman, John (2002), p.436.

27 Bill of Complaint, lodged at the Court of Chancery by the Mayor, Aldermen and Burgesses of the Borough of Newport against the South Wales Railway Co. and Her Majesty's Attorney-General, 15 August 1857, pf M160 625 SOU in Newport Reference Library.

28 Bill of Complaint.

29 Bill of Complaint.

30 Bill of Complaint.

31 The Newport Reference Library copy of the Bill of Complaint has Hunt's undertaking to appear on it (in writing).

32 Act of Parliament, 2 August 1858.

33 Star of Gwent, 17 October 1874.

34 *Cooperative Congress Newport* (1908), p.127, CWS: Manchester.

35 Biddle, Gordon (2003), pp.584–586, *Britain's Historic Railway Buildings*, p.448, Oxford University Press: Oxford.

36 The contractors for this work were Messrs Rennie, Logan and Co., contractors for the bridge, the tunnel, and some portions below Cardiff, *The Ancient & Modern History of Newport*, (1847), p.94.

37 Morgan, Aubrey Niel (1977), p.34, *David Morgan 1833–1919*, The Starling Press Ltd: Risca.

38 Newman, John (2002).

39 Trounce, W.J. (1918), *Cardiff in the 50's*.

40 See Chapter 9 'Openings and Blockades' in Jones, Stephen K. (2005).

41 Hamlin, William (1954), *The Story of Cardiff, Part III, the Town and City*. Filmstrip notes.

42 Matthews (1898), vol.3, p.494. For a summary of the origin of this school and the role played by Thomas Bates Rous, see Jones, Stephen K., *The Manor of Michaelston with particular reference to Cwrt-yr-Ala and the Rous Family*, pp.37–39, Local History Diploma Dissertation, University College, Cardiff, 1981.

43 *The Cambrian*, 11 April 1818.

44 Rees, William (1969), p.203. St John's School was enlarged and rebuilt over the years, in recent years it housed the Cardiff College of Art and finally the Friary Adult Education Centre before being demolished to make way for Principality House.

45 Morgan, Dennis (1995), pp.83-84, *Discovering Cardiff's Past*, D. Brown & Sons Ltd: Cowbridge.

46 Jones, Stephen K. (2005), p.158.

47 Strange, Keith (2005), p.56-57, *Merthyr Tydfil Iron Metropolis*, Tempus Publishing: Stroud.

48 Jones, Stephen K. (2005), p.157.

49 Williams, John (1995). pp.14-35, *Was Wales Industrialised*. Gomer Press: Llandysul. See also Davies, John (1996), p.116, *The Making of Wales*, CADW/Sutton Publishing Ltd: Stroud.

50 Jones, Stephen K. (2005), p.39, 212.

51 Jones, Stephen K. (2005), pp.38-9. George Thomas Clark, along with the new manager, William Menelaus (1818–82), brought the Dowlais works into the steelmaking era.

52 The bare-knuckle fighter, Shoni Sgubor Fawr (Johnnie Great Barn) of Penderyn, who had staged a fight in 1840 as one of the unofficial celebrations of the opening of the TVR, was to play a leading role in disrupting the turnpikes during the Rebecca riots in 1843, for which he was eventually arrested. See Jones, Stephen K. (2005), p.166.

53 Williams, David (1955), pp.201–209, *The Rebecca Riots*, University Of Wales Press: Cardiff.

54 Eleven deaths, attributable to injuries either on the day or in the weeks following, and 420 wounded have been attributed to the massacre. Reid, Robert (1989), p.191, *The Peterloo Massacre*, William Heinemann Ltd: London

55 Spring, Howard (1940), *Fame is the Spur*, Collins: London.

56 See Wakeford, C., Cardiff Directory 1855, 1863. Ewen, J., Guide and Directory for the town of Cardiff 1855.

57 The building houses the 'Prince of Wales', a J.D. Wetherspoon public house.

58 These and the following quotes can be found in Matthews, John Hobson (1898–1911), *Cardiff Records: being materials for a history of the county borough from the earliest times*, vol.6, Cardiff Corporation: Cardiff.

59 *Cardiff and Merthyr Guardian* 22 June 1850 and *The Cambrian* 21 June 1850.

60 Richards, John (2005), pp.72–73, *Cardiff: A Maritime History*, Tempus Publishing: Stroud. A story concerning John Batchelor as the Cardiff Police Magistrate (and Mayor of Cardiff) is told in Jones, Stephen K. (2005).

61 Trounce, W. J. (1918) p.14 *Cardiff in the 50's* .

62 Winstone, John (1879–83), p.85, *Old Cardiff*, Cardiff Naturalists Society.

63 Jones, Stephen K. (2005), p.108.

64 Richardson had been articled to Brunel during the construction of the Thames Tunnel and worked on a number of Brunel's works including the Bristol & South Wales Union Railway and was to champion the construction of the Severn Tunnel, being engineer for six years before Sir John Hawkshaw was brought in.

65 Diary of Charles Richardson 30 November 1837. I am extremely grateful to Peter Griffin for kindly bringing diary entries of Charles Richardson to my attention. The diary is in possession of Howard Beard of Stroud and the subject of an M. Phil. thesis by Peter Griffin (University of Gloucester, 2005).

66 Letter written Sunday 22 December 1839 and part of *The Correspondence of William Henry Fox Talbot* Project hosted at Glasgow University and directed by Professor Larry J. Schaaf, see http://www.foxtalbot.arts.gla.ac.uk/default.htm.

67 Cardiff Corporation (1974), pp.10-11, *Cardiff 1889–1974 the story of the County Borough*.

68 Lewis, E.D. (second edition 1963), *The Rhondda Valleys*, p.69, Pheonix House: London. See also;

Jones, Stephen K. (2005), pp.214-5.

69 See Jones, Stephen K. (2005), pp.203-205, and Mountford, Eric R. and Sprinks, Neil. (1993), p.7-9, *The Taff Vale Lines to Penarth*, Oakwood Press: Oxford. The PHDR's third Act was obtained on 22 June 1863 and authorised the lease period of 999 years. The lease for the tidal harbour and railway from Penarth junction to the harbour was to take effect from 1 January 1864.

70 John Lewis of Merthyr Tydfil for murdering his wife.

71 Lyons, E.T. and Mountford, Eric R. (1979, reprinted 1986), p.55, *An Historical Survey of Great Western Railway Engine Sheds 1837–1947*, Oxford Publishing Co.: Poole.

72 Cardiff Corporation (1974), p.36.

73 It was up against Caernarvon, Aberystwyth and Llandrindod Wells.

74 Cardiff Corporation (1974), pp.140-1.

75 See Jones, Stephen K. (2005), p.39, this was one of the last major changes seen through by G.T. Clark.

76 www.bbc.co.uk/wales/about/historyhunters/hh4.shtml

77 Spring, Howard (1939, reprinted 1944), p.62, *Heaven Lies About Us: A Fragment of Infancy*, Constable & Co. Ltd: London. This was Howard Spring's first volume of autobiography.

6

THROUGH THE GARDEN OF WALES

'... CALCULATED TO DESTROY THE TRADE OF THE TOWN'[1]

On leaving Cardiff the railway now crossed the river Taff, leaving the Cardiff or Kibbor Hundred to pass through the Vale of Glamorgan on its way west. Not a 'Vale' in the normal sense, the Vale of Glamorgan is bounded by hills to the north but the sea forms the boundary to the south.[2] The industrial heartland of Glamorganshire can be found beyond this northern ridge of hills and above the rich fertile countryside which has been known for centuries as 'The Garden of Wales'. The rock strata of the contemporary Vale of Glamorgan is also different from the uplands of the coalfields, being a deposition of Mesozoic rocks and well developed only in this location.[3] Before the railway reached the open countryside that typified the 'garden', it passed through Canton, a rapidly developing area that would be absorbed into Cardiff in 1875. At Canton a new locomotive shed was opened as a replacement for the original Newtown SWR shed, in June 1882. Offering four more roads than Newtown, Canton was a six-road straight shed designed by William Dean, the Chief Mechanical Engineer.[4] At this point the railway was originally at road level, the line being realigned and raised as a major engineering work to be financed as a Government loan scheme aimed at reducing unemployment levels in the late 1920s and early 1930s. The new lines would do away with three level crossings at Canton (Leckwith Road), Sanatorium Road and Moore's Lane and involved the construction of bridges at Leckwith Road and Grosvenor Street.[5] From Canton, the line progressed through the hamlet of Ely. At this point the SWR could have crossed the TVR, or rather the proposed Ely Branch (one of the TVR's original branches) serving the dock at the mouth of the river Ely. Such a line was revived in 1855 and became a reality on 21 July 1856 as the Ely Tidal Harbour & Railway, followed a year later by the Penarth Harbour Dock & Railway (PHDR).[6] The PDHR also authorised the construction of a dock near the opposite bank of the river Ely to the tidal harbour, but the PHDR would open first to the tidal harbour on 4 July 1859, crossing the SWR on its way. At Ely the first station on the SWR after Cardiff would be found, but it would not open until several months later 2 September 1850. In contrast, the PHDR (operated by the TVR) would only provide a goods station at Ely.[7]

An important industry here at Ely, and different to those exploiting the water of the Ely wells through brewing, was the paper mills. Founded in 1865, the paper mill had a works branch line to the SWR, part of which was photographed on 15 June 1932, showing a mixed-gauge turntable.[8] The turntable was laid with 'Barlow' rails for both standard and broad gauges. The branch line sidings, along with and the turntable, survived until the rail access was abandoned in the 1970s. Next came the first river crossing since the Taff and the line now crossed and re-cross the river Ely several times over the few miles.

What would have normally been considered as the next most important town after Cardiff was Cowbridge, but its leading citizens decided against the benefits of the railway and the route of the SWR avoided the town altogether. Roads through the Vale of Glamorgan, from the prehistoric portway, Roman road and turnpike, would all run through the settlement that was to become Cowbridge. But its citizens, or the Corporation of Victorian Cowbridge, do not appear to have extended a welcome to this latest mode of transport. The route of the SWR, as published in the 1844 prospectus, would not pass through Cowbridge, which was to be served from Llantrisant. Later in that year (September 1844), a director of the Bristol & Gloucester Railway, stated that:

Mixed-gauge turntable at Ely Papermill in the 1930s. (Courtesy of National Museum and Galleries of Wales, WI&MM collection)

... it has been reported that the proposed railroad will run through the coal works about five miles to the north of Cowbridge, and the good people of that ancient borough are well pleased to be left undisturbed, as no symptom of any wish to have the railway nearer has been evinced.[9]

The main reason for the line avoiding Cowbridge, however, does appear to have been for good engineering reasons, i.e. taking the line via Pontyclun to take advantage of the easier gradients presented by the valleys of the Ely and Ewenny on the way to Bridgend rather than a direct route through Cowbridge, which would involve considerable engineering works. At least one or two individuals of Cowbridge, such as the Revd Thomas Edmondes, did try to persuade the SWR to reconsider, but the initial hostile reaction to the railway and engineering considerations set the line firmly away from the town.[10] Ironically, a broad-gauge locomotive did pass through the centre of Cowbridge in 1849:

... the first (and it is probable the last for many years to come) steam engine and tender passed through this town.... Although a locomotive, its passage through Cowbridge was impelled by twenty-two of the most beautiful draught horses this part of the county ever produced, belonging to Messrs. Rennie & Co. Its destination was Pyle, where it is employed by the above spirited contractors on the works of the South Wales Railway.[11]

What was also interesting in the context of Cowbridge and its railway hopes was that this locomotive was called *Phantom*.[12] Cowbridge would eventually get its own railway, not on the broad gauge, but instead on the standard-gauge Cowbridge Railway supported by the Taff Vale Railway.[13]

Llantrisant marked the next major station after Cardiff, serving, as the above episode was to reveal, not just its own locality but the wider and rural Vale of Glamorgan, including Cowbridge. Opened as part of the main Chepstow to Swansea section in 1850, the SWR station of Llantrisant was actually not in Llantrisant but situated some two miles away at Pontyclun,[14] which at the time consisted of little more than a bridge over the river Clun and an old farmhouse called Pontyclun Fawr. The station here was one of four to be built for the SWR by Messrs Thomas Hughes & Co., who had also built stations for the Chester & Holyhead Railway.[15] It offered:

... a typical SWR wayside facility, with up and down platforms and a goods siding serving a goods shed and loading bank. The station building, on the up platform, was of characteristic 'Brunelian' style, with an overhanging hipped roof providing shelter on all sides.[16]

A small village was to build up on the north side of the line, along with the first hotel of the locality, the Windsor Hotel, in January 1858. Near Pontyclun was the house and estate of Talygarn, which was to be acquired by George Thomas Clark in 1865. Clark, as we have seen, was to be instrumental in taking the Dowlais Works into the steelmaking era; he would also expend much expense and effort in rebuilding the house so he could finally move from Dowlais House.[17] As the anonymous author of a number of guidebooks promoting the GWR, *Guide Book to the Great Western Railway* (1839) and *The History and Description of the Great Western Railway* (1843, 1846) and later in supplying reminiscences for Isambard Brunel to use in his biography of his father (published in 1870),[18] it was clear that Clark admired Brunel, although not his style of management! Some interesting volumes of Brunel interest would come to light during the sale of Talygarn and Clark's library in 1922, namely a Brunel family tree and a copy of the multi-volume work, *The Modern System of Naval Architecture*, by John Scott Russell (Brunel's collaborator on *Great Eastern*).[19]

Back to the line and the village of Pencoed would next be traversed by the SWR, the occasion marked by the permanent feature of the Britannia Inn being open for business,. It is said, '… on the same day that the very first train ran through the village', i.e. 18 June 1850.[20] That year was also notable for the completion and opening of Stephenson's Britannia Bridge, which appears to have a bearing on the name of the new hotel. Outside of the major products of Welsh industry, such as iron, coal and slate, and the demands of the farming and county communities, there were now opportunities for manufacturers to set up and serve the local or regional market. Such businesses would grow along with the railway and a few would be in demand from further afield as in the case with the Pencoed Brickworks, whose terracotta bricks would be used to face Birmingham Town Hall.[21]

It was reported on October 1847 that construction of the line was, '… proceeding with vigour' near Bridgend, with more than 100 men at work.[22] The *Monmouthshire Merlin* reported that 600 men had been laid off until the spring, confirming, in another column, that:

> … the works… have been suspended, in consequence of the monetary pressure. It is said that about four hundred men have been discharged, but we understand that the contractors have sent down a considerable number of their "navvies" to push on their contract at Bridgend…[23]

Before the money scares of 1847 there were scares of another kind at Bridgend; William Lewis, the undersheriff for Glamorganshire, had written to Lord Bute (John Crichton Stuart, second Marquis of Bute, 1793–1848), the Lord Lieutenant of Glamorgan.[24] He was reacting to a number of proposed deviations being sought by the SWR; the one of concern to Lewis was the deviation from Coychurch to Margam. Lewis was to write, 'at the request of a great number of my fellow Townsmen' on 13 February 1846, and is concerned about the proposed deviation of the SWR which he believes is, '… calculated to destroy the trade of the Town'. He then refers to the line:

> … originally selected by Mr. Brunel, and which no opposition whatever was offered by any one, & which has been sanctioned by Parliament, passed, as no doubt your Lordship may probably be aware, about a mile to the South of this Town, but it is now proposed to abandon that line, and to adopt another which will pass about three miles to the North of the Town, and the Company are now applying to Parliament for an Act to enable then to carry out this scheme.

The north Wales coastline with the sweep of Nefyn Bay and Porthdinllaen, the objective of an Irish railway terminus and port by
~nel and Vignoles, beyond. (SKJ photograph)

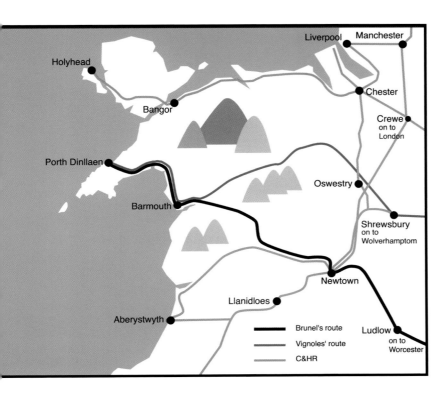

2 Map of railway
proposals by Brunel and
Vignoles through north
Wales to Porthdinllaen.
(Cartography by Owen
Eardley)

3 *Completed around 1835, the Seiont Bridge near Caernarvon today has been partly rebuilt but represents an early work by William George Owen. Shortly afterwards he joined Brunel's staff and was engaged on Great Western Railway (including the South Wales Railway) matters for the rest of his life. (SKJ photograph)*

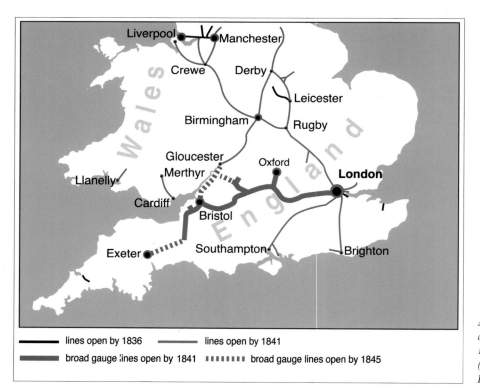

▬▬▬ lines open by 1836	▬▬ lines open by 1841	
▬▬▬ broad gauge lines open by 1841	∎∎∎∎∎∎ broad gauge lines open by 1845	

4 *Map of railway development between 1836 and 1845. (Cartography by Owen Eardley)*

Gloucester station in the 1970s, illustrating the long platform, a legacy of Brunel's one-sided station design in which the trains crossed over to access sections of the platform. (SKJ photograph)

Looking west towards Lydwey, the railway line runs alongside the river Severn near Purton. (SKJ photograph)

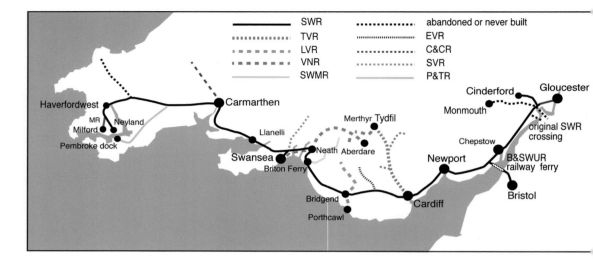

7 Map of railway companies engineered by or associated with Brunel in south Wales. Only two standard-gauge (4ft 8½in) railways are shown on this, the Taff Vale Railway (see vol.I) and the Pembroke & Tenby Railway which was promoted and built following the lapse of the SWR's powers to build their Pembroke Dock branch. (Cartography by Owen Eardley)

8 Chepstow station in 2006. As one of only two surviving SWR pavilion-style buildings, with hipped roof and wide overhanging to form a canopy, this is a Grade II listed structure. (SKJ photograph)

Opened in 1852, Brunel's Wye Bridge underwent major renewals in 1948 (land spans) and 1962 (main river truss). In 1989 a new ~ad bridge was built alongside as shown in this 2006 view. (SKJ photograph)

▷ View from the footbridge showing sidings and the original broad-gauge goods shed, the building nearest the railway line, at ~hepstow in the 1970s. (SKJ photograph)

11 *A section of the wrought-iron tube from the Wye Bridge, now on display at the Fairfield-Mabey works, the site of the later works of Edward Finch & Co. of Chepstow. Fairfield-Mabey (then the Fairfield Ship Building & Engineering Co. Ltd) were responsible for taking down Brunel's river span in 1962 and erecting the replacement Warren truss span. See page 249. (SKJ photograph)*

12 Above: *Showing Brunel's girder design, this section of one of the Chepstow land spans survives at Brunel University in Uxbridge. See photographs on the renewal of these spans on pages 246–247. (SKJ photograph)*

13 Right: *A SWR policeman's truncheon on display at the Hon. Sir William McAlpine's railway museum at Fawley. (SKJ photograph, courtesy of the Hon. Sir William McAlpine)*

Looking from England into Wales showing the 1962 railway deck of the Wye Bridge with the 1989 road bridge alongside. Moving directly upwards from a point between the two bridges to the horizon, it is possible to see Bellevue House (now known as 'High Trees') between the trees. This was the home of William George Owen, Brunel's senior resident engineer. See page 88. (SKJ photograph)

Windsor Bridge, Brunel's major bow string girder bridge across the Thames. (SKJ photograph)

16 *Newport tunnel, Brunel's broad-gauge tunnel, on the left, alongside the later bore. The tunnel, which bears the date 1848, takes the line under Stow Hill and both east and west portals consist of round-headed arches of rock-faced voussoirs. See photograph on page 110. (SKJ photograph)*

17 *The former SWR carriage sheds at Newport in 2006. See contemporary photographs of locomotives outside these sheds, with original glazed screens, on pages 106 and 107. (SKJ photograph)*

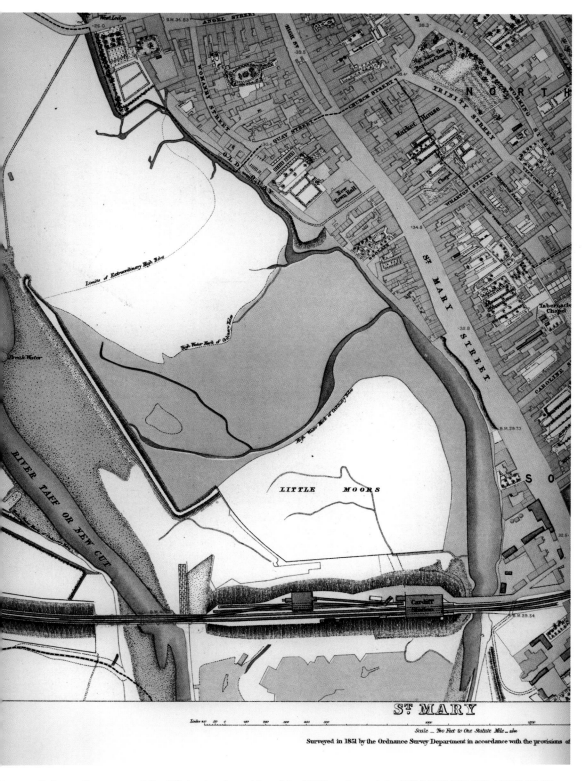

8 *1851 Ordnance Survey map of Cardiff, showing the position of the SWR station and the 'RIVER TAFF OR NEW CUT'.*
The viewing point for the painting overleaf would have been just to the right of the station on the bridge shown. Compare this with
the map on page 119 and the photographs on page 117. (Courtesy of Glamorgan Record Office)

19 Cardiff: a view of the river Taff as it flowed in 1840; note the gap in the building line on the west side of St Mary Street, caused by the erosion of the river over the years. The water colour is by Mrs H.G. Baden-Powell and bears the caption 'Cardiff 1840 St Mary St. & the River Taff before it was diverted by the GWR Co. One side of the street was washed away by the river.' (Courtesy of Cardiff Central Reference Library)

20 Cardiff: a view of what is now the old course of the river Taff by an unknown artist in the early 1850s; note part of the SWR station and the approach road bridge on the left. (Courtesy of the National Museum and Galleries of Wales)

Looking north with the Millennium Stadium beyond the masonry railway bridge serving Cardiff station; note the river bus and landing stage. The station's (now disused) concrete water tower can also be seen on the right of the bridge in this 2006 view. (SKJ photograph)

Looking south with Brunel's new cut alongside the Millennium Stadium. See also pages 113–116. (SKJ photograph)

23 *Statue of John Batchelor outside the department store founded by David Morgan. Batchelor was to lose his shipyard with the building of the SWR and David Morgan himself recalls walking through the railway tunnel at Newport before it was opened and travelling to Cardiff on one of the first excursions run by the SWR on the day after the opening. (SKJ photograph)*

24 *Bridgend, coloured lithograph depicting the station shortly after opening in 1850. Compare this with the early photograph of Bridgend station on page 132. (SKJ collection)*

Crossing Landore and the river Tawe: Brunel's timber viaduct runs through a landscape made lifeless by copper smelting. View by unknown artist in the early 1850s. (Courtesy of the Science Museum, London)

26 In this enlargement of the above, a Firefly class locomotive, with the only signs of human life, can be seen heading a train across the viauct.

Model of the centre section of Landore viaduct, with the Robert Howlett photograph of Brunel above, flanked by views of the ~~d~~uct, as it was once displayed at the Royal Institution of South Wales, now Swansea Museum. (SKJ photograph)

28 Landore viaduct with sp
replacement work being carr
out in 1979. See also pages
145–146. (SKJ photograph)

29 Remains of the high
level viaduct of the Swansea
Harbour Railway in 1974.
(SKJ photograph)

30 Clunderwen, a flying ar
road bridge near the station
that was replaced in 1985. S
photograph on page 165. (S
photograph)

Loughor viaduct in 2006; although much altered it is still on the original alignment and the only remaining Brunel viaduct in which timber still plays a structural role. Part of the road bridge carrying the A484 can be seen in the top right-hand corner. See also pages 157–158. (SKJ photograph)

Abermawr Bay in 2006; Brunel's proposals to create a port here as part of the terminus of his South Wales Railway would not be realised. (SKJ photograph)

33 *The original Vale of Neath Railway terminus at Aberdare. A surviving Brunel timber all-over roof station, it was photographed in 1979 along with the goods shed behind, but both were destroyed by fire in 1982. (SKJ photograph)*

34 *Rhydycar, the VNR railway bridge built over the Glamorganshire canal bridge, the road on the course of the canal, now forms part of the Taff Trail. Brunel had designed the two side arches to accommodate towpaths for the canal, but the canal company insisted that the main arch include both the canal and towpath. Brunel simply scaled (up to a 40ft 7in square span) the elliptical arch of this skew bridge to accommodate them – the side arches being retained and redundant from the start! (SKJ photograph)*

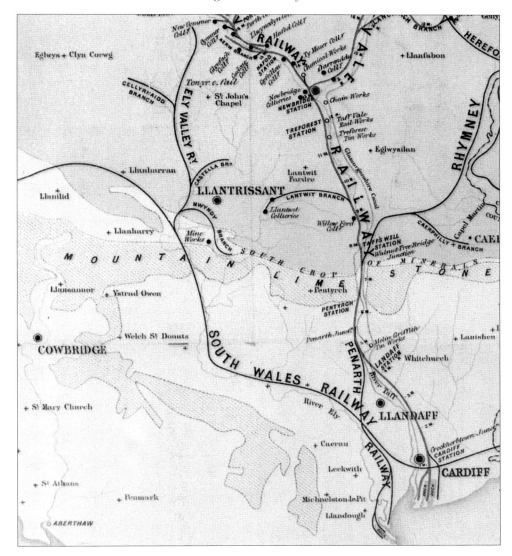

Map showing railway development in 1875. (SKJ collection)

The reason is, according to Lewis, the exploitation of mineral rights '... without regard
to the interests of the public...' It was to prompt a public meeting at the Town Hall 'on
Saturday last', which was chaired by Lord Adare (1812–71).[25] A number of resolutions
were raised by the meeting, which despite including persons connected with the
mining districts, was, according to Lewis, '... the most respectable meeting ever held in
this Town'. It was determined to petition Parliament on the subject, Lord Adare being
requested to present a Petition to the House of Commons, and it was resolved to ask
Bute to present one to the House of Lords. Lewis objected to the deviation of the line,
the original being, '... the most convenient line for the Farmers of the Vale... selected by

Mr. Brunel'; however, after this selection was made Brunel was called to adopt the upper line it was 'confidently asserted' by Lewis, on the urging of Mr Talbot. This is Christopher Rice Mansel Talbot (1803–1890), the important landowner and industrialist, whose estates could be found at Margam Park and Penrice Castle, and who was to play an increasing role in the development of the SWR. Lewis makes his argument based on three points: firstly, that, 'The Upper line is objectionable…' on account of sharp curvature and steep gradients – rendering it more unsafe for travelling; secondly, because the line travels through old coal workings, '… the passage of heavy Trains over such ground might cause serious displacements, and that accidents of a frightful character might frequently happen'; finally, the potential of a major security risk is now played, it appears to Lewis to be highly objectionable that, 'an important trunk Railway, which will be used for the conveyance of Troops for embarkation to Ireland, and possibly for the defence of our own Coasts', is taken '… through a densely populated Mineral District'.

Lewis talks about workmen, saying that they, 'frequently evince great discontent', and that they are constantly in disputes with their employers which are brought before the

Inside the modern booking hall alongside Brunel's surviving station at Bridgend station where a plaque commemorating Brunel was unveiled during the 200th anniversary in 2006. Left to right; Chris Gray, chairman of ICE Wales, Gordon Masterton, ICE president, and Brunel himself (aka Chris Code)! (SKJ photograph)

magistrates. He then takes a giant leap, based on the likely increase in the local iron and coal trade, in saying that, '… the lawless population of which might at any time by taking up the Rails at once stop all communication between the Metropolis and Ireland'.

He concludes his letter with, of course, the appropriate courtesies and admits that the 'upper line' is shorter by about two miles, but due to the curves and gradients it would be more costly to work and slower than the 'lower line'. But this is not enough for Lewis, as he then adds a full-page 'PS', adding that they will be drawing the attention of this matter to the Duke of Wellington and Sir James Graham:[26]

> … viz, the insecurity of the ground & the probability that in times of popular excitement the communication with Ireland & indeed I may also say with the important Dock Yard at Pembroke may be seriously interrupted. I am afraid that though we have petitioned parliament we shall not be able for want of friends to carry out our opposition.

The response from the Iron Duke was not what might have been expected. Lewis relays his response in a letter to Bute five days later, which is that Wellington claims no official control over railways and that application should be made to the president of the Board of Trade. This recommendation, according to Lewis, would be acted upon immediately.[27] Interestingly, Wellington was to step down from politics in 1846, at the same time that the Home Secretary, Graham, resigned after supporting Peel with the Corn Law Repeal Act, but Wellington would not completely leave public life behind, as Commander-in-Chief and with the new post of Lord High Constable of England, he organised the military response to the threat posed by the Chartist march on London in 1848. Back to 1846 and less than a month after William Lewis had proposed calling the attention of Wellington and the Home Secretary, Sir James Graham had cause to single out Sir John Guest, 'and members of his family', in a Parliamentary debate on education as evidence of improvements carried out since the Newport Rising of 1839.[28]

Did Lewis genuinely believe railway wrecking in the Bridgend area was a possibility? Industrial unrest was a threat and had been evidenced in the industrial districts of south Wales, notably Merthyr in 1831, and more recently with the Chartist attack on Newport in 1839. There were now attacks in rural areas and county towns with the 'Rebecca Riots' of 1839 and 1842–43.[29] Wellington did not need to join in the argument over Bridgend and its railway, as the threat of diversion did not last long, and the line reverted back to its proposed route through Bridgend. What does, however, come over strongly is the level of argument, if somewhat over-dramatised, that was put forward by Lewis, backed by Lord Adare and a Town Hall full of protestors, to retain their direct link to the railway, compared to the apparent indifference shown by Cowbridge. As it turned out, the Coychurch to Margam deviation would be rejected by the South Wales Railway Committee of the House of Commons, Lord James Stuart writing to his brother on 29 May 1846, stating that, 'The rail will pass as before intended by Merthyr Mawr & the shoreline.'[30]

Bridgend station was another typical SWR wayside facility with its hipped-roof pavilion with overhanging roof, all of which still survives and presents an impressive

Early photograph of Bridgend station looking west with up passenger train. (Courtesy of National Museum and Galleries of Wales, WI&MM collection)

façade today. The contractors, Merchant & Williams, had been successful in winning the station building contract and began work there in December 1849, although with some delay, *The Cambrian* telling its readers that:

> The foundation being cut… it was fully expected that the first stone would have been… laid on Wednesday last; but in consequence of some misunderstanding the stone was not laid until Thursday. It is expected that the station will be completed about the middle of May next.[31]

It was ready in time for the opening, the pavilion consisting of a single-storey building of Pennant sandstone rubble with tooled freestone dressings and round arch openings. The original building, now without its original roof pantiles, has a later, but similar style building alongside all of which was refurbished and restored in 1979.[32] Some years earlier the building was threatened with demolition, which resulted in public support being raised for its retention, backed by campaigners such as Sir John Betjeman, the Poet Laureate.[33] The rejection of the diversion of the main line may have stimulated the promotion of the Lynvi Valley Railway (LVR) on 7 August 1846,[34] but progress of this railway was painfully slow. It was authorised to construct a steam railway but did little beyond purchasing (under a further Act) the horse-drawn Duffryn Llynvi and Porth Cawl Railway. It was not until a further Act in 1855 that the LVR was

The railway at Bridgend showing the Coity Road bridge with a modified wrought-iron balloon flange girder used to provide an additional line for sidings. (SKJ photograph)

Coity Road Bridge at Bridgend, now demolished, showing a modified balloon flange girder. (SKJ photograph)

Margam Park in 1852. (Courtesy of Richard Morris)

moved to construct this line, converting from a tramroad into a broad-gauge railway, which was connected to the SWR at Bridgend.[35] By 10 August 1861 the LVR was running into the Bridgend station's goods yard at Coity Road.[36] The LVR is covered in greater detail in Chapter 9. No doubt because of the traffic of the LVR, additional sidings were required at the goods yard, some of which were accommodated by the widening of the bridge across Coity Road on the up side by the use of a wrought-iron balloon flange girder. This appears to have been a redundant girder brought from another location on the railway and also to be a modified shape in terms of the original top flange shape. The masonry bridge over Coity Road and this girder section has been swept away with the reconstruction of the Coity Road as part of the Mid Valley road link.

The next station on the line was at Pyle, the district to which Rennie's locomotive was being dragged by horses on its way through Cowbridge. Pyle was an important staging post and boasted a first-class coaching inn, the Pyle Inn, built around 1791 by Thomas Mansel Talbot (1747–1813), the father of the already mentioned C.R.M. Talbot.[37] Possibly it was his knowledge of the benefits of such establishments that led C.R.M. Talbot to become the principal proprietor of the Great Western Royal Hotel at Paddington.[38] Although the hotel fronted the station, it was not designed by Brunel although he was to take a close interest as the chairman of the hotel company's board. Brunel took advantage of the accommodation at Pyle on several occasions during the construction of the line in 1849 and 1850. Five years earlier, in 1845, it had been the venue for the inaugural meeting of the local 'Roads Board' set up to replace the Turnpike Trust and the despised toll gates following the aftermath of the Rebecca Riots. A less serious, but no doubt just as intensive, session was also spent here when Lady Charlotte Guest took the opportunity of her time there to translate part of the 'Kilhwen and Olwen' stories (part of the *Mabinogion*), when her husband was visiting his nearby properties at Newton.[39] Thomas Telford not only stayed here in 1825 but he used the Pyle Inn as a base to present his proposals for highway improvements through Glamorgan, including a bridge across the Neath at Briton Ferry. The opening of the line brought an end to its position as a coaching inn, and, like numerous other inns that Brunel had patronised when he relied on his own horse and carriage or stage coaches to get around the country, it was unable to survive on the limited business trade of the locality, and closed in 1886.[40]

The line now progresses through Margam, where the Tudor Gothic mansion of C.R.M. Talbot can be seen at Margam Park, along with the remains of the monastic buildings of Margam Abbey and the capacious Orangery built by his father, Thomas Mansel Talbot. The railway may have been seen from Margam Park, but Talbot stipulated that he did not want to hear the sound of passing trains from his house, and Brunel ensured that the track was laid well towards the sea on Margam Moors.[41] Talbot had followed the lead of his father in building up the industry of the location and from 1841 was responsible for the growth of a new town to which he gave his name, Port Talbot. His house, dubbed 'Mr Talbot's New Palace' by his friend Lewis Weston Dillwyn (1778–1855), was started in 1830 and completed five years later; it stands in a commanding position against the wooded hills enjoying views towards the sea.[42] Industrialisation had yet to make its mark on the landscape, a few coalmines and the Cwmavon copper works, situated away from the coastal plain, being the main intrusions. The line continued to Briton Ferry, a location described as follows; 'The South Wales Railway passes, on an embankment, through the once secluded bay, and has a busy little station at the point where it crosses the main street'.[43]

At Briton Ferry a connection would be later made with the South Wales Mineral Railway (SWMR), running from the SWR at Briton Ferry to the Glyncorrwg mineral district. Here also at Briton Ferry, Brunel would design a dock, with his buoyant lock gate design. All of this was in the future and before he fixed his line through Briton Ferry, he considered his options. In his 1836 proposal, Brunel talked about Neath being reached, '... without greater difficulties of Country... From Neath of course a branch of extension be formed to Swansea the nature of which must depend materially upon the manner in which the Neath river may be ultimately crossed'.

He goes on to say that that, '... Neath or Swansea must be considered as the natural terminus of the Southern line' because of the difficulty of crossing the different navigable rivers to be found between these places and the western terminus. This is

Above: *Briton Ferry station; note the policeman on the extreme right. (Courtesy of National Museum and Galleries of Wales, WI&MM collection)*

Left: *Another view of Briton Ferry station in broad gauge days. (Courtesy of National Museum and Galleries of Wales, WI&MM collection)*

Broad gauge track at Neath. (From The Railway *magazine, vol.II, 1898)*

Neath timber viaduct across the river and canal. (Courtesy of National Museum and Galleries of Wales, WI&MM collection)

The same scene in 1979. (SKJ photograph)

Llansamlet station about 1867; a 'fantail' signal can be seen on the left. (Courtesy of National Museum and Galleries of Wales, WI&MM collection)

Llansamlet flying arches; of the four three are in one group as seen in this photograph. (SKJ photograph)

reinforced by Brunel: 'I should recommend adopting Swansea or Neath as the present Terminus…' However, the position for a line across the whole of the south Wales coast is clearer in 1844 but how Swansea would be connected to the main line of the railway proposed in the 1845 Act would not become clear until 27 July 1846 with the second SWR Act.[44] The position that Swansea found itself in and the part played by Neath has led to speculation that Brunel had considered taking the SWR across the river Neath at Briton Ferry over the burrows and into Swansea from the east.[45] As late as 1889 it was still being alleged that it was the determined opposition of the Neath authorities that had led Brunel to adopt the present route through Neath and Landore, 'Swansea off the Main Line has been its curse. Swansea on the Main Line would have been its blessing'.[46] Was Brunel following the lead of Telford who had proposed a crossing at Briton Ferry; if so would it have been a timber crossing as he had proposed for the Severn?[47] It appears not, as at one of the SWR meetings held at Neath on the morning of 24 September 1844, Brunel responded to concerns raised by John Rowland (the prominent Neath banker criticised in the above pamphlet), his first being that the port of Neath might be obstructed by a bridge over the estuary, moving a motion to support the SWR, '… provided the free navigation of the river be not interfered with'.[48] Brunel replied that he had recommended a line through the town of Neath in his 1836 proposals and his view had not changed, 'In fact it would be to the interest of the Company to construct the line with as much respect as possible for the preservation of the free navigation of the Neath river, for the trade of Neath was far too important to be overlooked'.[49]

As Paul Reynolds explains in his article, even though Brunel was obviously keen to get the support of the Neath audience, there appears to be no grounds to suggest a proposal existed to build the line across the river at Briton Ferry. That same afternoon another meeting was held at Swansea and the *Cambrian* newspaper does not record any discussion about this short cut across the river. River crossings at this point would have to wait until the demands of the motor age, although the later Rhondda & Swansea Bay Railway (R&SBR) had proposed a bridge crossing and then a tunnel, which despite the attention of the veteran tunneller S.W. Yockney as engineer for the 1,490 yards-long tunnel under the mouth of the river at Briton Ferry, work was to be abandoned by 1885.[50] The swing bridge that was eventually built by the R&SBR was the lowest crossing of the river until a road bridge was built in the 1950s, this bridge being the last major riveted steel-girder bridge built in the country.[51] It has since been joined by the M4 crossing.

Another factor that Brunel may have considered was the connection to another railway, indeed an important part of this broad-gauge 'communications and coal' network, the Vale of Neath Railway (VNR), which was incorporated on 3 August 1846.[52] The main line of the VNR would run from the SWR at Neath to Merthyr Tydfil via the Vale of Neath and the Cynon Valley. Ironically, the VNR would later build its own branch into Swansea, the Swansea & Neath Railway, to avoid the tortuous section of the SWR when sending its coal trains to Swansea. So Brunel was committed to taking the line around Neath, crossing the river to the north of the town bridge. On the way to Neath the SWR went through the Briton Ferry ironworks, as evidenced by a report and estimate of the damage and loss sustained by the Neath Abbey Coal Co. due to the construction of the SWR through their works and lands adjacent to their collieries at Briton Ferry.[53] As well as industry it also passed through a district rich in the history of early Welsh tramroads, as evidenced by the 'waggonways' shown on George Yates' map of 1799.[54] With the opening of the SWR an address was given by the Mayor, Mr Sankey Gardner, on behalf of the Corporation.[55] With the opening of the Vale of Neath Railway, Neath station became severely congested and was described as being the most inconvenient of stations on the SWR. In 1855 the *Cambrian* reported that, '… the place is still uncovered and the passengers are exposed to all weathers',[56] and two years later commented on the operating difficulties:

> Such is the pressure and confined space at this important station that the traffic on the line is much interfered with. The passengers' trains are detained daily for want of room to come on to station, and goods trucks cannot be brought to the siding to be discharged without great delay.[57]

After Neath the line took a sharp turn to the left, passing close to the Neath Abbey ironworks, the famous works that was managed, like the Neath Abbey Coal Co., by the Quaker family of Price. Brunel had met these gentlemen before, particularly

Llansamlet flying arches; one of the arches was erected to resist the movement of the cutting. (SKJ photograph)

Llansamlet flying arches from rail level. (Courtesy of National Museum and Galleries of Wales, WI&MM collection)

Henry Habberley Price (1794–1839), who in 1832, along with William Brunton (1777–1851), proposed a line between London and Bristol.[58] Following a stiff climb up Skewen bank with its ruling gradient of 1 in 88, the line was now running over the type of ground that would alarm William Lewis. These were marked by old coal workings, where the passage of heavy trains could '... cause serious displacements'. The displacement that Brunel was most worried about, however, was of the sides of a steep cutting at Llansamlet. Brunel had an early experience of a cutting 'slip' when a GWR down goods train ran into a huge mound of earth in Sonning cutting in Berkshire on Christmas Eve, 1841. Pulled by the 2-4-0 engine *Hecla*, eight third-class passengers died and seventeen were injured when their two third-class carriages were crushed due to the force of the seventeen goods wagons behind. *Hecla* was seized under the ancient law of *deo dandum* (to be given to God) but the Board of Trade later exonerated Brunel and the GWR from all blame.[59] Very heavy rain had dislodged the earth from the sides of the cutting and Brunel must have been mindful of this when he came up with a safeguard for Llansamlet following a slip soon after the opening.[60] Brunel designed masonry 'flying arches' which spring from the sides of the deep cutting. One example of this kind had been erected on the Bolton & Preston Railway at Chorley in 1841.[61] The Chorley flying arches are, in fact, dissimilar in style to the

Llansamlet flying arches, and consist of sixteen thin masonry arches (little more than a foot thick at the centre of the arch) acting as struts between masonry retaining walls on either side at a span of 25ft 3in. In contrast, the four substantial Llansamlet arches span 70ft from the sides of the bare cutting, the design and weight of the arch providing sufficient force to resist the thrust of the side.[62] This weight is achieved with heavy copper slag which extends above the high parapet wall and forms a mound on the top of each arch; despite the weight involved only one of these arches has required underpinning near the springing of the arch.

Brunel's most substantial timber work, not just on the SWR, but as far as his work was concerned for any railway company, was to be found in the vicinity of Swansea. Crossing the river Tawe and the Landore marshes, the Landore viaduct formed a continuous timber work, exactly one-third of a mile long, with thirty-seven spans ranging from 40 to 100ft wide. The assistant engineer in charge of the construction of the viaduct was Lavington Evans Fletcher (1822–97). Fletcher had not worked under Brunel before, but had been engaged as an engineer to Messrs Barrett, Exall and Andrews of the Katesgrove Ironworks in Reading, who had supplied a steam engine and pumping equipment to the GWR for draining one of the shafts of the Box Tunnel.[63] The Landore viaduct contract had gone to Hennet of Bristol, presumably the same engineer (George Hennet) to whom William George Owen had been articled from 1828, then a civil engineer of Guildford Street, London, but with at least one other office in Liverpool.[64] Hennet was successful as the contractor for the permanent way and rails for the entire length of the SWR.[65]

A watercolour view of the viaduct was painted soon after the opening by an unknown artist; the sweep of the elongated study, to suit the subject matter, shows a landscape that at second glance is surreal. Apart from the driver and fireman seen on the Firefly-class locomotive passing over the viaduct, not a soul can be seen. There are cottages, houses and mine workings overlooked by the brooding castle on the hill, but no trees or foliage of any description and a lifeless river. And then behind the viaduct can be seen the reason for no vegetation and little sign of life – the copper smelters of Landore. Some literary accounts of the Landore landscape, such as that provided by John Murray, the railway handbook writer, are perhaps more graphic:

It [the railway] rapidly descends into the Vale of Tawe, which hereabouts and all the way to Swansea exhibits an unparalleled scene of desolation, to which a beautiful contrast is offered on the right by the distant hills at the head of the Swansea Valley. The soil is naturally infertile. The deleterious influence of the fluoric or arsenical acids from the copper works arrests the stunted vegetation, so that there are no trees, and instead of grass a dry yellow sickly growth of chamomile barely covers the ground. To the traveller who crosses the Landore viaduct at night, the livid glare from the numerous chimneys, the rolling, fleecy, white clouds of smoke which fill up the valley beneath him, the desolate-looking heaps of slag on either side, might well recall Dante's line; 'Voi che entrate, lasciate ogni speranza'...[66]

Landore viaduct looking south, Swansea Canal in the foreground. (Courtesy of the National Museum and Galleries of Wales, WI&MM collection)

Looking north at the Landore viaduct crossing the Swansea Canal. Note the five masonry piers. (Courtesy of National Museum and Galleries of Wales, WI&MM collection)

It was reputedly made from Canadian Pitch Pine and cost £20,000 to build, and opened with the running of the first train between Chepstow and Swansea on 18 June 1850. Not only was the viaduct to be virtually replaced some thirty-six years later, but the length of the bridge would be considerably reduced. This was done by embanking part of the viaduct in a programme of work that started in September 1886. The embankment was formed on the eastern side by tipping slag from the nearby Hafod copper works around and into the timberwork of the viaduct to form an embankment. Railway traffic continued as normal during the work. A steel truss replaced the timber main span bearing the legend, 'Edward D. Finch & Co. Steel Builders, Chepstow 1889'. Palmer of Neath was responsible for the side spans with new masonry piers being built by Abraham Kellett of London.[67] The cost of these works was £30,000 and the work was completed by October 1889. An extensive programme of works was undertaken by British Rail in 1978/79 to replace the wrought-iron girders. Today Landore viaduct straddles new roads and development brought about as part of the extensive reclamation of the lower Swansea Valley. The whole area has been revitalised with business and retail parks and the sporting venue of the Liberty stadium. Part of Brunel's original design can still be seen in the form of four masonry stone piers, each pierced with two arches, on the west side of the river Tawe close to the Neath Road.[68] The stumps of timber piers in the river bed and timberwork encased in the embankment, some of which had ignited causing smoke to issue from the trackbed, are all that remains of Brunel's *magnum opus* in wood.[69]

Next was the important junction for the branch to Swansea. Construction of the station at Landore was begun at the same time as the viaduct, 2 August 1847, and it remained busy as the main junction station for Swansea until the 1920s, even though the Swansea West Loop had been opened on 5 March 1906 to do away with the need to change at Landore.[70] The official opening of the SWR between Chepstow and Swansea on 18 June 1850 was celebrated with a breakfast on the Swansea Burrows, '... Mr Brunel, in responding to the toast, made a humorous and effective speech which however, was almost entirely lost upon us, as we experienced the greatest difficulty in hearing him. He sat down amid protracted cheering'.[71]

Despite the concerns of later Swansea writers who felt the drawbacks of being 'off the main line', the SWR received considerable support from Swansea and the town had recognised Brunel's talents at an early stage. There was also considerable financial support; the English Copper Co., one of the many companies responsible for the 'desolate-looking' feature of copper smelting areas such as Landore, took 500 shares, while many small tradesmen signed up for twenty shares at a time. Informed opinion was that Swansea as a whole, had taken 2,000 shares, but this was before the course of the line, as it affected Swansea, had been determined.[72] Further details on the association of Brunel with Swansea will be picked up in Chapter 9, but with the first section of the SWR between Chepstow and Swansea now open, the line was continuing its progress west.

Landore viaduct in the 1880s with tipping to form the embankment.

Landore viaduct during the rebuilding in the 1880s with new masonry piers being built.

Left: *Landore viaduct during reconstruction in 1979. (SKJ photograph)*

Below: *Landore viaduct in 2006. (SKJ photograph)*

Swansea station at the opening in June 1850. (SKJ collection)

Swansea station before rebuilding in the 1930s. (SKJ collection)

Opposite below: *View looking east across the Landore viaduct. (SKJ collection)*

Interior of Swansea station before rebuilding in the 1930s. (SKJ collection)

NOTES

1 Quote from a letter by William Lewis to Lord Bute, 13 February 1846, see Bute correspondence, L91/97i.

2 Picton-Turbervill, Edith (second edition, 1947), p.8, *In the Land of My Fathers*, Western Mail & Echo Ltd: Cardiff. Today the Vale of Glamorgan is defined by the county borough of the same name.

3 George, T. Neville (1937, second impression of third edition 1975), p.111, *British Regional Geology; South Wales*, HMSO: London. They form an exceptional deposit as far as the southern half of Britain is concerned because of their close proximity to contemporary shores.

4 Williams, B.P. (1994), p.5, *Cardiff Canton 1882–1994*, South Wales and West Railway: Cardiff.

5 Carried out as part of the Relief of Unemployment Measures, this work was completed by 1932, photographs of the level crossing at Ely Paper Mill, made redundant by under bridges on the raised section can be seen in Billingham, Nigel and Jones, Stephen K. (1999), p.120, *Ely, Caerau and Michaelston-super-Ely*, Chalford Publishing Co.: Stroud (reprinted by Tempus Publishing: Stroud).

6 See Jones, Stephen K. (2005), p.203-205, and Mountford, Eric R. and Sprinks, Neil (1993), p.7-9, *The Taff Vale Lines to Penarth*, Oakwood Press: Oxford. The PHDR's third Act was obtained on 22 June 1863 and authorised the lease period of 999 years. The lease for the tidal harbour and railway from Penarth junction to the harbour was to take effect from 1 January 1864.

7 Billingham, Nigel and Jones, Stephen K. (1996), p.120, *Ely, Caerau and Michaelston-super-Ely*, Chalford Publishing Co.: Stroud (reprinted by Tempus Publishing: Stroud).

8 Billingham, Nigel and Jones, Stephen K. (1999), p.19, *Ely Common to Culverhouse Cross*, Tempus Publishing: Stroud. A view of the branch line and works locomotive in 1967 can

be seen in Huntriss, Derek (1996), *The Heyday of Steam in South Wales*, Ian Allan Publishing: Shepperton.

9   Chapman, Colin (1984), p.7, *The Cowbridge Railway*, Oxford Publishing Co.: Poole.

10 See Chapman, Colin (1984), pp.6-12, for the story of how Cowbridge eventually gained its railway.

11 *The Cambrian*, 12 January 1849.

12 *The Cambrian*, 12 January 1849, this locomotive is later mentioned in a progress report, working on the Pyle to Taibach section. See *The Cambrian* for 26 April 1850.

13 See Chapman, Colin (1984).

14 The name 'Pontyclun' did not come into official use until 1893. See Francis, David J. (1976), p.134, *The Border Vale of Glamorgan*, Stewart Williams: Barry.

15 *Monmouthshire Merlin*, quoted in *The Railway Times*, 15 January 1850. The firm had also won contracts for the stations at Newport, Cardiff and Swansea.

16 Chapman, Colin (1996), p.13, *The Llantrisant Branches of the Taff Vale Railway*, Oakwood Press: Headington.

17 See Jones, Stephen K. (2005), for the Clark and Brunel connection (mainly Chapter 11) and for an account of Clark and Talygarn see Derek C. Kingham's chapter, *Clark of Talygarn* in James, Brian Ll. ed. (1998), *G.T. Clark, Scholar Ironmaster in the Victorian Age*, The Making of a Scholar Ironmaster, University of Wales Press: Cardiff.

18 Brunel, Isambard (1870, reprinted 1971), p.97, *The Life of Isambard Kingdom Brunel*, Longmans, Green & Co: London (reprinted David & Charles: Newton Abbot). See also Jones, Stephen K. (2005), p.206-209.

19 Listed in the auction catalogue published by Gottwaltz & Perry of Cardiff, for auction at Talygarn on 5–22 July 1922.

20 Francis, David J. (1976), p.86. Pencoed station would not open until 2 September 1850, along with Ely, Pencoed and Briton Ferry.

21 Francis, David J. (1976), p.86.

22 *The Cambrian*, 5 November 1847. Only a week earlier work near Newport had been suspended, it is believed because of money problems.

23 *Monmouthshire Merlin*, 23 October 1847.

24 Bute correspondence, L91/97i, 13 February 1846.

25 Davies, John (1981), p.126-7, *Cardiff and the Marquesses of Bute*, University of Wales: Cardiff Press. Edwin Wyndham-Quin, third Earl of Dunraven (Lord Adare) was supported by Bute for the Tory nomination, C.R.M. Talbot being the liberal candidate, both represented Glamorgan until 1852, Talbot continuing as an MP until his death in 1890.

26 Sir James Robert George Graham (1792–1861) was Home Secretary in Sir Robert Peel's administration, Wellington (1769–1853) was also in Peel's cabinet, but without portfolio.

27 Bute correspondence, L91/110, 18 February 1846.

28 Bessborough, Earl of, ed. (1950), p.176, *Lady Charlotte Guest Extracts from her Journal 1833–1852*, John Murray: London. Sir James Graham complimented Guest personally in his speech on the Dowlais schools and their management.

29 See Chapter 5.

30 Bute correspondence L91/208, 29 May 1846, NLW.

31 *The Cambrian*, 21 December 1849.

32 Newman, John (1995), p.162, *The Buildings of Wales: Glamorgan,* Penguin Books/University of Wales Press: London. Bridgend is a Grade II listed building, CADW record no. 11306.

33 The refurbished station was formerly reopened by the Rt. Hon. Nicholas Edwards, MP, Secretary of State for Wales on 30 November 1979. On 10 June 2005 it was officially reopened for Vale of Glamorgan passenger services by Andrew Davies, AM, Minister for Economic Development and Transport, Welsh Assembly Government.

34 9 & 10 Vic., cap.353, 1846. see Chapter 3 and 9.

35 MacDermot, E.T. (revised by Clinker, C.R., 1964), vol.1, p.305.

36 Smith, Clive (1985), pp.14-15, *Railways of the Lynfi Valley,* Alun Books: Port Talbot. Access into Bridgend station, with its own facilities, was achieved in 1866.

37 Griffiths, Barrie (2001), p.41-2, *The Inn at Pyle,* The Kenfig Society Monograph No. 19, Kenfig.

38 Hughes, John Vivian (second edition 1978), p.27, *The Wealthiest Commoner: C.R.M. Talbot,* West Glamorgan County Council: Port Talbot.

39 Guest, Revel & John, Angela V. (1989), p.107, *Lady Charlotte A Biography of the Nineteenth Century,* Weidenfeld and Nicolson: London.

40 Griffiths, Barrie (2001), p.52-3. The Pyle Inn was converted to flats and the building survived until 1959.

41 Hughes, John Vivian (second edition 1978), p.26. A railway halt was sited between Pyle and Margam for his convenience.

42 Newman, John (1995), p.430. The Talbot male line died out in 1890, the house has survived a major fire and is now restored as a centrepiece of Margam Country Park.

43 *The Handbook of the Vale of Neath* (1852).

44 9 & 10 Vic., cap.239, 1846, SWR Act of 27 July 1846, in Newport Reference Library (qM000625 SOU), section vii. Jones, T.I. Jeffreys ed. (1966), p.87, ccxxxix (L. and P.) (585).

45 See *Neath Antiquarian Society* Transactions 1980–81, article by Paul Reynolds on *The Neath River Railway Tunnel*, pp.7–14. This is area further explored by Frank Llewellyn-Jones in Bulletin 60 (February 1994) of the South West Wales Industrial Archaeology Society.

46 Pamphlet by E.E. Rowse, *Proposed re-opening of Wind Street and Swansea on the Main Line,* quoted article by Paul Reynolds, *The Neath River Railway Tunnel*, p.7.

47 Rhys D. Phillips refers to an earlier suspension bridge; 'An Act of Parliament of 1801-2 and another tempo. George IV. sanctioned the construction of a Suspension Bridge to carry a new road across the Nedd at Briton Ferry; this was to be at least 200 ft. wide and 90 ft. high, above the spring tide. The bridge was not built.' See Phillips, Rhys D. (1925), p.346, *The History of the Vale of Neath,* Rhys D. Phillips: Swansea.

48 From Paul Reynolds, *The Neath River Railway Tunnel*, p.8.

49 *The Cambrian*, 28 September 1844.

50 See Paul Reynolds, *The Neath River Railway Tunnel*. The firm of Yockney had many associations with tunnelling work for Brunel.

51 Rhys D. Phillips refers to a proposed road bridge of 1918–20, See Phillips, Rhys D. (1925), p.346.

52 9 & 10 Vic., cap.341, 1846. See Chapter 3 and 8.

53 Report by Joshua Richardson, 5 March 1850, see *Neath Antiquarian Society* Transactions 1978, article by Harry Green on *Briton Ferry Ironworks: A Myth Destroyed*, pp.111-5.

54 Mackworth's earliest line dates back to 1697 see Lewis, M.J.T. (1970). p.247-50, *Early Wooden Railways*, Routledge & Kegan Paul: London, and colour plate 8 of Jones, Stephen K. (2005) for Neath Abbey, showing horse drawn trams and a horse-worked 'gin' and map on page 51.

55 Jenkins, Elias (1974), p.245, *Neath and District: A Symposium*, Elias Jenkins: Neath. Jenkins notes that the first train seen at Neath, presumably testing the track, is variously recorded on the 11 or 18 May 1850, a month or more before the inaugural opening.

56 *The Cambrian*, 26 January 1855.

57 *The Cambrian*, 12 June 1857.

58 The scheme for the 'Bristol and London Railway' was issued on 7 May 1832. See MacDermot, E.T., revised by Clinker, C.R. (1964), *History of the Great Western Railway*, vol.1. Ian Allen: London. See also Jones, Stephen K. (2005) p.73, 96.

59 Hammond, Rolt (1956), p.7, *Engineering Structural Failures*, Odhams Press Ltd: London. The Inspector General; Sir Frederic Smith, could find no error in the construction.

60 The slip at Llansamlet must have occurred in the summer of 1850. *The Cambrian* of 30 August 1850 covered the half-yearly meeting of the SWR at which the slip was reported. By the next half-yearly meeting, in February 1851, the arches had been built; *The Cambrian* of 28 February 1851.

61 These featured in the Minutes of Proceedings of the Institution of Civil Engineers in 1844. See Rennison, R.W. ed. (1981, second edition 1996), p.219, *Civil Engineering Heritage: Northern England*, Thomas Telford Publishing: London. The Llansamlet flying arches can be found in Cragg, Roger ed. (1986, second edition 1997), p.82, *Civil Engineering Heritage: Wales & West Central England*, Thomas Telford Publishing: London.

62 MacDermot, E.T., revised by Clinker, C.R. (1964), p.297, vol.1.

63 Obituary notice Proc. MICE, 1897.

64 *Cardiff and Merthyr Guardian* and *Glamorgan, Monmouth and Brecon Gazette*, 22 June 1850.

65 *The Cambrian*, 17 August 1849.

66 Correctly; '*Lasciate ogne speranza voi ch'intrate*' or 'Abandon all hope you who enter here', from one of the most remarkable visions in Western literature; *The Divine Comedy* by Dante Alighieri. Written between 1308 and his death in 1321, it represents an allegory for his and future ages with the poet doomed to suffer eternal torment for vices exhibited and sins committed on earth – Dante's *Inferno* presenting an image, as far as John Murray was concerned, that could be Landore.

67 I am grateful to Paul Reynolds for pointing out the references in *The Cambrian* (12 March 1886, 20 April 1888 & 4 October 1889) and reporting that comment on the streets of Swansea at that time was that people regretted the passing of the old bridge and that there was nothing wrong with the old one!

68 Illustrations of the viaduct show five such piers but only four are extant today.

69 This happened before BR refurbishment in the 1970s and appears to have been fuelled by the remains of Brunel's timber piers but not considered a danger as trains continued to travel over it during this time.

70 Thomas, Norman Lewis (1965), p.172, *The Story of Swansea's Districts and Villages*, Neath.

71 Report on the opening of the SWR 18 June 1850, *Cardiff and Merthyr Guardian* and *Glamorgan, Monmouth and Brecon Gazette*, 22 June 1850.

72 *Monmouthshire Merlin*, 5 October 1844.

7

FINAL DESTINATION
'LETTER FROM SKIBBEREEN'[1]

Although the line had been opened from Chepstow to Swansea more or less as proposed, serious cracks in the original plan were beginning to show. Two years earlier, in late January 1848, the directors were pushing to open the line as soon as possible and they ordered the contractors to finish the Swansea to Newport section as quickly as possible. It was not until 15 September 1848, however, that *The Cambrian* announced:

> The works on the intended line of railway are to be wholly discontinued from Haverfordwest to Swansea, it having been determined to push forward with all possible dispatch that portion of line from Swansea to Gloucester, so that it might be opened as early as practicable. The works connected with Neath are carried on with much activity. Mr. Kirkhouse is making great progress with the bridges and road. A great number of the permanent rails are arriving from Cardiff.[2]

At the half-yearly meeting of the SWR, held on 26 February 1849, the company chairman, Charles Russell (1786–1855), said that although when money had been abundant it had been sensible to go for the whole line, now things were different and money was scarcer. Sections of the railway would now be opened as built – Newport to Swansea as being the most lucrative, Grange Court as being a link with the rest of the Great Western system and west of Swansea in due course.[3] Many of the directors of the SWR had been seeking to make changes regarding the western end of the line, a process that would take not place until June 1852 when it finally overcame opposition to do so. As part of this process, Russell would resign because of the clash of interests between the SWR and GWR, Russell acting as chairman to both companies. His successor was C.R.M. Talbot, the man who William Lewis had claimed 'urged' Brunel to change the route of the SWR and who was now the Lord Lieutenant of Glamorgan.[4] When Sir John Guest broke the news of Talbot's Lord Lieutenancy to Lady Charlotte, she confided in her diary, 'I think they might just as well have appointed Merthyr [her pet name for her husband] himself who is quite as rich, if not more so, and has much more influence in the County...'[5]

Guest may have been wealthy, but not for nothing was Talbot known as 'The Wealthiest Commoner'.[6] First elected to Parliament in 1830, he became the 'Father of the House of Commons' in 1874 and went on to serve as an MP for sixty years until his death in 1890. His skills as an orator were well known (and noted by Lady Charlotte Guest) but it was claimed that he only spoke once in the House, which was to ask someone to close a window because of the draught! The truth is he rarely spoke, which is more than can be said of a fellow MP on the GWR board of directors, indeed the chairman, Sir Daniel Gooch, who was proud that he had been a silent member.[7] Talbot had been a shareholder of the SWR from the start and encouraged friends and political colleagues to do likewise; with financial constraints biting hard in 1849 he came forward with a major contribution to enable the SWR to go ahead, 'Here, gentlemen, is a cheque for £500,000 to complete your line'.[8] Brunel got on well with Talbot and eventually, with Brunel acting as mediator between Russell and the GWR on one side and Talbot and the SWR on the other, a workable agreement was finally made, as related in Chapter 5. Talbot was related to William Henry Fox Talbot and in a letter to his cousin in 1853, gave an interesting insight on Brunel based on an occasion when both were travelling on the GWR, Talbot making the observation:

Partial opening out of Cockett tunnel, Swansea. (Courtesy of National Museum and Galleries of Wales, WI&MM collection)

The rebuilt east portal at Cockett and the later, brick-built, 'flying arches' at Cockett, Swansea. (SKJ photograph)

Did you but know how your life depends on the signalmen at the parts where other railways meet and cross! I said one day to Brunel when we were coming up 'I am always glad when we have passed the Reading points, they are so complicated' I wanted his assurance there was no danger, but his reply was; 'and so am I'.[9]

The line continued from Swansea, passing through the 789-yard long Cockett Tunnel, a tunnel that would later suffer from subsidence and partially collapse in 1899, causing traffic to be diverted over the London & Northern Western Railway's lines through Swansea.[10] During the reconstruction of the tunnel, part of the hillside was excavated and brick versions of Brunel's flying arches were built to prevent slippage. Prior to the opening in 1852 a fatal accident had occurred at the tunnel which the *Cardiff and Merthyr Guardian* referred to as the 'Lloughor' tunnel, reporting that John Coughan, alias William Smith, was employed on the construction as a haulier, leading a horse-drawn wagon in the tunnel when his foot slipped and he fell under the wagon, when crushed both his legs. Despite being taken to Swansea Infirmary and amputations undertaken, 'he expired in about an hour'. A native of Ireland, he was thirty years of age.[11]

Next came the crossing of the river Loughor by a timber bridge that can claim to be the last of his timber viaducts still in use. Designed by Brunel, again with Lavington Evans Fletcher acting as resident engineer, it was 750ft long with a swing bridge at the Swansea end which provided an opening of 40ft with seventeen further spans of similar size. The swing bridge had last been used in 1887 and was officially, and permenantly, closed to river traffic by major work carried out on the viaduct during 1908–09. Wrought-iron girders replaced the timber trusses around 1880 with Brunel's original trestle work remaining but with the work completed in 1909, the design was changed from a three-pile group to a four-pile group (see drawing on page 157).[12] The bridge was refurbished in 1979–81 in a sympathetic fashion and still retains a considerable percentage of original timber up to the lower walling[13].

At Llanelly the SWR first crossed the main line of the Llanelly Railway and then the Dafen branch on the level. As this line was built to the standard gauge, no junction was possible. Indeed, the first engineer to the Llanelly Railway had been Brunel's resident engineer on the TVR, George Bush.[14] The Llanelly Railway was one of the first locomotive railways in Wales, having ordered two locomotives, *Victoria* and *Albert*, from Timothy Hackworth & Co., in 1839.[15] On 1 June 1853 the Llanelly Railway opened a branch across the head of the dock to the SWR station to run their trains to a platform alongside. In 1858 a short, broad-gauge branch was added to bring SWR traffic to the dock.[16] In order to tranship coal between the standard-gauge Llanelly trains and the broad-gauge, Brunel designed apparatus to

The west portal of Cockett tunnel. (SKJ photograph)

facilitate this, resembling a giant 'pair of scales' and similar to one in use at Bristol for like purposes.[17] In taking the railway through Llanelly, Brunel was to divert the course of the river Lliedi and take the railway along the foreshore under the supervision of the Woods & Forests, the SWR Act of Parliament containing the following clause, '… that as the foreshore belongs to her Majesty the Queen in right of her Crown, the SWR shall be made through Llanelly under the supervision of the Woods and Forests, as it is to be made upon the foreshore which belongs to the Crown'.[18]

William Chambers, Jr (1809–82), was one of the original subscribers listed in the South Wales Railway Act of 1845. In 1836, along with his father, William Chambers, Snr (1774–1855), he had promoted the Llanelly Railway with George Bush (c.1810–41) as engineer.[19] Despite having forfeited the bond he had put up for a contractor that had failed on a TVR contract, Chambers, Jr, was prepared to invest in another Brunel project; indeed, he was probably behind an Address of Congratulation by the Llanelly Chamber of Commerce in 1852.[20] At a General Special Meeting of the Llanelly Chamber of Commerce held on 8 September 1852, the chairman, Mr B. Jones, announced that it had been resolved (unanimously) to present an address to the directors of the SWR, on the opening of the line from Swansea (Landore) to Carmarthen. This was given as the 17th instant (i.e. 17th September) and it was further resolved (also unanimously) that Mr Chambers, Jr, along with seven others including the chairman,

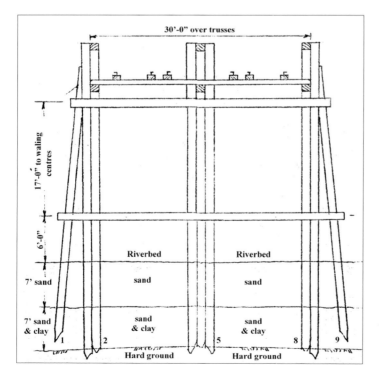

The drawing shows the 1852 arrangement of the viaduct, consisting of seventeen groups of timber piles. Note the gauge is broad and standard. (Drawing based on engineer's notes)

Loughor viaduct, seen here in its original condition (three-pile group) prior to the reconstruction of the rail deck around 1880. The opening section, a wrought-iron swing bridge, allowed river traffic to pass through the first span of the viaduct and can be seen on the left (Swansea side); see also the colour section for a view of the viaduct today. (Courtesy of National Museum and Galleries of Wales, WI&MM collection)

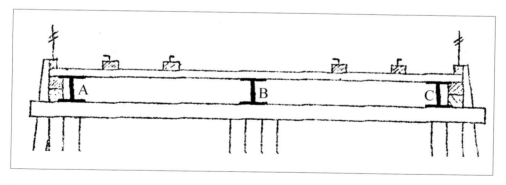

Later in the nineteenth century the timber trusses were replaced by three wrought-iron girders (A, B and C) on which Barlow rail was laid laterally between the three to form decking. (Drawing based on engineer's notes)

Loughor viaduct in 1979. Photograph taken during a major (three-year) refurbishment. Brunel's original three-pile group was changed, in, 1909 to a four-pile group. (SKJ photograph)

The former Loughor station in 1980 before its demolition to accomodate the new road (A484) leading to the replacement bridge across Loughor. (SKJ photograph)

secretary and treasurer, be requested to form a deputation to present the address which ran as follows:

> ... This Chamber has watched, with much anxiety, the circumstances which have attended the projection and construction of this Line ; and for the continuous efforts and energies of your Board,- supported by one of your number, locally connected with Llanelly, with whose ['known' is marked through here] views this Chamber has been acquainted – that it was of vast importance that the South Wales Railway should be extended below Swansea ; and for the valuable services rendered by your Chairman, under the vicissitudes which pressed all Railway Companies, more or less,- this Chamber is anxious to express its warm acknowledgements; and to congratulate your Board, your Company, and the Country, on this important occasion.[21]

During the Rebecca Riots of 1842–43, father and son were the only resident magistrates in Llanelly. Although the son, Chambers, Jr, had sympathy for the peaceful protestation of the daughters of Rebecca, he took an active role in arresting the perpetrators when the destruction of property was concerned in the form of attacks on gates.[22] Continuing the journey westward, part of the canalbed of the Kidwelly & Llanelly canal to Pembrey Harbour was used to form the trackbed for the SWR.[23] There were permanent way problems on the next section of line, caused by a shortage of Barlow rails delaying the public opening from 17 September to 11 October 1852.[24] Seen as low-cost alternative to bridge rail on baulk timbers, Barlow rail proved to be unreliable and prone to spreading under load. By 1856 the SWR was forced to replace them and on 11 April 1857 sought tenders for the purchase of about 400 tons of rails, offering to deliver to any station on the SWR between Newport and Carmarthen; 'Any further particulars can be obtained of Mr. W G Owen, SWR, Gloucester'.[25] Much of it was to end up as fence posts and used for other engineering purposes, and as we have seen, Barlow rail was pressed into use as decking for Loughor viaduct in the 1880s. The same edition of the *Cardiff and Merthyr Guardian* reports that the second line of rails between Carmarthen and Neyland had been opened. With up and down tracks now open, there was an opportunity to initiate a timetable better connecting with the Irish boat traffic. A night train would now arrive and leave Neyland three times a week on the departure of the Irish packets:

> The express which now leaves London at 4.50 pm and which at present proceeds no farther than Cardiff, will then run the whole way to Neyland, arriving there about two o'clock in the morning, just before the departure of the packets. The packets, moreover, arrive at Neyland shortly after midnight. A train will, after the first of May be despatched for London immediately after their arrival, which will reach London by 11 o'clock in the morning. These new arrangements will be an invaluable boon to all travellers proceeding to and returning for Ireland.[26]

The next town along the coast from Llanelli on the line, Kidwelly, had responded some years earlier and in a grander way to the prospect of its connection to the railway, as

FERRYSIDE.

Lithograph of Ferryside showing the railway. (SKJ collection)

Problems with Barlow rail: a derailment near Carmarthen caused by the rail spreading under the weight of a broad gauge train. (From The Railway *magazine, vol.II, 1898)*

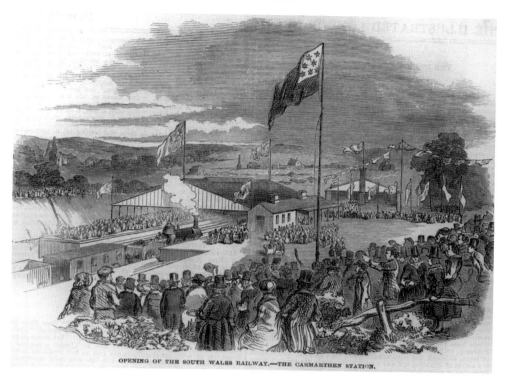

OPENING OF THE SOUTH WALES RAILWAY.—THE CARMARTHEN STATION.

Opening of the line to Carmarthen which took place on 17 September 1852, but the timetable did not begin until 11 October, and this Illustrated London News *image prematurely shows a completed station and an all-over one at that! The station became 'Carmarthen junction' with the opening of the Carmarthen & Cardigan Railway's station (which was nearer Carmarthen) in 1860. (SKJ collection)*

Brunel once commented to the contractor, Francis Roubiliac Condor (1815–89).[27] According to an account later published by Condor, Brunel told him the following story when he and Condor were travelling on the SWR to Neyland and were passing through the town of Kidwelly:

> ... I always feel very sneaking when I pass this place. When we first obtained the Bill for the line, the good people here were overjoyed. They held a public meeting, and resolved to present me with the freedom of the town. It was drawn out in form, and sent me with a letter from the mayor, and in fact, in a gold-plate box. Of course I felt gratified, and I waited a day or two before acknowledging the letter, as I was extremely busy, and wished to do so in suitable terms. So a week or two slipped by, and I thought that I must make my apologies in person. But from that time to this the opportunity has not presented itself. I am ashamed to say that I have never even thanked them, and I feel as if I must rush through the town whenever I have to pass it, from being unable to excuse my neglect.[28]

This honour appears to have been conferred around 1845 but could it have been made after the next episode? On 23 January 1846 the Mayor of Kidwelly, John Williams, made a statement that the SWR proposed to, '... erect a fix[ed] bridge across Gwendraeth Fach River...'[29] A fixed bridge would obstruct and impede navigation and the Town Clerk was instructed to write to the SWR's solicitors and caution them from erecting such a fixed bridge. If they persisted in such action, the Borough of Kidwelly would write to the Lords of the Admiralty and HM Commissioners of Woods and Forests. Kidwelly got its opening bridge, a timber trestle with thirteen spans, the centre span lifting up to allow a 20ft-wide clearance for vessels bound for Kidwelly.

Throughout this period and particularly during 1846 and 1847, *The Cambrian* and the *Cardiff and Merthyr Guardian* reported on the famine that was gripping Ireland and the Scottish Highlands in a vice of misery. Scotland was suffering much hardship and distress from the spread of blight, destroying the potato crop and the main source of food for the rural population. However, on the sheer scale of tragedy, it was the Irish Potato Famine or 'The Great Hunger' that has etched itself in popular memory as one of the great human tragedies of modern times. In the period of the famine leading to 1850, almost 1 million perished out of a population that stood at 8.5 million at the time of the 1841 census. A further million would emigrate to escape the famine and something like a further half a million births would be lost as a direct result of 'The Great Hunger'. *The Cambrian* reported: 'Ireland – the Irish journals continue to furnish the most lamentable accounts of the awful state of destitution and distress to which the poor of that country are now reduced'.[30]

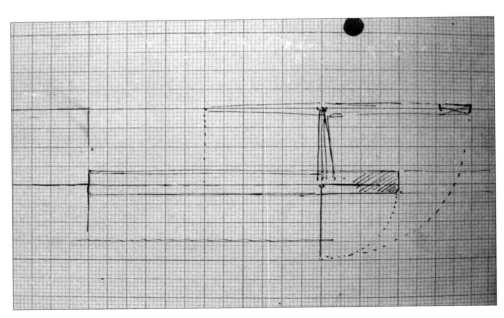

Opening bridge sketch for Carmarthen, from small sketchbook 30, f.7, 4 October 1852. (Courtesy of University of Bristol special collections)

The original roll-back opening bridge at Carmarthen. (SKJ collection)

Carmarthen was the only one of Brunel's opening bridges to be replaced by an opening bridge. In 1908–11 a steel rolling bascule bridge replaced the original superstructure with a 50ft bascule-type opening span. (SKJ photograph)

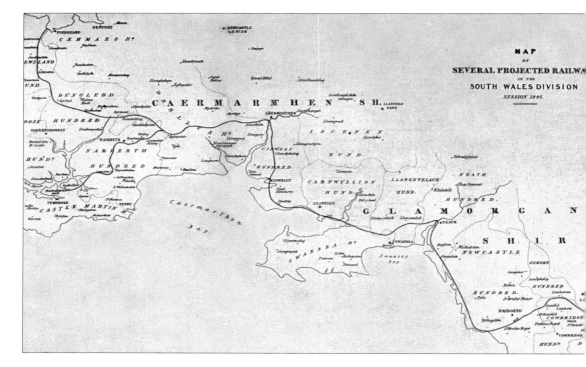

Section of the Parliamentary map of the South Wales Division, Session 1845, showing the proposed terminus at Fishguard. (SKJ collection)

St Clears station, the next station after Carmarthen. St Clears, or rather its turnpike gates, were visited regularly by 'Rebecca'. Interestingly the town became the home of Hugh Williams, the man regarded by many as the real 'Rebecca', after 1851. All that remains of the station complex today is a fragment of the platform. (Courtesy of National Museum and Galleries of Wales, WI&MM collection)

The Skibbereen area was one of the worst affected and was to become notorious as the centre of some of the most harrowing suffering endured by famine victims throughout the country. The quotation above comes from a letter from Skibbereen (dated 20 December 1846) that was published in the *The Cambrian* on 8 January 1847. From accounts such as this, Skibbereen started to become infamous for the destitution and hardship caused by the failure of the potato crop. In the famine graveyard at Abbeystrewery near Skibbereen some 8,000 to 10,000 unidentified souls are buried. Famine caused by potato blight was not unknown to Ireland, which had suffered on a number of occasions since potatoes had become the staple food of the country in around 1700. But the famine of 1846–47 has stood out as the high-water mark of suffering in Ireland. It also was to impact on the aspirations of the SWR, both in completing the line to Fishguard and the proposed branch lines in Ireland itself. Despite such a backdrop, Brunel managed to give an upbeat report on progress in February 1847.[31] The effects of the Irish famine on the SWR caused much anxiety to the SWR directors, who saw trade being eroded before they had even commenced. There was also much fall out from the financial crises caused by Railway Mania, bringing down several financial houses and railway companies with many schemes being shelved in this period, including some of the SWR branches. The SWR agreement with the GWR allowed the latter to run the SWR and the SWR being guaranteed a dividend, subject to the SWR opening their line through to Abermawr, near Fishguard. When the SWR was forced to suspend the works on to Fishguard, the GWR ceased to make dividend payments to the SWR. This naturally became a heated debate between the two companies. Eventually, the SWR

Opened on 2 January 1854 as 'Narbeth Road', Clynderwen station straddled the old counties of Carmarthen and Pembroke. The role of the roof awnings in covering one of the staggered platforms can be clearly seen in this photograph of the pavillion-style station buildings. In 1866 with the opening of the Pembroke & Tenby Railway's Narbeth station the name 'Clynderwen', and more recently 'Clunderwen', was adopted. See the colour section for the bridge photograph. (SKJ collection)

Clarbeston crossing, note the disc and crossbar signal at 'All right' with the board or fantail signal below it at 'caution'. (Courtesy of National Museum and Galleries of Wales, WI&MM collection)

OPENING OF THE SOUTH-WALES RAILWAY.—THE NARBERTH-ROAD STATION, HAVERFORDWEST.

Opening of the line to Haverfordwest. Mr W. Walters, the Mayor of Haverfordwest, welcomed the SWR and following the customary speaker and a ball that evening, 'A brilliant display of fireworks was given by the directors of the South Wales Railways, to the great delight of a numerous crowd.' (SKJ collection) moved to proceed in the construction of a harbour terminal that would allow for trade with Ireland and across the Atlantic. Following an extensive survey Brunel came forward with Neyland Point, located on an arm of the Cleddau, which fed into the Milford Haven waterway, where suitable facilities could be built. The railway would run from Haverfordwest and the SWR obtained an Act of Parliament to carry out these plans and abandon their works to Abermawr on 17 June 1852. regular traffic on the SWR to Carmarthen began on 11 October 1852 with a station at Myrtle Hill, later to become Carmarthen Junction with the opening of the Carmarthen & Cardigan Railway.[32]

The portion of trackbed completed up to that day in the spring of 1851 has remained virtually untouched; it had been suggested that later lines could use the workings – the Manchester & Milford Railway and the GWR's branch to reach Fishguard in 1905. All of them, however, avoided the abandoned trackbed in Treffgarne and in the 1970s Roger Worsley, together with fellow enthusiasts from the local historical society, decided to take a closer look at the workings and carry out a survey:

> … it was found we had something unique on our hands – a length of broad gauge trackbed just as Brunel's navvies and engineers had left it in 1851; and as it was incomplete, we could see how his thinking went, how he divided up his gangs of men when sinking a cutting (first, a 6' wide trench on the line, then a second, half way down to datum, of full 30' width,

Opening bridge at Haverfordwest. (SKJ collection)

Left: *Broad gauge carriages in the sea near Neyland. (From* The Railway Magazine, *vol. III, 1898)*

Below: *Opening bridge at Haverfordwest. (SKJ collection)*

then the third down to trackbed level and ballasted, the men following each other, making for easier removal of earth by hand barrowing); we could see a crossing, with its keeper's hut and garden. We could see the reinforcement of drystone walling to take the sideways pressure of high speed trains on Brunel's broad gauge.[33]

Roger also talks of the navvy villages in Treffgarne with the floors soon liberally sprinkled with the broken remains of discarded Kilmarnock Whiskey bottles![34] The GWR's later time to Fishguard could have used most of the alignment but instead came up the middle of the valley on a massive embankment. At Treffgarne excavations revealed rock strata containing fossils of great interest to geologists, which would become known as the 'Brunel Beds'.[35] With the new terminus now settled on, opening of the line continued in sections, Carmarthen to Haverfordwest on 28 December 1853 and then to Neyland on 15 April 1856, where the railway was welcomed by illuminated images of Brunel and his associates which were lit at night. On the new section of single line to Neyland, which was laid with ordinary bridge rails as Barlow rail had been found unsatisfactory on the Carmarthen section, one of Brunel's opening bridges could be found just outside Haverfordwest. S.W. Allen recalled a 'A Narrow Escape' concerning this bridge in his *Reminiscences* published in 1918. The bridge opened to allow sailing vessels to pass by the raising of the 30ft wrought-iron bascule section by a hand winch and chains, assisted by a balance weight – in all a slow moving operation. One day, he recalls, the bridge was still open but the engine driver, taking his train in the direction of Neyland, was under a misunderstanding about the signal and. '… dashed towards the open bridge at great speed'. Close by the bridge was the town gas works, the 'good lady' of which was in her garden at the time and, immediately appreciating the danger, attempted to stop the engine diving into the river Cleddau by:

> … clambering up the steep embankment, wildly gesticulated for the driver of the train to pull up, which he did by reserving the valve gear of the engine and turning on full steam, and, at the same time, applying the screw hand brakes, which was the ordinary system in use at the time, pulled up the train with the front portion of the engine projecting over the edge of the bridge. The Bascule on the opposite bank being raised to a vertical position… the bridge man also seeing the danger, could not lower the bridge quickly enough, climbed to the top of the Bascule, so as to add his own weight to hasten its descent.[36]

Not everyone was happy with the decision to terminate the line at Neyland. Those who felt aggrieved over the abandonment of the Tenby and Pembroke dock branch would form the Pembroke & Tenby Railway, the SWR and later the GWR offered a route to Tenby via Neyland, with the fare presumably including the ferry charge and road coach costs, to Tenby up to the opening of the P&TR in 1866. Neyland was to be called 'Milford Haven', until 1859, reverting to its correct name 'Neyland' for a few months and then 'New Milford'. This lasted until 1906 when it reverted to its correct name. Calling the terminus 'Milford Haven was not enough for Colonel Greville who appealed to the SWR to bring the line instead to the actual town of Milford Haven. Brunel considered that Neyland had the advantage of being sheltered and it was also opposite the Government dockyard, which was not served by a railway, and would be suitable for the Irish packet service. Colonel Greville wrote from his residence, Castle Hill, on 26 March 1855, 'If they go to the wrong place at first they will be forced to go to the right place at last. Therefore with regard to rails and docks at Milford it is but a question of time'.[37]

Greville promoted a line from Milford to join up with the SWR at Johnston and obtained an Act of Parliament in 1856. The first sod of the Milford Junction Railway was cut in a field near the brewery on 26 August 1858 with the line being completed on 26 September 1863. In July 1857 Brunel visited Neyland and Milford Haven, speculation in the *Telegraph* newspaper that his visit may be in connection with settling a location to establish a home port for his PSS *Great Eastern* then under construction at Millwall, the protracted launch of which would occupy much of his time from

The abandoned trackbed of Brunel's line to Abermawr, near Fishguard. (SKJ photograph)

Close up of the abandoned trackbed showing masonry work, at Treffgarne gorge. (SKJ photograph)

SOUTH WALES HOTEL.

THE SOUTH WALES HOTEL, NEW MILFORD, is immediately adjacent to the New Milford terminus of the Great Western Railway, and is pleasantly situated on rising ground, overlooking Milford Haven. Ornamental grounds intervene between the Hotel and the station, which, while they give privacy to visitors, afford a convenient and ready access to the station. The Hotel contains spacious Coffee Room, Private Sitting Rooms, and Billiard Room.

Steamers leave New Milford for Waterford about 2.0 a.m., and arrive from Waterford about 1.30 a.m. and the Hotel is open at these times for the convenience of Passengers arriving and departing by the Steamers and Trains. *Address Manager.*

Advertisement for the South Wales Hotel at Neyland (known in this period as New Milford); note the facilities offered. (SKJ collection)

Showing broad gauge carriages. (From The Railway Magazine, *vol. III, 1898)*

31 January 1858. In October 1858 Brunel and his wife Mary visited Neyland and were to enjoy the hospitality offered by the Lord Nelson Hotel at nearby Milford Haven.

The Tenby, Saundersfoot & South Wales Railway, authorised on 27 July 1846, had already fallen by the wayside and with the lapse of the SWR's powers to build their branch to Pembroke Dock, local interests now took over.[38] A survey was made for a line between Pembroke Dock and Tenby which was promoted in 1858 as the South Wales, Pembroke & Tenby Junction Railway. In July 1859 supporters of the proposal were authorised to construct a line of railway between Tenby and Pembroke Dock, a distance of some eleven and three quarter miles. By the time of the line being opened, the company was calling itself the more familiar Pembroke & Tenby Railway (P&TR). It was through the P&TR that the first conversion of broad gauge to standard took place in Wales. The P&TR built a railway from Pembroke Dock to Whitland, in two sections: Tenby to Pembroke Dock, opened in 1863; Tenby to Whitland, opened in 1866. At the latter point it connected with the SWR, although by the time the connection was made, the SWR had been taken over by the GWR. Built to the standard gauge the P&TR now wanted to extend its railway to Carmarthen where the GWR's major rival, the London & North Western Railway, had access via the Vale of Towy and Central Wales Railways. It obtained an Act of Parliament in 1866 to extend its line to Carmarthen but within the Act was a schedule whereas if either party gave notice to the other, a standard-gauge connection would be laid down on the GWR and running powers be granted for the P&TR to run through to Carmarthen. In 1868 such notice was given by the P&TR and a payment of £20,000 was made for the conversion and rights. The GWR decided, however, that traffic to Neyland was not sufficiently high to justify double-track usage and converted the up line to standard gauge for the benefit of the P&TR, who had paid for fifteen miles of track to be re-gauged. The P&TR started running through goods traffic in June 1868 and this was followed by passenger trains in August 1869.

Despite his attention, Brunel's plans for Neyland would be doomed to disappointment and C.R.M. Talbot was to confess that his 'visions of greatness' for the western terminus had faded away.[39] The SWR opening receipts were not encouraging; the first week's receipts, i.e. from 18 June 1850 covering passengers and parcels, amounted to £918 16s 7d, and so it continued:

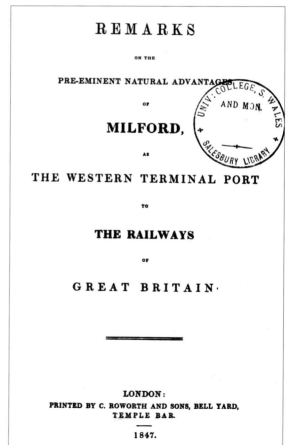

One of the many books and pamphlets published extolling the maritime arguments for Milford Haven. (Courtesy of Brian Ll. James, formerly of Salisbury, librarian at Cardiff University)

REMARKS

ON THE

PRE-EMINENT NATURAL ADVANTAGES

OF

MILFORD,

AS

THE WESTERN TERMINAL PORT

TO

THE RAILWAYS

OF

GREAT BRITAIN.

LONDON:
PRINTED BY C. ROWORTH AND SONS, BELL YARD,
TEMPLE BAR.

1847.

Neyland, the end of the South Wales Railway. Coaling staithes and other works being designed by Brunel for its position as a port along with a number of 'second-hand' buildings from elsewhere on the line. (SKJ collection)

Corresponding week in 1851	£1,090	
Corresponding week in 1852	£1,755	(note Wye Bridge not yet open)
Corresponding week in 1853	£3,531	(note through traffic from London as far as Carmarthen)
Corresponding week in 1854	£5,255	
Corresponding week in 1859	over £7,000[40]	(note line now fully open)

Against this background the facilities at Neyland were sourced as cheaply as possible. The engine sheds had been used at Chepstow (West) from the opening of the SWR in 1850 but had become redundant after the Wye Bridge at Chepstow was completed and the line opened through to Gloucester. They were taken down and re-erected at Neyland under order of a SWR minute dated 13 October 1854. These sheds were later extended by an addition to the 'northern' side at Neyland, and the original two-road shed continued in service until the end of steam in September 1963. The June 1865 timetable of the GWR shows that express trains from London to Neyland took 9 hours and 35 minutes for the 285¾-mile journey via Gloucester. There were three through down trains on weekdays and two on Sundays with a similar number for the up service.

While working on the western end of the SWR, Brunel would have had the opportunity to meet up with his old mentor Nicholas Roch (*d.* 1866), at his house, Paskeston Hall, near Cosheston, close to Pembroke Dock. Roch was a prominent Bristol businessman from an old Pembrokeshire family who had played an important role in starting Brunel's career in that city. Although there is a story that the SWR was at one time going through his Pembrokeshire estate, Roch was very much in touch with developments of this sort, in the run up to the SWR's obtaining its Act of Parliament he had kept in touch with Brunel. He submitted evidence in support of the SWR Bill as regards traffic returns and was one of the principal subscribers listed along in the first Act of the SWR granted on 4 August 1845. His monument in the Roch chapel of the nearby church refers to, 'His energetic and beneficent life'. The two men had benefited from their association. On 13 August 1832, Brunel records in his diary, 'Went to Osbourne's – met Mr. Roach [sic] then it appears I am to be consulted on the best means of scouring the float…'[41] From the dock commission, with the help of Roch, came the Bristol Railway or, as it was soon to become known, the Great Western Railway. The Great Western Railway would eventually merge with the South Wales Railway on 1 August 1863. C.R.M. Talbot, the SWR's chairman, became a GWR director, and W.G. Owen remained on as engineer for this section of the GWR before becoming chief engineer of the GWR in 1868.

NOTES

1   Letter from Skibbereen, letter dated 20 December 1846 to *The Cambrian*, 8 January 1847. It includes the line: 'Distress, disease, and death are running rampant here.'
2   *The Cambrian*, 15 September 1848. William Kirkhouse had been successful for the Swansea Division No.1 contract.
3   *The Railway Times*, 17 March 1849.
4   William Lewis, the Undersheriff for Glamorganshire, had written to Lord Bute on this matter, Talbot became Lord Lieutenant in 1848. Bute correspondence, L91/97i, 13 February 1846. See Chapter 6.
5   Hughes, John Vivian (second edition 1978), pp.24-5, *The Wealthiest Commoner: C.R.M. Talbot*, West Glamorgan County Council: Port Talbot. Bessborough, Earl of, ed. (1950), p.211, *Lady Charlotte Guest Extracts from her Journal 1833-1852*, John Murray: London.
6   Hughes, John Vivian (second edition 1978).
7   Hughes, John Vivian (second edition 1978), p.16. Martin, Sir Theodore, (originally published 1892, Nonsuch edition 2006), p.231, *Diaries of Sir Daniel Gooch*, Nonsuch Publishing Ltd: Stroud.
8   Hughes, John Vivian (second edition 1978), p.26.
9   Hughes, John Vivian (second edition 1978), p.27.
10 Innes, John (1902), *Old Llanelly*, Western Mail: Cardiff.
11 *Cardiff and Merthyr Guardian*, 31 May 1851.
12 *GWR Magazine*, 1910, article by H.W. Beckley, pp.228-229. Newman, John, (1995), p.416, *The Buildings of Wales; Glamorgan*, Penguin Books/University of Wales Press: London.
13 I am indebted to Colin Lucas (formerly British Rail Western Region bridge engineer) for advising me on the 1979–1981 work and to Andrew Clayton of Network Rail for further information and for commenting on my text. See also *Railwest* issue No.7, March 1981, p.7 for article on the viaduct.
14 Bush had left the Llanelly Railway to take up his post on the TVR, see Jones, Stephen K. (2005), pp.111-113, *Brunel in South Wales vol.1 In Trevithick's Tracks*, Tempus Publishing: Stroud.

15 Smith, D.J. (1971), p.77, *Shrewsbury to Swansea*, Town & Country Press Ltd: Bracknell.

16 MacDermot, E.T. revised by Clinker, C.R. (1964), p.42, *History of the Great Western Railway*, vol.1, Ian Allen: London.

17 Smith, D.J. (1971), p.35.

18 Innes, John (1902).

19 See Jones, Stephen K. (2005), pp.111–3, for the involvement by Chambers and Bush with the Llanelly Railway.

20 Address of Congratulation by the Llanelly Chamber of Commerce, 8 September 1852, bound in a copy of SWR Act 17 June 1852, in Newport Reference Library.

21 Address of Congratulation by the Llanelly Chamber of Commerce, 8 September 1852.

22 Williams, David (1955), *The Rebecca Riots*, University of Wales Press: Cardiff, pp.13–14, and Jones, Stephen K. (2005), pp.164–6.

23 Gladwin, D.D. & J.J. (1974), p.39, *Canals of the Welsh Valleys*, Oakwood Press BN 95.

24 MacDermot, E.T., revised by Clinker, C.R. (1964), p.42.

25 *Cardiff and Merthyr Guardian*, 11 April 1857.

26 *Cardiff and Merthyr Guardian*, 25 April 1857.

27 Condor, Francis Roubiliac (1983), *The Men Who Built Railways*, edited by Jack Simmons, Thomas Telford Ltd: London. Originally published by Hodder & Stoughton in 1868 under the title *Personal Recollections of English Engineers*.

28 Condor, Francis Roubiliac (1983), p.129.

29 Borough of Kidwelly minutes, 23 January 1846, p.361, WHM (Bill Morris collection), Carmarthen Record Office.

30 *The Cambrian*, 8 January 1847, accounts of the suffering and fund raising in south Wales to help the relief efforts appear on a regular basis before and after this date.

31 *The Cambrian*, 26 February 1847.

32 Lodwick, J.V., *History of Carmarthenshire*.

33 Brinton, Piet & Worsley, Roger (1987), p.123, *Open Secrets: Explorations in South Wales*, Gomer Press: Llandysul.

34 Brinton, Piet & Worsley, Roger (1987), p.120.

35 George, T. Neville (1937, second impression of third edition 1975), p.23, *British Regional Geology; South Wales*, HMSO: London.

36 Allen, S.W. (1918), p.21, *Reminiscences*, Western Mail Ltd: Cardiff.

37 Rees, J.F. (1954), p.57, *The Story of Milford*, Cardiff.

38 9 & 10 Vic., cap.256, 1846. See Chapter 4.

39 Rees, J.F. (1954), p.59.

40 Trounce, W.J. (1918), *Cardiff in the 50's*, Cardiff.

41 The two had become involved in the Bristol Riots of 1831, see Jones, Stephen K. (2005), p.83, Brunel diary entry in University of Bristol, Special Collections, IKB Private Diary, p.338, 13 August 1832. It is interesting to note that in Brunel's diaries Roch is spelt several ways, as Roach and Roache, but it is not until Brunel actually saw his name written down (for a Bristol Railway committee meeting on 25 February 1833) that he adopts the correct spelling, with Brunel crossing out the 'a' in his spelling for that day's entry.

8

RETURN TO THE IRON CAPITAL
'... THE DIFFICULTIES WERE INSURMOUNTABLE'[1]

The story of the Vale of Neath Railway (VNR) is not a straightforward one or a railway project that was finished when the work planned and executed by Brunel was over. The line was one of apparently insurmountable difficulties and contradictions; it was primarily a mineral line that was also promoted for scenic tours; it was a line with numerous branches that sought to access every possible source of revenue but did not appear to put the canal, at least in the Vale of Neath, under pressure. There was also later development with the Newport, Abergavenny & Hereford Railway. Space denies telling the latter story and what now follows is a snapshot of Brunel's Vale of Neath line.[2] Whilst Brunel may have considered his coastal route, as a strategic line of communications to have the, '... requisites and character of a good line', he could not make the same claim regarding the VNR, the emphasis here being on how railway technology could be pushed to the limit in the exploitation of mineral wealth.[3] His understanding of the terrain dates back, at least, to his 1835 surveys for the G&SWR where he gained first-hand knowledge of possible routes for a Vale of Neath line. In December 1835 *The Cambrian* reported, 'Mr Brunel, the celebrated engineer, who has surveyed the several proposed lines of communication between Merthyr and Neath...'[4] Shortly after this he was approached in connection with a proposed turnpike road to Neath, the route of which he later claimed to have personally surveyed up the valley. It was a commission he would turn down, advising William Meyrick, the solicitor representing the Turnpike Trust, that they should, '... procure the assistance of some other professional man...'[5] The Neath district was a historic location for Welsh tramroads, with examples dating back to around 1695 with Sir Humphrey Mackworth's wooden railed 'waggonway'.[6] This primitive tramroad continued in use until about 1705, using horse-drawn vehicles, although at one time Mackworth experimented with sails on his wagons to harness the wind.[7] Mackworth also constructed a short tidal cut, just about 300 yards long, from the river Neath to serve his Melyn lead and copper works, but the first major canal work in the area was the Neath Canal authorised in 1791 from Neath to Glynneath.[8]

Vale of Neath Railway seal. A broad gauge railway incorporated in 1846 with a main line running from Neath to Aberdare, against heavy gradients, opening in 1851 with the Merthyr branch following two years later. (Courtesy of GWR Museum, Swindon)

The naturalist and surveyer, Alfred Russel Wallace 1823– 1913. Wallace was employed as one of the VNR's surveyors. (SKJ collection)

The idea of the VNR was raised and promoted by Henry Simmons Coke, who as well as being an attorney, was also town clerk and clerk to the magistrates for the borough and hundred of Neath.[9] Coke went to London on 21 May 1845 to propose a line from Neath to Merthyr in front of an audience that included the Earl of Jersey and the directors of the SWR and the GWR.[10] A company was formed in July 1846 which was incorporated on 3 August 1846 with authorisation for the construction of the main line of the VNR from the SWR at Neath to Merthyr Tydfil with four branches and a capital expenditure of £550,000 in £20 shares. The line would leave the SWR at Neath and proceed up the broad vale towards Glynneath where it would begin its ascent up to a tunnel near the summit in order to pass through to the Cynon Valley. Running along the hillside through Hirwaun to a junction known as Gelli Tarw or Aberdare Junction, the main line proceeded through Abernant, taking a sharp left and tunnelling under the Aberdare mountain and thus making a return to the iron capital, Merthyr Tydfil, for Brunel. Of the branches, one was planned to run down the Cynon Valley to Middle Duffryn colliery, meeting with the Aberdare Railway on the way, but no through communications would be possible as the Aberdare Railway was a standard-gauge railway.[11] The Amman branch (spelt that way by the VNR) also served collieries with a third branch coming off it (the Dare branch) to terminate at Bwllfa Dare. A surveyor who worked on the levelling of the line referred to the line as, '… a branch of the Great Western and South Wales Railway then making, and was for the purpose of bringing the coal and iron of Merthyr Tydfil and the surrounding district to Swansea, then the chief port of South Wales'.[12]

The surveyor was none other than the (later world-famous) explorer and naturalist, Alfred Russel Wallace (1823–1913), who was to co-publish his theory of evolution by natural selection with Charles Darwin in 1858, but in 1846 he was engaged in laying out the line of the VNR.[13] Born in Usk, the Natural History Museum describes Wallace as being an outstanding explorer, collector, naturalist, geographer, anthropologist and political commentator, but he was also an accomplished surveyor and architect. In 1841 Wallace, with his elder brother William, arrived in Neath to undertake surveying and mapping work for the parish of Cadoxton-juxta-Neath. Cadoxton then extended from the Neath parish for some fifteen miles towards Pont-Nedd-Fechan at the head of the Vale of Neath. The brothers worked together on various surveying jobs in the locality and at one stage Wallace and his brother would lodge with one of the colliery surveyors working for the Neath Abbey ironworks, the famous works where Wallace's younger brother Herbert would later be employed. Wallace also took a keen interest in the Neath Mechanics' Institute, helping to form it in 1843 where he was to teach a number of classes himself.[14] Associated with the Mechanics' Institute was a telescope for which Coke, the town clerk, had allowed a piece of land to be used to erect an iron pillar or base for its use. For a time Wallace moved away when work was scarce but returned in 1845 following the death of his brother William. William had been returning to Neath when he caught pneumonia through travelling in a GWR third-class railway carriage, and died in Bristol. The carriage sounds like the type of third-class carriage built about 1844 that the VNR themselves would later acquire, 'It had a flat iron roof which protected it from above but was of little avail against wind or driving rain'.[15] Wallace took over his brother's surveying business in Neath and recalls that he heard of a civil engineer in Swansea who wanted all the surveyors he could get, and that they all had two guineas a day, and often more. This was probably Rhys W. Jones, Brunel's assistant in laying out the VNR.[16] Wallace wrote to the engineer concerned who then called in to see him asked if he could do levelling:

> ... he told me he wanted a line of levels up the Vale of Neath to Merthyr Tydfil for a proposed railway, with cross levels at frequent intervals, and that he would give me two guineas a day, and all expenses of chain and staff men, hotels, etc. He gave me all necessary instructions, and said he would send a surveyor to map the route at the same time.[17]

In his autobiography Wallace talks about the work starting in mid-summer, hard work which kept him busy until the autumn, but which he enjoyed immensely. He talks about the scenery in terms of the '... wildest and most picturesque little glens' he had ever explored but that there were obstacles, huge rocks as big as houses and having to '... take cross-levels up steep banks and precipices all deeply wooded'.[18] It is not surprising that he found the scenery to be wild and picturesque as nowhere else in Wales is as celebrated for its beautiful scenery and waterfalls, all of which, no doubt, was to whet his appetite as a naturalist for future explorations and give a foretaste of the natural problems that had to be overcome by the engineer. The ability to overcome such natural obstacles and the gradients involved, climbing from Glynneath for about four miles at 1 in 50 and then descending down from the summit near Hirwaun to Aberdare at a similar rate for two miles, laid the company open to professional criticism, 'Mr. Stephenson, "whose name was European," declared before a House of Commons committee,' "that it was impossible to make it a line adapted to the transit of minerals – that the difficulties were insurmountable"!'.[19]

Third-class carriage, built about 1844 by the GWR and a type that the VNR would later acquire. It had a flat iron roof which gave little protection against wind or driving rain. (Courtesy of National Museum and Galleries of Wales, WI&MM collection)

Cover of VNR's handbook showing the mouth of the river Neath as it flows into the Bristol Channel. The river Neath would receive Brunel's attention as part of his work in improving the access to Briton Ferry Docks. (SKJ collection)

SCENERY

OF

THE NEATH VALLEY.

To Excursionists and Tourists.

The Directors of the Vale of Neath Railway Company
Have provided

COVERED FIRST CLASS

AND

OPEN EXCURSION CARRIAGES,

*Especially adapted for viewing the justly Celebrated Scenery of this
Valley, and its Tributaries.*

Parties taking not less than Twelve Tickets, may have an Excursion Carriage attached to either of the Ordinary Trains; or a Special Engine may be obtained on giving due notice to the undersigned, or to Mr. FREDERICK CLARKE, South Wales Railway, Swansea: from either of whom the Terms of hire may be known.

The principal Waterfalls in the Valley are—
"Melincourt,"
"Yscwd Einon Gam,"
"Yscwd Gwladis,"
"Upper" and "Lower Cilhepste,"
"Upper," "Middle," and "Lower Clyn Gwyn."

☞ The first of these may be reached by any of the ordinary Trains from the Resolven Station; the remainder, together with the far-famed "Porth yr Ogof Cave," the "Dinas Rock," and the "Bwa Maen," from the Glyn Neath Station; but Special Trains may be stopped at the option of the Passengers.

By order,

JOSHUA WILLIAMS.

1

VNR's handbook to the scenery of the Vale. (SKJ collection)

Map from the VNR's handbook showing the junction at Neath with the SWR. (SKJ collection)

This was Robert Stephenson, who was called by the TVR, and it is ironic that Stephenson, once acting for the Marquess of Bute against the TVR and Brunel over the proposed dock at Ely, should now be acting for the TVR but still against his friend and professional rival, Brunel. By threatening the 'territory' of the TVR with his proposals for the VNR, Brunel had burnt his bridges with the former company and once again faced Stephenson, who was not the only one to criticise the route. *Herapath's Journal* wrote a scathing account of the line, stating that the line is for mineral traffic to be conveyed down to the sea, 'but strange to say, it has to lift trains up gradients and over the mountains…' It continues by passing on the opinion of a professional man, 'Of all the sections I have seen, I never saw one with such gradients for a mineral traffic. Had the line been laid out by anyone else but Brunel, it would have done him for life.'[20]

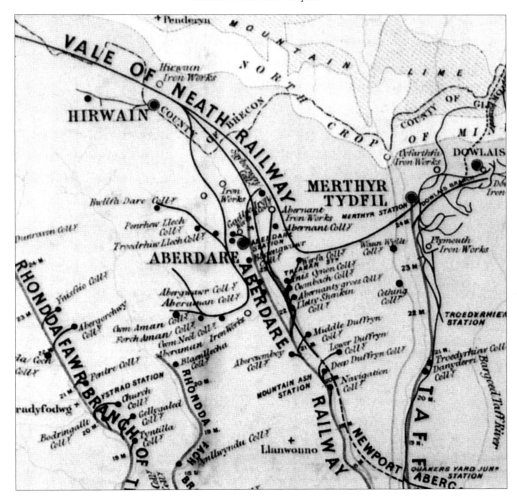

Map showing railway development in the Aberdare area in 1875. (SKJ collection)

After the first rough levels were taken, the engineers were able to mark out the line provisionally and Wallace went over the actual line to enable the sections to be drawn as required by the Parliamentary Standing Orders. For the Aberdare branch the name of Thomas Joseph, '... a knowledgeable and respected local mining engineer...', has been put forward as surveyor.[21] By the autumn of 1846 Wallace had to go to London to complete the plans and reference books for Parliament. He and other surveyors, draughtsmen and clerks were accommodated in a large hotel in the Haymarket, working in a large room on the upstairs floor, and although they could order what food they wanted everyday they were forced to work very late, often past midnight towards the end of November and for the last few days of that month, working all night in order to complete the work. As Wallace states, it was a year of wild speculation, with plans and sections for 1,263 new railways

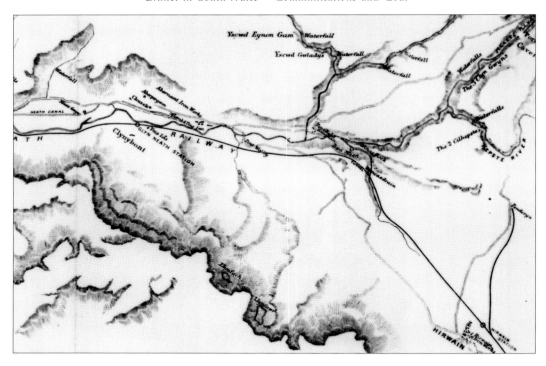

Map from the VNR's handbook showing the line up the Vale of Neath and into the Cynon Valley. (SKJ collection)

being deposited, with a proposed capital of £563,000,000. The sum that was required to be deposited by the promoters at the Board of Trade was so much larger that the total amount of gold in the Bank of England and notes then currently in circulation. It is not surprising that the public got frightened and a panic ensued with the result that shares in the new lines which had been at a high premium crashed to almost nothing, with even the established lines being greatly depreciated. Wallace is also concerned about the activities of proposals put forward for purely speculative reasons, some of which sought to be bought off by opposing lines which had a better chance of success. Wallace illustrates this by the fact that the VNR was dogged by a potential competitor with the grand sounding name of the 'East & West Junction Railway.' This was a line running from Swansea to Yarmouth by way of Merthyr, Hereford, Worcester and across the agricultural district of the Midlands; Wallace believe that it had no chance of passing and that a number of other companies agreed to buy off its opposition to their own scheme. He is scathing on the utter waste of money on these schemes in that, 'Not one-tenth of the lines proposed that year were ever made and the money wasted upon surveyors, engineers and law expenses must have amounted to millions.'[22] By 1847 larger premises for the Neath Mechanics' Institute were required and Wallace was successful with his design for the new building.[23] Shortly after this Wallace decided to give up his surveying and architectural work and pursue his quest for exploring plant and animal life, leaving in April 1848 for the Amazon basin. The rest is history or, rather, natural history.

Not all those living in the Vale of Neath welcomed the new railway and the benefits it brought; D. Rhys Phillips, whose book, *The History of the Vale of Neath*, was published in 1925, records how the landlord of the Plough Inn at Abertwrch believed that the smoke of the locomotives, passing so close to his house, would destroy the horses in the stable, an interesting comment from a landlord, Joe Warlow, who dealt in disabled horses.[24] Sian Glover, living at Pontwalby, feared that the, '... puff of the engine would sour the contents of the milk-pans from Llanfaglan to Pencaedrain!'[25] Some of the older inhabitants felt the railway was something to fear, although the saying, 'a mountain being made out of a molehill', comes to mind for the following prophesy:

Ni fydd dim llaeth gan warthog mwyn Y lloi yn feirw y waen
Daw'r twyni'n goch gan sychyn O ofn y train a'r injin![26]

Which loosely translates as:

There will be no milk from gentle cattle, the calves will be dead on the moor
The hills will become red with drought from being frightened of the train and the engine!

A number of contracts were let on 7 July 1847 and the first sod of earth was cut in August 1847. No.1 contract extended from Neath to Tydu (Hamlet of Clun) and was allotted to Mr Bevan of Cwmavon. No.2 from Tydu to Clynybont (parish of Glyn-corrwg) was given to Mr Hopkins, listed as a road surveyor of Bridgend. Eight contracts were let altogether from Neath to Hirwaun,the Aberdulais cutting being one of the last major works. Contract No.2 included a cast-iron aquaduct to carry the Resolven brook over the railway instead of the railway being carried over the brook as first projected, which, 'effected a decided improvement in the line'.[27] The VNR had returned to Parliament July 1847 to obtain authority to construct additional branches, one of which was an additional junction with the SWR at Neath, providing a west-facing spur and a more direct link from Aberdare to the Merthyr Tunnel. [28] The gradients for this were 1 in 16 for 546 yards and 1 in 13 for 730 yards; not surprisingly, this was later dropped.[29] The line was a double broad-gauge road with stations at Neath, Aberdulais, Resolven, Glynneath, Hirwaun and Abernant. Anticipation of the long-awaited opening was flagged up in May 1851:

This most important line is on the verge of completion. The line has been carried out most satisfactorily, and at the same time economically. We may also conclude that at no distant day we shall see capacious dock accommodation at Britonferry... What a change will then be effected in the Vale of Neath, the town of that name, and the neighbourhood of Britonferry, as this line will, in all human probability be the means of improving the western districts alluded to just as greatly as the Taff Vale Railway benefited Cardiff.[30]

Brunel's cast-iron aqueduct carrying the Clydach brook over the railway at Resolven. The ironwork was supplied by George Hennet from his Bridgewater ironworks in 1849. As can be seen from this photograph taken in 1979, the railway that the brook is carried over has been reduced to a single tack and is the last surviving stretch of the VNR's main line from Neath, the section being left open to serve Aberpergwm colliery. (SKJ photograph)

Opposite above: *Close up of the 60ft-high masonry viaduct over Nant Gwrlych at Pontwalby. (SKJ photograph)*

Opposite below: *Contemporary lithograph of the Cwm Gwrelych or Pontwalby viaduct. (SKJ collection)*

The 'no distant day' dawned on Tuesday 23 September 1851 with an opening ceremony of the Neath to Aberdare section taking place in the presence of the chairman, Lord Villiers, and the secretary, Joshua Williams.[31] The opening was celebrated by the train proceeding to Aberdare for lunch and a public address, from where they returned to Neath for a 'public breakfast' presided over by the Mayor of Neath, Alexander Cuthbertson. Additional musical accompaniment was provided by Crawshay's Band who were picked up at Hirwaun on the return trip and played on route. Delays with the Merthyr terminus, and the Merthyr Tunnel, meant the line here would not open until 1853. The VNR was to pay the price for surmounting 'insurmountable' difficulties by having to cope with a four-mile climb out of the Vale of Neath from Glynneath at a gradient of some 1 in 50 whilst over the summit it descended down to Aberdare at a similar gradient for two miles. Stationary engines were originally proposed to assist but it was decided that it would become unnecessary with the continuing improvement being made by locomotives, but it was not to be an easy ride.

The VNR shared the SWR station at Neath and the first and longest timber viaduct on the line, 270 yards long, extended from its junction with the SWR. Proceeding up the valley the next station was Aberdulais, the railway crossing the river Neath alongside George Tennant's 340ft-long canal aquaduct.[32] As with the SWR, Brunel was confident to specify timber viaducts for suitable crossings on the line, notably over the canal and river at Neath and Aberdulais. The principal ascent on the line towards Hirwaun was from Glynneath up the Rhigos bank, a gradient of 1 in 50. At Pontwalby was the structure of Cwm Gwrelych, '... consisting of four bays each of 43ft span and 60ft high'.[33] The tunnel at Pencaedrain was completed by the contractor, William Ritson, who moved over to finish the troublesome Merthyr Tunnel, 2,495 yards long, a tunnel that had ruined two contractors and was now being built by direct labour. Following preliminary work in 1847, two contractors and their men had begun working on eight shafts of the Merthyr Tunnel in August 1848, but both failed by February 1850.[34] Despite Ritson's efforts the tunnel was not completed until August 1853. Less than a year later the *Cardiff and Merthyr Guardian* told its readers about a incident that had occurred near the Pencaedrain tunnel involving a sheep and, '... one of those magnificent engines of the company...' in which the sheep had strayed on the line and had her forequarters entirely cut off. Good taste does not seem to have worried the newspaper about what it said, referring to a recent fashionable dance called 'Pop goes the weazle' and altering it to 'Pop goes the lamb'. However, it does complete the story by saying that, '... this little black lamb (not a weazle) is doing well under the care of a local protector'.[35]

Wallace was not the only one who found the scenery of the Vale of Neath to be of a wild and picturesque quality as the VNR would promote the locality, the beautiful scenery and waterfalls by the publication of a handbook. It also provided for excursion parties by the introduction of an, '... elegant saloon carriage of unique construction, the seats being grouped so as to afford views in every direction'. Tourists were also advised to look from the Cwm Gwrelych viaduct as, '... the view of Glyn Neath is indescribably magnificent'.[36]

However, not everyone appreciated and respected the natural environment along the route. On Sunday 28 April 1850, a party of Irish labourers, working on the VNR, conceived the idea of overturning the Rocking Stone at Yscwd Gwladis on the chance of finding hidden treasure![37] Described as a 'Sunday frolic' the stone, which Wallace had recorded seeing in 1846, was overturned and fractured:

> ... so that no human skill could replace it in its original position. These modern barbarians, but too well knew the powers of block and lever, through ignorant as savages of every consideration which endeared such a curiosity to the Philosopher, the Antiquarian, and the Bard. There lies the ruin of this venerable antiquity, a monument of English Vandalism in the 19th century, and one amongst many proofs, that Education is yet far in the rear of our national requirements.[38]

The waterfalls were a favourite resort, '... an irresistible attraction to the tourist, and formed the chief beauty of the Vale...'[39] They formed the focus for numerous picnic parties during the summer months and were much enjoyed by the population at large, particularly the readers of the *Cardiff and Merthyr Guardian*. The newspaper brought the following story to their readers' attention on 11 April 1857, believing

Pencaedrain tunnel; the northern portal of the 526-yard-long tunnel has been obscured by earth works for the A465 'Heads of the Valley' road. (SKJ collection)

Aberdare end of the 'troublesome' tunnel through to Merthyr Tydfil. (SKJ photograph)

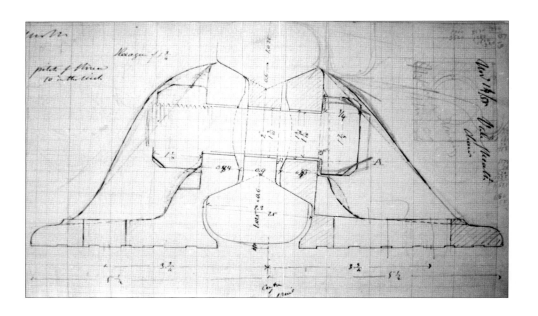

that the waterfalls, '… are likely to be made the site of a gunpowder manufactory by a London company…'[40] This was the Vale of Neath Powder Co., which set up its gunpowder works on the site of the Dinas Bridge Fire Brick Works, situated above the village of Pontneddfechan.[41] Needless to say, the gunpowder works did not blight the location and the beauty of the waterfalls could still be enjoyed.

As already mentioned, Brunel had erected a number of timber viaducts on the line, particularly of the fan style, in which the main timber members conducted the deck loads directly to the piers in converging straight lines. These main members were typically of 12in square sections of yellow pine, and up to five of these might converge in a special cast-iron shoe placed on top of a brick or stone pier. It was said that a good repair gang could renew any of the sections in an hour and the timber could be expected to last thirty years.[42] On the Amman and Dare branches could be found two of Brunel's timber fan viaducts, the Dare and Gamlyn viaducts. In August 1857 Brunel reported on an effect caused by the expansion of the rails on the Dare viaduct; it was '… a curious and unexpected result of the heat of the season'. Those branches were closed to traffic from 1 September 1939 but the timber viaducts remained until 1947, being demolished in that year.[43] As such, they were the last complete examples of Brunel's famous timber structures to remain in active use and never passed into British Railways' ownership.

Until the Merthyr tunnel was completed in 1853, a temporary station a few miles out of Hirwaun was opened for the convenience of Merthyr inhabitants. From here a brake conveyed passengers between the station known as Merthyr Road and Merthyr, a Mr Williams having the arrangements. Serious falls occurred in the tunnel due to colliery workings in 1874. In the previous year, on 16 May 1873, a disaster took place when a coupling of a wagon belonging to the Plymouth Iron Co. broke in a coal train as it was entering Merthyr Tunnel. The consequence was that twenty-one loaded coal wagons and the brake van ran back down the incline to collide with a Brecon & Merthyr Railway passenger train, coming to halt at Merthyr Terminus, the collision resulting in one death and fifty-two injuries.[44] Passing through the tunnel and down towards the valley floor, the line was taken over the Glamorganshire Canal by the Rhydycar bridge; this was a substantial skew bridge with three arches accommodating the canal and towpaths, the main arch having a square span of 40ft 7in, and a skew span of 48ft 6in.[45]

Opposite below: *Sketch of the rail chair and bullhead rail designed by Brunel for the VNR. The use of Barlow rails on the VNR had been found unsatisfactory for heavy traffic and was liable to move under the weight of a moving train. As a replacement Brunel designed a special chair to allow the life of the rail to be doubled, other types of double headed rail chair caused indentations to the bottom rail head making it unsuitable for re-use. Small sketchbook 32, f.13, 14 November 1858. (Courtesy of University of Bristol special collections)*

On the Dare and Aman branch of the VNR there were two timber viaducts. These two viaducts were the last of Brunel's timber structures to remain in active use, being closed to traffic in 1939 and dismantled in 1947 after a life of ninety-two years. The Dare or Cwm viaduct shown here was 70 ft high and 450 ft long, the masonry piers for both still survive. (SKJ collection)

The Dare viaduct showing the TVR's Dare Valley Railway running underneath. (SKJ collection)

Dare viaduct in the course of demolition in 1947. (SKJ collection)

View of the rail deck; note the large number of chairs holding the rails in place. (SKJ collection)

Gamlyn viaduct; this viaduct at 70 ft high and 600 ft long, was the larger of the two viaducts on the Dare and Aman branch. (SKJ collection)

Because of the problems of cross-valley access to the VNR, trade by the canals was not killed off overnight. Indeed, the canals tended to retain their existing customers, which in general were on the opposite side of the river to the VNR. In 1875 the clerk of the Neath Canal wrote that he felt that the canal had held its own against the VNR for twenty years, although, 'It is only the old Collieries that continue to use the Canal, those newly opened all go to the Railway'.[46] In the Cynon Valley the Lletty Shenkin colliery sent its coal, 'on to the Vale of Neath Railway across the canal wharf at the canal head'.[47] For the Aberdare Canal Brunel had apparatus erected in the Aberdare station yard for the transfer of coal (and other materials) to and from the canal tramroad and then to or from VNR wagons in November 1851. When the line was extended to the canal head half a mile away in June 1853, Brunel appears to have been lax in not providing similar interchange facilities for the canal boat cargos. Facilities were eventually provided, but these proved to be unsatisfactory due to the, '… serious cost of transit and material damage to the Coal…' which led to an extension line, known as the Aberdare Valley Railway, being built and leased to the VNR.[48] Thomas Powell (1784-1864), the coalmaster who had supported the TVR in 1835, was one of the first to develop a form of iron container, which was used on the Aberdare Canal, coal being loaded into boxes which could easily be transferred from tramroad wagons to canal barges.[49] Brunel took this idea forward and had special flat or platform trucks constructed for the VNR that would carry four iron containers; these containers could be lowered by special apparatus at the dock into the hold of a ship. Then, the containers which had hinged trapdoors

Above: *Broad gauge engine working in the Dare Valley near Bwllfa Colliery with Bwllfa House in the background; it is dated to between 1867 and 1872. (Courtesy of Rhondda Cynon Taff Library Service)*

Right: *Reconstruction of Barlow rail permanent way on the original alignment of the Dare and Aman branch of the VNR, now in the Dare Valley Country Park. (SKJ photograph)*

would open and deposit the coal with minimum breakage, the coal being of a friable nature. Through the photographs taken of the Swansea north dock bridge accident in 1865, which involved a train of these container trucks, we can see that Barlow rail was pressed into use to form the base to hold the containers. Barlow rail was to be used on the Dare and Aman branches, but like everywhere else it was tried, including the final section of the SWR, it was soon found to be unreliable and replaced. The rail, 12 to 13in wide, was seen as an economic alternative to bridge rail on baulk timbers, but it had to be very carefully packed with ballast to prevent spreading under load.

Despite the setback Brunel had encountered when he ordered the first locomotives required by the GWR, by giving inadequate specifications to various locomotive companies, resulting in engines far from equal to the task, Brunel decided to once again enter this arena. This time, no doubt, he had a greater understanding of the practical considerations and could draw upon the expertise of Daniel Gooch, who had rescued the earlier situation. The locomotives specified were to emerge as a development of Gooch's 'Corsair' class 4-4-0 ST locomotive whilst Brunel's specified locomotives Nos 13–15, were six-coupled locomotives built by the Vulcan Foundry and fitted with modified Dodds Wedge motion. They had full-length saddle tanks of 1,500 gallons capacity, inside plate frames, wheelbase 7ft 1½in + 8ft 1½in, wheels 4ft 9in, cylinders 18ft x 24in and weighed 40 tons. Unfortunately, whilst Brunel had specified a greater engine weight to provide sufficient adhesion in hauling trains up the Glynneath bank, they turned out to be too heavy for the permanent way and were altered to tender engines in 1860–61.[50] In order to strengthen the permanent way, Brunel designed a special rail chair which would take a heavier form of double-headed rail, a chair design that ensured that the underneath of the rail was not marked and avoid the problem of double-headed rail chairs.

In *Song of the Earth*, the second book of the *Rape of the Fair Country* trilogy, Alexander Cordell writes of a confrontation between canal and railway. This account, he told the author, was based on one of scores of interviews he had carried out as research for his novel and he used one particular interview as a basis for a scene of confrontation between canal bargees and railway navvies during the building of the railway, 'at this confrontation Brunel, he said, was present, as told by his grandfather'.[51]

	VALE OF NEATH RAILWAY	
24 September 1851	Neath Junction with SWR to Aberdare	19 miles
June 1853	Aberdare to Canal Head	41 chains
2 November 1853	Gelly Tarw Junction to Merthyr	6 miles 23 chains
7 November 1854	Gelly Tarw Junction to Dare Junction	2 miles 38 chains
7 November 1854	Dare Junction to Nantmelyn Colliery	1 mile 15 chains
	ABERDARE VALLEY RAILWAY	
November 1856	Aberdare, Canal Head to Middle Duffryn Colliery	2 m
November 1856	Dare Junction to Cwmaman Colliery	2 miles 70 chains
1 June 1857	Nantmelyn Colliery to Bwllfa Dare Colliery	34 chains

Total VNR broad-gauge mileage at 31 December 1857 = 34 miles 61 chains.

Drawing of VNR 0-6-0 locomotive No. 14, a saddle tank engine designed to Brunel's specifications in order to overcome the gradients of the Glynneath Bank. (SKJ collection)

After 1861 additional mileage gave the VNR access to Briton Ferry Dock and Wharf and the Swansea Harbour Railway; the Swansea & Neath Railway being opened on mixed gauge.[52]

All the Merthyr ironmasters appeared to have had an interest in the VNR. William Crawshay took 1,000 shares in the VNR and Lady Charlotte Guest frequently wrote about the progress on the construction of the line in her diary as on 21 April 1854, 'Some Engineering Difficulties arising about our Vale of Neath Branch...'[53] Criticism about Brunel's progress in completing the line was raised by, amongst others, Henry Austin Bruce (1815–95) who had extensive interests in the locality, living at Duffryn House near Aberdare, becoming the MP for Merthyr on the death of Sir John Guest and chairman of the VNR in 1859 on the death of Lord Villiers.[54] At a board meeting on 15 March 1850 he gave notice that he was going to recommend that Brunel's salary be reduced from £1,000 to £600 at the next board meeting because of the time being taken to complete the line![55] In 1858, Joshua Williams, who had been secretary since 1849 and had subsequently taken over the Traffic and Locomotive Departments since the opening of the line, now took over the Engineering Department, relinquishing the role of secretary to John Swain. The directors pointed out that, 'Mr. Brunel will still be connected with the Line in the capacity of Consulting Engineer'.[56] Consulting Engineer was not a title Brunel approved of, but there were greater concerns, notably the Taff Vale Extension of the Newport, Abergavenny & Hereford Railway and moves to bring a standard gauge route to Middle Duffryn and then running, by the use of a third rail on the broad-gauge VNR, through to Neath and Swansea.

Aberdare, originally a terminus station of the VNR, became a through station less than three years after the opening when the line was extended to the canal head, half a mile away, in June 1853. The Brunel timber all-over roof station can be seen in the middle of the photograph which was taken about 1899. (SKJ collection)

Inside the VNR terminus station at Aberdare which was being used as a furniture warehouse before its destruction by fire in 1982. See colour photograph of the exterior. (SKJ photograph)

This would take place after Brunel's death as would the succession of Bruce to the chairmanship of the VNR. This was at a time of great depression for the company and a Committee of Investigation was undertook to examine the future of the VNR. The engineer; T.E. Harrison, undertook the survey covering issues of track, rolling stock and traffic arrangements. A major area of dissatisfaction was the route its trains had to take to get to Swansea docks by the SWR, and although it obtained concessions from the SWR to operate its own coal trains to Swansea over the SWR, the final solution was for the VNR to promote the Swansea & Neath Railway, which was passed on 19 July 1861.[57] Avoiding the tortuous Skewen curves of the SWR, the line ran from the VNR at Neath through Coedfrank, Llansamlet and St Thomas to proceed over the high-level harbour railway at Swansea to the north-east side of the railway bridge crossing Wind Street, with a branch railway commencing opposite the 'Red House' in St Thomas, and terminating by a junction with the Swansea Vale Railway, with powers to use the Swansea Harbour Railway.[58] The line was amalgamated with the VNR in 1863 with the branch opened on 14 July 1863. Opening bridges spanned the river Tawe (new cut) and the north dock entrance, both of which were supplied by Sir William Armstrong. The serious accident mentioned earlier occurred on this line on 29 November 1865 involving a VNR mineral train on its way to the south dock, the driver being given the signal 'line clear' but the bridge:

> ... which spans the lock, was at that time open. The train, which at that time was drawn by one of the company's most powerful broad-gauge engines, started, and not withstanding that the signal indicated 'danger,' it appears to have been unobserved by either the driver or the stoker, and the train was allowed to proceed on its journey, and the lock of the north dock proved to be its final receptacle.[59]

The driver and stoker lost their lives, but the engine and many of the wagons, once extracted from the water, were found to have little damage, the engine only requiring £250 worth of repairs, and the lock was cleared and reopened for traffic on 4 December. In Swansea the passenger station was to be found on Little Wind Street, by the side of the Wind Street bridge, with the booking office located in one of the arches of the viaduct with a bold flight of steps within it forming the approach to the railway platform, built on top of the viaduct, 260ft long by 16ft wide. As a passenger station, Wind Street was closed on 1 March 1873, with passenger traffic being diverted over Landore viaduct to High Street station.[60]

The first excursion train on that route and to that station by the VNR took a Sunday school outing of some 1,304 scholars from the Tabernacle Chapel, Aberdare, on a train journey from Aberdare station via Briton Ferry Road to Wind Street, Swansea, in August 1863.[61]

Ironically, the VNR appears to have knocked down more than its fair share of chapels when it came to demolishing buildings on the route of the railway. One such casualty on the Merthyr branch was the Moriah Chapel in Llwydcoed, a Welsh Calvinistic Methodist chapel, demolished to make way for the line around 1851.[62] This was not the only one making way for the VNR, a high-profile example being Capel Shiloh in the centre of Merthyr Tydfil. The VNR wanted the site of the Shiloh Welsh Wesleyan

Chapel, to make way for an entrance to the station from the High Street and legend has it that the VNR's engineer was prepared to design a replacement, hence the design being credited to Brunel.[63] The new chapel was erected a few hundred yards away in Church Street, Merthyr, and opened on 14 March 1854:

> The New, handsome, and spacious Chapel recently erected by the Welsh Wesleyans of Merthyr, was opened this week; and the internal arrangements confirmed the favourable and pleasing impressions produced by the external form.[64]

The real architect(s) of this building, however, are revealed in another *Cardiff and Merthyr Guardian* report on the laying of the foundation stone, less than a year earlier; it refers to the original Shiloh Chapel, now purchased by the VNR, and that the chapel elders had now chosen a site for another chapel, one that was, '… once intended for the much-talked-of new town hall, which was always coming, but never came…' The foundation stone was laid on 22 April 1853 by Mr David Rosser who described the new chapel as a 'handsome and commodious edifice'. Finally, the report states that, 'The new chapel is designed by Messrs. Wilson and Fuller of Bath. It is to be in the Norman style; and the contract has been let for £1,000.[65] Newman refers to it as one of the temple-like chapels built in a Romanesque style, with corbelled gables rather than pediments and that, 'The Welsh Wesleyan chapel of 1853 at Merthyr Tydfil, attributed to *I. K. Brunel,* and now a mere shell, is the earliest example'.[66] The chapel is also an early example of such a building being given up as a place of worship, becoming the Miners Hall in 1921, when the building was extended and the tower truncated. The rundown of the mining industry led to a change of use and its acquisition as a night club, but a series of fires, the most serious in 1991, reduced the building to an empty shell. The chapel architects were only partners only for a short time; James Wilson, an architect much favoured by the nonconformists, is best known for Cheltenham College whereas Thomas Fuller (1823–98) was known for his English Gothic style.[67] In its original form Chapel Shiloh enjoyed Fuller's maxim, 'Light, God's eldest daughter, is a principal beauty in a building'.[68]

Lithograph of the VNR line, from Aberdare, crossing the Taff Vale Railway near Merthyr Tydfil. (SKJ collection)

The Miners Hall, Merthyr Tydfil, in 1979. This was originally a chapel built as a replacement for the Shiloh Welsh Wesleyan Chapel that the VNR acquired and demolished in order to make way for an entrance to its station from the High Street. Opened in 1854 it had long been assumed that the VNR's engineer, i.e. Brunel, was responsible for the design of the replacement Shiloh Chapel, but although built as a result of the construction of the VNR, Brunel was not the architect. (SKJ photograph)

The approach to the former TVR station at Plymouth Road, Merthyr Tydfil, with tracks now lifted and the VNR line on a series of arches to the right. (SKJ collection)

Above: *General view of Merthyr High Street station, on 30 August 1951. Note Shiloh Chapel/Miners' Hall on the skyline. (Courtesy of Ian L. Wright)*

*High Street station, Merthyr Tydfil,
16 May 1874. The aftermath of
a locomotive crashing through the
buffers and the wall of the former
Vale of Neath terminus, now GWR
and standard gauge. (Courtesy of
Merthyr Tydfil Reference Library)*

Right: *Barlow rail being used as a fence post
at the entrance to the now demolished goods
station at Merthyr Tydfil. (SKJ photograph)*

Opposite below: *Interior view of Merthyr
High Street station, taken on 4 August 1952.
(Courtesy of Ian L. Wright)*

Notes

1 Phillips, D. Rhys (1925), *The History of the Vale of Neath*, D. Rhys Phillips: Swansea, p.342. BN 41–3.

2 For the complete story see Jones, Gwyn Briwant and Dunstone, Denis (1996), *The Vale of Neath Line: from Neath to Pontypool Road*, Gomer Press: Llandysul. The Aberdare section of the VNR is covered in Mear, John F. (1999), *Aberdare, The Railways and Tramroads*, John Mear: Aberdare.

3 University of Bristol, Special Collections, PLB 2, G&SWR, pp.56–64, 21 September 1836.

4 *The Cambrian*, 5 December 1835.

5 University of Bristol, Special Collections, Letter Book 2, p.196, Brunel wrote to W. Meyrick on 5 December 1836, see Jones, Stephen K. (2005), p.108. See also Jones, Gwyn Briwnant and Dunstone, Denis (1996), p.27.

6 Later examples showing Welsh tramroads ('waggonways') in the Neath district can be seen in a map of 1799 along with a 1804 view of Neath Abbey, showing horse-drawn trams and a horse-worked 'gin', in Jones, Stephen K. (2005), p.51 and colour plate 8. See also Chapter 9 for further information on Mackworth's industrial interests.

7 Jenkins, Elias (1974), *Neath and District: A Symposium*, Elias Jenkins: Neath, p.244.

8 Hadfield, Charles (second edition 1967), pp.62–63, *The Canals of South Wales and the Border*. David & Charles: Newton Abbot (in conjunction with University of Wales Press: Cardiff).

9 *Slaters Commercial Directory*, 1858–1859. Coke's office was in the Parade where he was also an insurance agent representing the Eagle Co.

10 Phillips, D. Rhys (1925), p.342.

11 The Aberdare Railway would become part of Brunel's only standard gauge, the Taff Vale Railway, see Jones, Stephen K. (2005), p.200–202.

12 Wallace, Alfred Russel (1908), *My Life: a record of events and opinions*, Chapman and Hall: London, p.243.

13 Wallace's idea of Natural Selection was arrived at independently of that of Charles Darwin but both men agreed to the publication of a joint paper in 1858.

14 Eaton, George (1986), p.9, *Alfred Russel Wallace, 1823–1913, Biologist and Social Reformer*, George Eaton: Neath.

15 Ellis, Cuthbert Hamilton (1949), *Nineteenth century railway carriages in the British Isle: from the eighteen-thirties to the nineteen-hundreds*, Modern Transport Pub. Co.: London. BN 48

16 Jones, W.H. (1922), p.177, *History of the Port of Swansea*, Spurrell: Carmarthen. Jones was also the engineer to the Swansea Valley Railway, see Chapter 9.

17 Wallace, Alfred Russel (1908), p.242.

18 Wallace, Alfred Russel (1908), p.242.

19 Phillips, D. Rhys (1925), p.342.

20 Mear, John F. (1999), p.109.

21 Mear, John F. (1999), pp.98 &106.

22 Wallace, Alfred Russel (1908), p.243.

23 Eaton, George (1986), p.9, Eaton, George (1986), p.28. The building is now the Neath Museum.

24 Phillips, D. Rhys (1925), pp.342 & 354.

25 Phillips, D. Rhys (1925), p.342.

26 Phillips, D. Rhys (1925), p.342. From an 'old manservant of Ynysgerwyn'.

27 Phillips, D. Rhys (1925), p.343. See also the *Swansea and Glamorgan Herald*, 14 July 1847.

28 See Chapter 4, Act 10 & 11 Vic., cap.74, 1847.

29 Jones, Gwyn Briwnant & Dunstone, Denis (1996), p.30.

30 *Cardiff and Merthyr Guardian*, 31 May 1851.

31 This was George Augustus Frederick Child-Villiers (1808–1859), who only held the title of 6th Earl of Jersey for three weeks following the death of George Child-Villiers, 5th Earl of Jersey (1773–1859).

32 Completed by William Kirkhouse in 1824.

33 Phillips, D. Rhys (1925), p.342. This has also been referred to as the Pencaedrain Viaduct and it actually has five spans but Phillips may have discounted one 'bay' which is blocked in stone, with a large rounded opening.

34 MacDermot, E.T. (1927, first revised edition 1964), *The History of the Great Western Railway*, vol. II, Ian Allan: London, p.6.

35 *Cardiff and Merthyr Guardian*, 25 March 1854.

36 *The Handbook of the Vale of Neath*, 1852.

37 Phillips, D. Rhys (1925), p.16.

38 *The Handbook of the Vale of Neath*, 1852.

39 *Cardiff and Merthyr Guardian*, 11 April 1857.

40 *Cardiff and Merthyr Guardian*, 11 April 1857.

41 See also Pritchard, Tom, Evans, Jack and Johnson, Sydney (1985, reprinted 1998), *The Old Gunpowder Factory at Glynneath*, Merthyr Tydfil & District Naturalists' Society: Merthyr Tydfil.

42 Sealey, Anthony (1976), *Bridges and Aqueducts*, Hugh Evelyn: London, p.90. BN 107

43 One of those involved in the demolition of the Dare viaduct was Jack Parsons. Following the RAF, one of Jack's first roles as an engineer was the demolition of the Dare viaduct. Correspondence with Jack Parsons of the David Owen Centre, University College, Cardiff, on 29 January 1979.

44 MacDermot, E.T., revised by Clinker, C.R. (1964), *The History of the Great Western Railway*, vol. II, Ian Allen: London, p.48.

45 Davies, W. L. (1992), p.135, *Bridges of Merthyr Tydfil*, Glamorgan Record Office publication in collaboration with the Merthyr Tydfil Heritage Trust: Cardiff.

46 Hadfield, Charles (second edition 1967), p.73.

47 Davies, Alun C. (1978), *A Welsh Waterway in the Industrial Revolution: The Aberdare Canal 1793–1900*, The Journal of Transport History, New Series IV, vol.3, Leicestert University Press: Leicester, pp.159, 160 & 161.

48 Hadfield, Charles (second edition 1967), p.125.

49 Powell wanted the Aberdare Canal Co. to permit the retrieval of empy containers for re-use, free of charge, Aberdare Canal Minutes 28 June 1842.

50 Waters, Laurence (1999), *The Great Western Broad Gauge*, Ian Allan Publishing: Shepperton, pp.85–6.

51 Correspondence with Alexander Cordell on 17 October 1977, then living in the Isle of Man, the name of the 'old gentleman' was not recalled.

52 MacDermot, E.T., revised by Clinker, C.R. (1964). p.326.

53 William Crawshay to Joshua Williams, February 1853, p.299, Nos 179–182, Crawshay Papers and Diary of Lady Charlotte Guest, vol.XVI, p.163, 21 April 1854, both in National Library of Wales.

54 Bruce would also become one of the trustees of the Guest empire, along with G.T. Clark as the first Baron Aberdare in 1873. See Jones, Stephen K., (2005), p.212, and *The Dictionary of Welsh Biography down to 1940 (DWB)* (1959), p.54, The Honourable Society of Cymmrodion: London.

55 This was not pursued, see Jones, Gwyn Briwnant & Dunstone, Denis (1996), p.34.

56 MacDermot, E.T. (1927, first revised edition 1964), p.7.

57 Obviously this was just one aspect of Harrison's report, the criticism over access to Briton Ferry dock will be dealt with in vol.3.

58 Jones, W.H. (1922, facsimile edition 1995), *History of the Port of Swansea*, Spurrell: Carmarthen (1995 West Glamorgan County Archive Service: Swansea), p.266.

59 Jones, W.H. (1922, facsimile edition 1995), pp.267–8.

60 Jones, W.H. (1922, facsimile edition 1995), p.267.

61 Jones, Alan Vernon (2004), *Chapels of the Cynon Valley*, Cynon Valley History Society: Llandysul, p.349.

62 Jones, Alan Vernon (2004), p.141.

63 The Welsh Wesleyan movement, in the absence of original documents, had also incorporated the legend.

64 *Cardiff and Merthyr Guardian*, 18 March 1854.

65 *Cardiff and Merthyr Guardian*, 30 April 1853.

66 Newman, John (1995), *The Buildings of Wales: Glamorgan*, Penguin Books/University of Wales Press: London, pp.86 & 438.

67 For Wilson see Taylor, Jeremy (1978), *The Architectural Medal: England in the Nineteenth Century*, Colonnade Books/British Museum Publications Ltd: London, p.207. For Fuller see Bristol Society of Architects website and article by Lance Wright: www.bristolarchitects.com/index.htm

68 Fuller's style is evident on a number of domestic and religious buildings in and around Bath. One design around the time of the Merthyr commission included the town hall of Bradford on Avon, complete with an octagonal tower. Fuller emigrated to North America in 1857 and went on to design the new Houses of Parliament building in Ottawa.

9

LANDSCAPE AND INDUSTRY

'ONE MUST NOT THINK OF THE BEAUTIFUL, BUT OF THE USEFUL, WITH A CAPITAL U'[1]

Of all the landscapes that Brunel was to take his railways through, none presented a more industrialised vista than that of Landore. Landore was the site of the Swansea area's first coppersmelting works of 1719, built on the banks of the river Tawe, some two miles from the centre of the town. This development and others along the Swansea Valley and in the town itself, provided stark demonstration of the physical cost paid by Swansea in becoming a world famous metallurgical centre. Swansea's position in the smelting of iron, tin, zinc and copper had been achieved on phyisical assets, the abundance of coal and its coastal location, all of which attracted ore miners and smelters to the locality of Swansea, or 'Copperopolis' as it became known due to its non-ferrous expertise, and Neath.[2] Indeed, Neath had been the first centre for smelting non-ferrous ores, through Sir Humphrey Mackworth (1657–1727) moving to the area on the marriage to Mary Evans of the Gnoll, Neath.[3] A Shropshire industrialist, he revitalised coalmining on his wife's estates by taking over the leases that had been acquired there by his wife's father and grandfather.[4] Mackworth developed Neath into a major centre for coppersmelting using its central location between Cardigan and Cornwall, the twin sources of his mineral supply, using local coal instead of charcoal in the smelting process.[5] To facilitate this he built the first tramroads or 'waggonways' in Wales, bringing the Shropshire railway system to Neath. These wooden waggonways were constructed in 1697, the wooden rail being improved some time before 1791 by plating the wood with iron.[6] By the 1750s Swansea had taken over as the centre for coppersmelting, becoming the source of half the smelted copper in Britain. The conversion rate to produce 1 ton of copper involved the smelting of 4 tons of rich copper ore with 18 tons of coal. The huge reserves of coal in the Swansea area, much of it in shallow seams, were exploited in this process but it was not the town's only asset. It was a town of considerable attraction as up to the mid-nineteenth century, Swansea could boast to be a fashionable summer and winter resort. A seafront promenade complete with respectable bathing facilities were much in evidence. Writing from Italy in the early nineteenth century, Walter Savage Landor (1775–1864) claimed that, 'The Gulf of Salerno is much finer than Naples, but give me Swansea for scenery and climate... I would pass the remainder of my days between that place and the Mumbles'.[7]

The town had a long tradition of being a fashionable location and no doubt an inspiration for one of its most famous sons, that most famous of all 'arbiters of elegance', Richard 'Beau' Nash (1674–1762). Swansea was likened to Brighton during the last quarter of the eighteenth century,[8] but would it have appealed in the late 1820s to young man like Brunel as a location to spend leisure time or relax and recuperate?[9] Brunel choose the real Brighton, hardly a suitable place for recuperation, hence his father's concern that he went from there to the quieter and less strenuous attractions of the West Country. By the beginning of the nineteenth century the threat of industrialisation to the 'Brighton of Wales' was evident. In 1804, the year the Oystermouth Railway was being mooted, John Evans stated that, '... it is the wish of the inhabitants that Swansea should be viewed in the light of a *fashionable resort*, rather than as a *trading town*; and a bathing place, rather than a sea-port'.[10]

The Oystermouth Railway (mentioned in the SWR Act) can be seen as part of this move towards industrialisation but as a mode of transport it was to take the innovative step of conveying visitors along the seafront in the pursuit of pleasure, becoming, in the process, the world's first passenger railway. The line was built between 1804 and 1806 from the basin of the Swansea Canal, at the top of the High Street in Swansea where the SWR was to site its passenger terminous, to a field on the shore opposite Oystermouth Castle. The story of what was the longest surviving railway, up to its ill-advised closure in 1960, began in July 1804 with a meeting in a Swansea hostelry. This was the Bush Inn, a public house that still exists on the High Street, and which in the twentieth century was to be frequented by Dylan Thomas.[11] Back in 1804 local businessmen engaged in quarrying and mining at Mumbles met to discuss the possibility of improving communications between Mumbles and Swansea. Trade in limestone and other minerals from Mumbles to the town of Swansea was conveyed by boat across Swansea Bay. The first proposition called for the construction of a canal along the foreshore of Swansea Bay, but this met with opposition from vested interests in shipping at Swansea, including the Swansea Harbour Trust, who feared the establishment of a rival dock at Mumbles. A tramroad was agreed as a compromise with the original Act of Parliament, which provided the necessary legal authority to create the five-mile railway in 1804, with a clause allowing the use of '... drawing by men, horses or otherwise' i.e. mechanical traction, in addition to horses, to draw the wagons and carriages.[12] This far-sighted inclusion came about because the promoters of the line were acquainted with the work being caried out at Samuel Homfray's Penydarren Ironworks at Merthyr Tydfil involving Richard Trevithick. The engineer and surveyor of the Oystermouth Railway, Edward Martin, who had been prepared to construct either a canal or tramroad to provide the link between the Mumbles and the Swansea canal, responded to criticism that the tramroad would not be an adequate substitute for a canal with the following point:

> ... I have no hesitation in declaring that if Mr. Trevithick's very ingeniuos machine is brought to that perfection, which some persons are confident it will be, and which from the very liberal patronage received from Mr. Homfray of Pendarran [sic] there is every reason to

hope for; that is of driving waggons on a tramroad at a cheaper rate by fifty per cent than it can be done by horses, that it will be most advantageous to the proprietors and the public to substitute an entire tramroad instead of a canal...[13]

Whilst the Oystermouth Railway would not follow the lead shown by Trevithick on the Merthyr Tramroad (it relied on horse transport until 1877), it would herald a world first. Benjamin French, a supporter of the tramroad scheme who acted as supervisor during the construction of the line, had a vision of the railway carrying passengers along the seafront. French agreed to pay the Oystermouth Railway £20 a year for the privilege of operating his passenger service using a specially designed iron carriage on the line which would run to a timetable. On 25 March 1807 the timetable was initiated, a day recognised as marking the commencement of world's first passenger railway service.

The two radically different worlds of Swansea, the resort and the trading town, had a strained co-existence which reached a point of no return in the 1850s with the construction of the South Dock and the high-level viaduct that served it running through the town. With industrialisation came an explosion of population; in 1821 the population stood at 6,099 but by 1881 the census recorded over a tenfold increase of 65,788. In 1882 Clark Russell would write, 'One must not think of the beautiful, but of the useful, with a capital U. Nobody talks of sea views or mountains here, but of how many ships were cleared last week, and what the export and import returns were and the like'.[14]

One of the principal families behind the almost complete industrial transformation and the raising of Swansea's metallurgical profile were the Vivians. Henry Hussey Vivian (1821–94) was the eldest son of John Henry Vivian, a merchant engaged in copper smelting and the MP for Swansea, who sent him to study metallurgy in Germany and France for two years. In 1842 he started to manage the Liverpool branch of the firm of Vivian & Sons and three years later managed the Hafod Smelting Works at Swansea for his father. In 1855, following the death of his father, he took full charge of the works and with the benefit of his European metallurgical knowledge he improved the copper-smelting process to obtain numerous by-products, such as obtaining sulphuric acid from copper-smoke. He was to take out several patents in connection with the manufacture of spelter, gold, silver, nickel, and cobalt and erected new works in 1871 at White Rock, near Swansea, to treat poor silver-lead ores. He served as the MP for Truro, Cornwall, from 1852 for five years, then Glamorgan from 1857 to 1885, and finally Swansea from 1885 to 1893. As an MP with specialised knowledge, he sat on the Royal Commission on Coal which reported in 1871. His interest in coal production led to his introduction of the 'sliding scale' method of calculating wages after the south Wales coal strike of 1889. He was one of the chief supporters of the Rhondda & Swansea Bay Railway and called for improvements to the harbour facilities of Swansea. His Swansea home, Singleton Park, now forms part of Swansea University.[15]

Swansea's raw materials such as copper ore came at first from Cornwall on ships that sailed up the river Tawe to wharves adjoining the smelting works. Locally mined coal was brought from pits on the western banks of the Tawe Valley by canal and tramroad. With the decline in the quality of Cornish ores, the raw material sustaining 'Copperopolis' was now being brought from the other side of the world, the crews of Swansea vessels earning the title of 'Cape Horners' by rounding Cape Horn en route to the copper-rich regions of countries such as Chile. Swansea dominated the British copper-smelting industry until the 1880s, with Vivian's Hafod Works leading the way as the largest and most up-to-date enterprise of its kind. With economics favouring ore smelting in the country of origin, decline was inevitable and Swansea ceased to smelt copper ore, turning instead to refining imported blister (i.e. semi-refined) copper.[16]

Brunel was aquainted with Swansea, in a professional way, since at least the year 1836 when he was engaged on the Gloucester & South Wales Railway survey. This survey included an extension or branch to Swansea, but at the time Brunel felt that, although the survey had extended beyond Swansea, there was little chance of any line being continued beyond that.[17] Ten years later and 1846 marked an important year as far as Brunel and Swansea were concerned. The G&SWR had been superceded by the SWR and its route into the town was now determined by Act of Parliament; the branch line would leave the main line at the sixty-seven and a quarter-mile mark, '... to the east side of High Street on the south side of Pottery Lane and also at or near a point on the Oystermouth Railway or Tramway...'[18] The site referred to as Pottery Lane (also known as the Pottery field) was the site of the present-day High Street station with a shipping place for minerals being situated upon the lower level of the Brewery wharf adjoining the river.[19] George Grant Francis (1814–82), the secretary of the Swansea Dock Co., was to criticise the location of both sites, in particular the branch to the

Lithograph showing the river Tawe and the floating harbour. Note the Swansea High Street station of the SWR on the right. (SKJ collection)

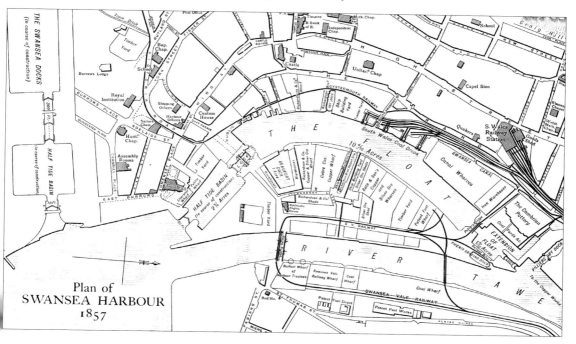

Plan of Swansea Harbour in 1857. (From W.H. Jones's History of the Port of Swansea, *Carmarthen, 1922)*

Brewery wharf which would have, '... a gradient of 1 in 56 or 27 feet in 504 yards' and, '... bounded on three sides by public roads, and with a frontage which will give layerage to three, or at most four ships, and that in a tidal harbour'.[20]

Francis suggested that the mineral branch communicated with the proposed South Dock by a viaduct or by a longer route to get around the severe gradients and run at the level of the Oystermouth tramroad to the dock. In the end a high-level viaduct, following closely to the line of the Oystermouth Railway, was built and extended to the South Dock as part of the Swansea Harbour Railway.[21] These were to become known as the Strand arches and allowed coal to be transported at a high level for tipping at the South Dock. The viaduct cut a swaythe through the town and presented clear evidence of the unstoppable march of industrialisation on Swansea. Brunel was also to be involved in the determination of the position of the dock. In September 1846, Henry Somerset, the 7th Duke of Beaufort (1792–1853), whose freehold interests covered most of the land known as the Town Reach or Burrows, instructed Brunel to prepare a report as to which site was most suitable for the construction of a new dock. Swansea had only recently completed shipping facilities that were an improvement on its previous status of being a tidal harbour, despite the aspirations of the harbour trustees to improve matters.[22] Several proposals to create a floating dock out of the river Tawe were proposed over the years since the Harbour Trust was formed in 1791.[23] In 1827 the Swansea MP John Henry Vivian took up the idea, realising that a Bill then going through Parliament would allow for the construction of a bridge over the river

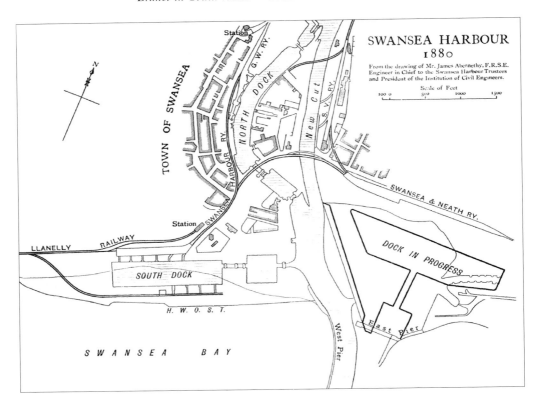

The accident that occurred on 29 December 1865 when a coal train, believing that the opening bridge across the north dock lock to be in position, proceeded to cross. The bridge was open and both the fireman and driver died in the subsequent fall into the lock. (From W.H. Jones's History of the Port of Swansea, Carmarthen, 1922*)*

Opposite above: *Plan of Swansea
Harbour in 1880 showing the Swansea
Harbour Railway providing a link to the
SWR (now shown as G.W.RY) and the
Swansea & Neath Railway. (From
W.H. Jones's* History of the Port of
Swansea, *Carmarthen, 1922)*

Right: *The aftermath of the accident of
a broad gauge container train that had
attempted to cross the north dock bridge
in 1865. The containers and their hinged
trapdoors can be clearly seen as well as the
use of Barlow rail in sub-dividing the flat
trucks. (SKJ collection)*

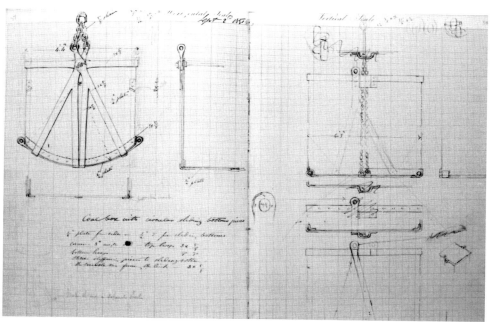

*On the Vale of Neath, Brunel introduced a container system for transporting coal of friable nature. This system
consisted of four iron boxes, 4ft 8ft cube, which were loaded onto platform trucks at the colliery and hauled to
Briton Ferry or Swansea Docks. At the docks, the boxes were lowered by machinery down into the hold of a ship,
with the coal being deposited by opening the hinged floor of the box. Large sketchbook 4, ff.37–38, 2 September
1851. (Courtesy of University of Bristol special collections)*

Tawe and facilitate the floating of the river.[24] Thomas Telford was consulted in the same year and he put forward three plans to enable a floating harbour to be formed.

It was not until 1831, however, that the Swansea Harbour Trust finally resolved to adopt the principle of constructing a floating harbour, offering a premium for the best plan. Six schemes were submitted and included separate submissions from the engineers, W. Brunton and Hy. H. Price.[25] To decide on the best plan the trustees consulted Jesse Hartley, of the Liverpool Dock Co., who put forward his own plan. This was adopted on 28 November 1831 but delays in aquiring an Act of Parliament and negotiations over the necessary land meant that, over ten years after the trustees' resolution, the float was still not open for shipping.[26] Such delays led to the formation of the Swansea Dock Co. by frustrated industrialists and a visit by Beaufort in September 1846 was seen as an opportunity to press him into giving his patronage to the undertaking. Beaufort admitted such an undertaking was essential to the prosperity of Swansea but sought the opinion of a competent engineer – hence the instruction to Brunel. The Swansea Dock Co. were looking to build their dock on the Burrows and there was also an alternative scheme east of the Tawe, in Fabian's Bay. The latter was put forward by Starling Benson (1808–79), one of the promoters of the Swansea Vale Railway and the landowner embroiled in the floating dock negotiations. Benson had previously employed George Bush (1810–41) to carry out surveys in connection with the Swansea Vale proposals of 1840.[27] He was also to consult Rhys W. Jones, another engineer connected with the Swansea Vale proposals and one who would work with Brunel in laying out the Vale of Neath Railway, on drawing up a plan for the dock. The plans for the Burrows scheme, now known as the South Dock, were prepared by James Page, the engineer to the Swansea Dock Co.[28] Brunel's report was dated 9 October 1846 and can be summarised as follows:

(1) Any extent of dock that could be so formed would be totally inadequate to the growing wants of the port, and subsequent extensions could not be made except at very great expense; (2) It would destroy the accommodation then offered to those vessels which could take the ground, without giving in lieu any more extensive accommodation for other vessels; and (3) it would diminish the quantity of water flowing through the harbour, and probably injure the entrance to the Port.[29]

Brunel believed that the efficiency of the dock, 'will be sacrificed unless the communication by railway through the town is secured', and suggested that:

A good railway communication (which would be worked by locomotive or any mechanical means must be carried upon a viaduct) must be effected between the docks and the extremity of the proposed branch of the SWR at a place called the Brewery, being carried somewhat in the direction of the Oystermouth Rly.[30]

Extending the canal to the docks was felt by Brunel to be of great imprtance, 'if not absolutely essential'. In his book *History of the Port of Swansea*, W.H. Jones highlighted

Swansea South Dock in 1865, a fascinating early photograph showing mixed gauge with broad and standard gauge trains. A VNR coal container train is prominently shown as well as the special loading towers on the dockside, the train would have travelled over the Swansea and Neath Railway, a line promoted by the VNR and opened in 1865. The broad-gauge 0-6-0 tank locomotive has dual-gauge buffers which facilitated the movement of wagons of either gauge. (Courtesy of the Royal Institution of South Wales)

the point made by Brunel who stresses that, because such a railway and canal would run through the built-up areas of the town and across public streets, the authorities and its inhabitants would have to be united in order to prevent any opposition, as well as to bear some portion of the expense. Brunel's opinion was issued by Beaufort as a public document. On 9 October Brunel visited Swansea as instructed to find the best place to build the docks. In the company of several gentlemen of the Dock Company, he made inspections opposite Cambrian Place, walked to the Pier Head and then, '… proceeded to example various places on the east side of the river'. During the week he spent in the town he also visited the Swansea Vale Railway and, '… furthered arrangements with the view of proceeding at once with the Vale of Neath Railway', of which he was engineer also.[31] Four years after the decision, and necessary Act, that determined Swansea's position with regard to the SWR, the High Street Station opened as a terminus station in 1850. Lewis, the publisher of *The Swansea Guide* in 1851, informs us that:

Swansea High Street station. (SKJ collection)

The SWR Co.'s termini at Swansea are bordering on High Street, one being for Passengers, and the other for the Goods traffic. There is another in the course of construction on the Strand, on the site of the Old Brewery for the mineral traffic. The latter will be communicated with by means of a Branch, which will extend into the new Floating Dock. The Passenger terminus is the largest on the line, and in point of appearance is remarkably neat, light, and airy, and is under the superintendence of Mr Relton. The SWR booking office is in Wind Street. It is neatly fitted up by Mr Probett, who is the sole agent for the coaching and parcel Dept., of the SWR.[32]

Brunel's original timber station and the facade presented to passengers was to change over the years by rebuilding and additional works. Firstly, in 1877–78 on the western side of the station, offices of Pennant stone were built with Bath stone dressings. Then the structural fabric of the station was changed from the original all-over roofed building to pitched steel-framed awnings of standard GWR 1930s pattern over the platforms in 1924–26, and the addition of a fifth platform. In 1934 the station was remodelled to accept longer trains and the main terminal block facing down High Street was added, the financial costs being offset from Government support available to alleviate unemployment, support that had also been taken up by the GWR for Cardiff Station and the western approaches to that station. The Swansea engine shed was open on the day the line opened from Chepstow to Swansea, to be extended in 1854. Replaced by Landore shed in 1874, it was converted into a goods shed, part of which – though much altered – still remains. Pedestrians walking from the High Street through a tunnel under the station platforms come out on the Strand where the high-level viaduct, consisting of rusticated masonry forming a row of round-headed blind arcading, carries the SWR's branch down to coal drops at the North Dock (the original floating harbour). The branch opened in 1852, and extended as the Swansea Harbour Railway, to the South Dock in 1859. The North Dock, the original floating dock scheme, was finally completed in 1852 by the diversion of the course of the river Tawe through a new cut and used the bed of

Belonging to C.R.M. Talbot, the paddle yacht, Lynx, was one of the first vessels to enter the South Dock. (SKJ collection)

the river as the dock. The scene of the major accident, already detailed, in the 1860s, it was to last as a working dock until 1928 and was filled in during the 1930s.[33]

The first survey for a modern locomotive railway up the Swansea Valley had been made in 1830, with a second around 1836 by William Kirkhouse. In 1840 George Bush, as it has been already noted, was brought in to survey the valley but there was opposition to the railway being built on the eastern side of the river Tawe, to which Bush pointed out that the estimated cost of three miles on the western side was equal to the cost of sixteen miles on the eastern side.[34] Bush's sudden death on 13 November 1841 was to cause a setback; however, in 1845 the Swansea Vale Railway Co. was formed as a non-Parliamentary company by Starling Benson, Joseph Martin and others. The story of the Swansea Vale Co. and the protracted and ultimately doomed negotiations with the SWR cannot be told in full here, suffice to say that it poerated as a horse-drawn line partly on the line of Scott's Tramroad before opened as a private railway, from Swansea to Graigola collieries in December 1852.[35] The line of tramroad being on the ground, however, meant that the SWR would have to cross it, hence Brunel's interest in it when he visited Swansea in October 1846. The level crossing was at Six Pit, so named after a local colliery that had six pits near Llansamlet, and a junction would later be formed between the two railways: the broad-gauge SWR and the standard-gauge Swansea Vale Railway. The latter agreed to provide broad-gauge rails from the junction to their terminus on the eastern side of the North Dock.[36] Going back to the time of the formation of the Swansea Vale Railway Co., there had been direct contact with the SWR, as the partners saw the potential for selling or leasing the railway, not just to the SWR but to narrow-gauge interests in the shape of the Welsh Midland Railway Co. By the beginning of 1846 the Swansea Vale Railway Co. were holding negotiations with both companies. The Welsh Midland Railway Bill was rejected by Parliament on 3 March 1846 to the great consternation of shareholders who lost a considerable amount of their investment. The Swansea Vale Railway Bill was also going through Parliament that year and on 7 July 1846 the Bill was being read for the third time in the House of Commons; it now passed to the Lords but was to fail on a technicality.[37] Negotiations resumed with the SWR in August 1846 with the Swansea Vale agreeing to sell their undertaking for £74,516 which was accepted (or rather £70,000 in SWR shares) by the SWR provided Brunel gave his approval. Louis Vigurs, the SWR deputy chairman, signed the agreement which also stipulated that the Swansea Vale were not to support any rival line along the Tawe Valley, a reference to their earlier association with the Welsh Midland Railway. Brunel was out of the country on business and here the story takes a strange turn of events as in October 1846, the SWR Board, under the mistaken impression that Brunel had given his consent to the agreement, introduced a Bill in Parliament for the purchase and extension of the Swansea Vale Railway. On 18 November Brunel informed the board that he could not approve the terms of the agreement, writing, 'There appears to have been some material error in the accounts on which the bargain was founded or at least a mode of stating the accounts which has led to a very considerable error on our part'.[38]

Negotiations continued with the SWR, a number of meetings taking place between Brunel, Charles Russell of the SWR and their solictors W.O. & W. Hunt on the one part and Benson on the other. The SWR, lacking powers to purchase the company directly, proceeded with the Swansea Valley Railway Bill, which was passed and gave powers to make a railway from Abercrave Farm near Ystradgynlais to Swansea, based on the original Swansea Vale Railway Bill.[39] The new Swansea Valley Railway never acquired the Swansea Vale Railway, however, and the SWR had no powers to subscribe to the new company and provide the purchase money itself. A suggestion made by Benson to Russell in September 1848, that the SWR run its branch to Swansea down the eastern side of the river instead of the western, was not taken further:

> … I told him that it had long ago been decided, that all the notices had been given and the works begun, that I had never heard of any disposition to alter it; but that Mr. Brunel was the proper person to speak to on the subject.[40]

In the meantime, work was proceeding with the construction of the SWR; by March 1850 it was necessary to effect the level crossing with the Swansea Vale; the latter company was to send a formal notice to the SWR about trespassing or interfering with their land despite the fact that the SWR's 1845 Act gave them the powers to do this. Possibly because of this formal notice, the SWR invoked their powers without warning. Benson discovered workmen, employed by the SWR surveyor Samuel Jones, in the process of raising the height of the Swansea Vale line by about 2ft for some 3 to 400 yards to enable the SWR to cross on the level. C.R.M. Talbot, who replaced Charles Russell as SWR chairman in May 1849, and who had been fully informed by Benson on the history of the Swansea Vale and its relationship with the SWR, on 18 March 1850, would now receive Benson's letter on this matter two days later:

> The men were gradually raising the blocks and rails so as to interfere as little as possible with the Coal Waggons passing over, and had already altered the level for about 100 yards. Mr S

Jones, the South Wales Surveyor, upon my calling at his Office, acknowledged that he had employed the Men & at my request gave me the enclosed Memorandum.[41]

The SWR had the authority to do this and Benson could only complain. Negotiations with the SWR officially came to an end in August 1851 and the Swansea Vale pressed on to Graigola. On the opening in December 1852, traffic was being worked by C.H. Smith using his ex-Liverpool & Manchester Railway locomotive *Bat*, the Swansea Vale acquiring two of its own locomotives the following year. The SWR were concerned about the level crossing, particularly now locomotives were being used and telegraphic bell signals were installed to warn the crossing keeper of the approach of SWR trains in April 1854. In February 1857 the crossing was done away with, the Swansea Vale being diverted under the main line, but not before a collision occurred in October 1856 between two mineral trains.[42] To carry passengers, the Swansea Vale needed to become a statutory company with an Act of Parliament; it finally achieved this in 1855 and passenger services between Swansea St Thomas and Pontardawe began in 1860. By 1874 the line had been opened as far as Ystradgynlais with branches to Glais and Brynamman. It was still an independent company and still chaired by Benson, but it had attracted the attention of the Midland Railway who became lessees in that year and absorbed the company by Act of Parliament on 11 August 1876.[43]

Another line with tramroad origins was the Llynvi Valley Railway (LVR), incorporated on 7 August 1846.[44] Authorised to construct a steam locomotive railway, it did little beyond purchasing (under a further Act) the Duffryn Lynvi & Porthcawl Railway, a horse-drawn tramroad that had opened in 1828 to haul coal from the Dyffryn Colliery to Porthcawl. The Bridgend Railway also connected Bridgend to the Duffryn Lynvi & Porthcawl Railway at Cefn Cribwr.[45] One of the longest lived associations with commercial coal exploitation was with the Coegnant district in the Llynvi Valley. In 1830 the Coegnant colliery was advertising, at its wharf at Porthcawl, 'Large Coal is for sale at 8s 6d per ton and small coal at 7s per ton'.[46] This link was broken after 150 years when the last representative of that colliery district, the Coegnant North and South Pits, wasclosed in 1981.[47] As well as coal, the tramroad was used in conjunction with a smelting works near Metcalfe Street, Caerau, with spelter or zinc ore

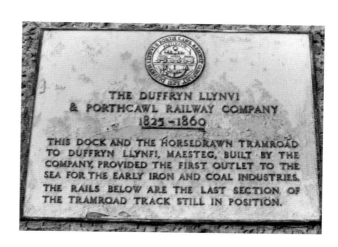

Plaque commemorating the Duffryn Llynvi and Porth Cawl Railway at Porthcawl. (SKJ photograph)

Later developments of the original LVR line, a bridge now demolished at Caerau. (SKJ photograph)

Branch line serving the Llynvi ironworks, now demolished. (SKJ photograph)

Remains of the Llynvi ironworks buildings at Maesteg in the 1970s. The large building, known as the 'Cornstores' was the steam engine house and has been incorporated into the Maesteg Sports Centre building. The remains of the furnice can also be seen. (SKJ photograph)

Maesteg station in GWR days. The passenger service was withdrawn in 1970 but the line, as far as Maesteg, was reopened in 1992 and there are proposals to extend this service to Caeran. (SKJ collection)

being brought into Porthcawl dock from Cornwall carried up the Llynvi Valley, the processed zinc then being taken back to Porthcawl and shipment.[48] The ironworks at Maesteg were also served by the Duffryn Llynvi & Porthcawl Railway at Garnllwyd.

The Duffryn Llynvi & Porthcawl Railway was the first dock and railway venture in south Wales, something that worried Lord Bute because of the potential to attract coal shipments away from the dock he was building in Cardiff. In 1837 he employed the engineer W.H. Harrison to survey a branch line feeding in to the TVR; this was the Llantwit Vardre branch, the construction of which, it was considered, would, '... check any intrusion from Porth Cawl Railway towards this district'.[49] The LVR was to return to Parliament twice in July 1847, on 2 July to seek extension[50] and on 22 July for authority to purchase the Duffryn Lynvi & Porthcawl Railway.[51] There was considerable agitation at the delays in forming this railway, the *Cardiff and Merthyr Guardian* complaining about the the lack of a decent mode of transport between Maesteg and Bridgend, 'The railway – so called (for in its present form it can only be deemed an apology for one) is prooverbial for unequalled slowness in travelling...'[52] It referred to the acquisition by the LVR of the old DL&PR and felt that the union of the two companies should have resulted in either a new line of railway or that the old line would be altered and improved to allow locomotive engines to be used, '... but the spirit of competition having once evaporated, the public is compelled to; "grin and bear the brunt" of it...' After several years of doing nothing, the LVR chose the easiest option and the LVR moved to obtain powers to ease some of the curves on the old DL&PR and use it as a locomotive railway – no doubt causing cries of outrage in the valley! The Bridgend Railway was acquired by the LVR in 1854 and a further Act in 1855 finally moved the LVR into completing this line, converting the tramroad into a broad-gauge railway branching off the SWR at Bridgend.[53] As the *Cardiff and Merthyr Guardian* had alluded to it in 1851 the spirit of competition was needed and something of the sort was behind the 1855 action, a threatened pincer movement by the SWMR and a proposed 'Maesteg Bridgend & South Wales Junction Railway'.

Isambard Brunel had only this to say on the LVR, 'The Llynvi Valley Railway is a short line, leading from the South Wales Railway at Bridgend into the coal and iron districts'.[54] The first sod was cut in connection with the line in 1858, and broad-gauge rails were laid from Bridgend, partly following the old Duffryn Llynvi and Porthcawl tramroad line from the mainline to Nantyffyllon in the Llynvi Valley. The Porthcawl branch started at Tondu and although easily graded south of the SWR main line at Pyle, it followed a tortuous route due to its tramroad ancestry. The LVR opened for goods on 10 August 1861 and the first passenger service commenced on 25 February 1864 from Bridgend to Maesteg, and to Porthcawl on 1 August 1865, passenger trains running from Porthcawl through Cornelly and Tydraw stations to the SWR Junction and continuing up the valley to Coegnant. On the Porthcawl branch a station was made close to the now GWR station at Pyle, but no junction was formed until 1876.[55] At Maesteg the first LVR station, managed by William Akehurts, the first station master, was situated near, what was recorded in 1958 as the Goods Yard.[56] Also in that year it was noted that, 'Llangynwyd Station was constructed much later and the old low platform [broad gauge] of that station can be seen beyond the road bridge just below the present station'.

The firm of John Brogden & Sons was the first to exploit the resources of the Llynvi Valley using the new railway. John Brogden, a succesful entrepreneur who had made his money through railway contracting and mining in Lancashire, come down to south Wales through the acquisition of the Tondu ironworks and its mineral estate in about 1854.[57] The Brogdens went on to develop the Garth Pit in 1864, the first of the new generation of larger and deeper coalmines to supply their blast furnaces and for the sale-coal market. The Brogdens were also heavily involved in the standard-gauge Ogmore Valley Railway which was to merge, despite the difference in gauge, with the LVR in 1866 to form the Llynvi & Ogmore Railway (L&OR).[58] By 1868 the third rail had been laid throughout, allowing standard-gauge operation on the combined network. The GWR was to take over the working and management of the L&OR on 1 July 1873, the system consisting of twenty-seven miles of railway serving twenty-six collieries.[59] Later, under the GWR, two 44xx class locomotives, the smallest of the Churchward standard 2-6-2T engines, with 4ft $1^1/_2$ in diameter driving wheels, were kept to operate the demanding and tortuous demands of the Porthcawl branch.[60] On this branch the line would pass Cornelly Quarry and run under the Porthcawl to Cornelly road, curves easing somewhat due to the flat ground leading to Nottage and the outskirts of Porthcawl. On passing Nottage Halt, the line was to dive through what was an unusual feature of the branch, the 63-yard-long Nottage tunnel, an artificial tunnel demanded by the landowner so that he would not see the railway from his house, before emerging alongside the Porthcawl to Cornelly road.[61]

Brunel appointed Captain McNair to the post of resident engineer on the LVR; this was a post that A.J. Schenk was also interested in, to whom Joseph Bennett was to write two days after McNair's appointment on 17 September 1858, informing him that there, '... is not any prospect...' of him being considered for the appointment.[62] Brunel appears to have had some interest in Schenk's position, however, judging from a comment Bennett makes in the letter that he hopes that he will continue to be in a better position, '... in a pecuniary point of view'. Less than two months later Brunel did have something for Schenk and offered him a position on the Swansea Harbour Railway as his inspector:

> ... Mr. Brunel will of course expect that you will devote the whole of your time to the works over which he has placed you, although he will still consider, that subject to his approval, you will not be debarred from keeping up your connection with Swansea. Of course you are aware that services of our Inspector will only be temporary. Will you be good enough to ascertain which Drawings that had been attached to the Contract were burnt as they will have to be supplied – I think Mr Lewis Thomas said the N[os] were 2, 3 and 5.[63]

Curiously, the salary for this was £300 and considerably more than the £225 offered to McNair for his post of resident engineer; indeed the salary that McNair had accepted was not sufficient to allow him to rent the accomodation he needed – prompting Brunel to write on the same day to Alex Macgregor of the LVR:

> ... I beg to say that the salary which I offfered was £225 per annum. I find that Captain McNair has had real difficulty in obtaining a house to reside in and the rent which he has to pay, and the high price of properties in the district to which he had gone, renders it quite necessary for me to appeal to the Directors on his behalf, and to recommend which I do most strongly that Captain McNair's salary should be £250 instead of £225...[64]

The last letter sent out on Brunel's behalf to the LVR was on 8 August 1859 when Bennett wrote to G.F. Saunders seeking payment of his account for professional services and disbursements from the commencement of his engagement with the company to 1 July 1859; if the company found it inconvenient to pay the whole of the account they could make a payment on account.[65]

Notes

1   Clark Russell writing in 1882, from a leaflet on James Abernethy published by Swansea City Council in 1985, as part of *Stony Stories: A Maritime Quarter Trail*.
2   A comprehensive study of the landscape of the first industrial period in Swansea has been carried out by Stephen Hughes of the Royal Commission on the Ancient and Historic Monuments of Wales (RCAHM) and published as *Copperopolis* (2000, reprinted 2005), Royal Commission on Ancient and Historical Monuments in Wales: Aberystwyth.
3   *The Dictionary of Welsh Biography down to 1940 (DWB)* (1959), The Honourable Society of Cymmrodion: London, p.606.

4 Evans, Sir Herbert and Evans, David.

5 Mackworth had mineral interests in the Gogerddan estates in Cardiganshire which he acquired in 1698.

6 Lewis, M.J.T. (1970). pp.247–50. *Early Wooden Railways*, Routledge & Kegan Paul: London. A 1799 map showing these early Welsh tramroads can be seen in Jones, Stephen K. (2005), p.51. Mackworth's railway disappeared with the closure of the pits in 1809–10.

7 Landor, Walter Savage, 1775–1864, English poet and essayist, educated at Oxford. After a quarrel with his father, he went to live in Wales, where he wrote the epic poem *Gebir* (1798).

8 'Swansea in point of spirit, fashion, and politeness, has now become the Brighton of Wales' from *The Gloucester Journal*, 14 August 1786, see Boorman, David (1986), *The Brighton of Wales, Swansea as a Fashionable Seaside Resort c. 1780-1830*, Swansea Little Theatre Co. Ltd: Swansea, p.1.

9 Brunel was sent away from London in order to rebuild his constitution following the Thames Tunnel, see Jones, Stephen K. (2005), p.77.

10 Evans, John (1804), p.168, *Letters written during a Tour through South Wales, in the Year 1803, and at other times*, London, quoted in Boorman, David (1986), p.90.

11 Dylan Thomas took his last drink here before setting off from Swansea on his final trip to America.

12 Gabb, Gerald (1987, second impression 1994), *The Life and Times of the Swansea and Mumbles Railway*, D. Brown & Sons Limited: Cowbridge, p.12.

13 Gabb, Gerald (1987, second impression 1994), p.12. Martin was responding to correspondence in the columns of Wales's first newspaper; *The Cambrian*, a weekly launched in January 1804.

14 Clark, Russell, 1882.

15 *The Dictionary of Welsh Biography down to 1940 (DWB)* (1959), p.1009.

16 British Copper Manufacturers took over the Hafod and Morfa works in 1924, amalgamating with ICI in 1928. The combined site was to produce copper plates and billets as Yorkshire Imperial Metals until closure in 1980.

17 University of Bristol, Special Collections, PLB 2, p.59, 21 September 1836.

18 The second Act granted to the SWR on the 27 July, 1846 (9 & 10 Vic., cap.239, 1846).

19 Jones, W.H. (1922, facsimile edition 1995), p.180, *History of the Port of Swansea*, Spurrell Carmarthen. Facsimile edition by West Glamorgan County Council, Swansea.

20 Jones, W.H. (1922, facsimile edition 1995), p.180.

21 Authorised in 1857.

22 Jessop had declined an invitation to survey the harbour in 1793 shortly after an Act of Parliament had been passed to preserve and enlarge the harbour of Swansea (the 6th Duke of Beaufort, the Earl of Jersey and others becoming Trustees).

23 Jeffreys Jones, T.I. ed. (1966), *Acts of Parliament Concerning Wales 1714–1901*, Cardiff: University of Wales Press, p.179. This was 31 Geo.III (24 June 1791) 83 (Pub.) 1352; 'An Act for repairing, enlarging and preserving the Harbour of Swansea, in the County of Glamorgan.'

24 Bayliffe, Dorothy M. and Harding, Joan N. (1996), p.30, *Starling Benson of Swansea*, D. Brown & Sons Ltd: Bridgend, p.179. Jones, W. H. (1922, facsimile edition 1995), p.157. The bill was to amend the Glamorganshire Turnpike Act of 1823.

25 Jones, W. H. (1922, facsimile edition 1995), p.164. Henry Habberley Price and William Brunton had proposed the first practical proposal for a railway between London and Bristol in 1832. See Chapter 1.

26 Full details of the floating harbour saga can be found in Bayliffe, Dorothy M. and Harding, Joan N. (1996), and Jones, W.H. (1922, facsimile edition 1995).

27 Bush was Brunel's resident engineer on the TVR.

28 Jones, W.H. (1922, facsimile edition 1995), p.178.

29 Jones, W.H. (1922, facsimile edition 1995), p.178.

30 Jones, W.H. (1922, facsimile edition 1995), p.178–79.

31 *The Cambrian*, 16 October 1846.

32 Lewis, J. (1851), *The Swansea Guide*, BN51

33 See Chapter 8.

34 Jones, W.H. (1922), *History of the Port of Swansea*, Carmarthen: Spurrell. See also Bayliffe, Dorothy M. and Harding, Joan N. (1996), p.182, and Jones, Stephen K.(2005), pp.130–31. Bush's comments appeared in *The Cambrian*, 24 November 1846.

35 Hadfield, Charles (1967), *The Canals of South Wales and the Border*, David & Charles: Newton Abbot, p.57. For the Swansea Vale Railway see Bayliffe, Dorothy M. and Harding, Joan N. (1996), Chapter XII.

36 MacDermot, E.T., revised by Clinker, C.R. (1964), *History of the Great Western Railway*, vol.1, Ian Allen: London, pp.302–3.

37 This hinged around the Duke of Beaufort's rights regarding watercourses. See Bayliffe, Dorothy M. and Harding, Joan N. (1996), pp.188–89.

38 Bayliffe, Dorothy M. and Harding, Joan N. (1996), p.189.

39 Act cl (L & P), 10–11 Victoria, 1847.

40 Bayliffe, Dorothy M. and Harding, Joan N. (1996), p.195. Letter by Charles Russell to W.O. Hunt, 1 October 1848.

41 Bayliffe, Dorothy M. and Harding, Joan N. (1996), p.196. Letter by Starling Benson to C.R.M. Talbot, 20 March 1850.

42 MacDermot, E.T., revised by Clinker, C.R. (1964). p.302–3.

43 Barrie, D.S.M., revised by Baughan, Peter E. (1994), p.207, *A Regional History of Great Britain*, vol.12, *South Wales*, David St John Thomas Publisher: Nairn.

44 9 & 10 Vic., cap.353, 1846.

45 MacDermot, E.T. (revised by Clinker, C.R., 1964), vol.1, p.43.

46 Lewis, David, *The Coal Industry in the Llynvi Valley* (2006), p.17 Tempus Publishing Ltd: Stroud.

47 Lewis, David (2006), p.17 & 146.

48 Davies, George F., Cambettie, Demetrie, compilers (1958), *Maesteg and District: Festival of Wales 1958*, souvenir brochure, Maesteg Urban District Council: Maesteg, pp.32–33.

49 Bute VI, Llantwit Vardre Branch October 1837, Cardiff Central Reference Library. A railway eventually to be built as Thomas Powell's Llantwit Vardre Railway in 1843. See Jones, Stephen K. (2005), p.190.

50 10 & 11 Vic., cap.72, 1847.

51 10 & 11 Vic., cap.295, 1847.

52 *Cardiff and Merthyr Guardian,* 31 May 1851.

53 MacDermot, E.T. (revised by Clinker, C.R., 1964), vol.II, p.43.

54 Brunel, Isambard (1870, reprinted 1971), p.89, *The Life of Isambard Kingdom Brunel,* Longmans, Green & Co.: London, 1870, reprinted David & Charles: Newton Abbot, 1971.

55 MacDermot, E.T. (revised by Clinker, C.R., 1964), vol.I, p.44.

56 Davies, George F., Cambettie, Demetrie, compilers (1958), p.36.

57 Lewis, David (2006), p.23. See also Chapter Nine and the Barrow monument.

58 Barrie, D.S.M., revised by Baughan, Peter E. (1994). *A Regional History of Great Britain,* vol.12, *South Wales,* David St John Thomas Publisher: Nairn, pp.179-80.

59 Barrie, D.S.M., revised by Baughan, Peter E. (1994), p.180.

60 Page, James (1979), p.94, *Forgotten Railways: South Wales,* David & Charles: Newton Abbot.

61 Page, James (1979), p.95.

62 University of Bristol, Special Collections, PLB 11, p.90, letter to A.J. Schenk, 17 September 1858.

63 University of Bristol, Special Collections, PLB 11, p.100, letter to A.J. Schenk, 8 November 1858.

64 University of Bristol, Special Collections, PLB 11, pp.100–1, letter to Alex Macgregor, 8 November 1858.

65 University of Bristol, Special Collections, PLB 11, pp.219–20, letter to G.F. Saunders, 8 August 1859.

10

LAST LINES

'AND IF THE INCOME SHOULD APPEAR TO BE
ADVANTAGEOUS TO THE SOUTH WALES RLY...'[1]

At the end of 1852 Brunel was in correspondence with Owen Bowen of Upper Thames Street, London, the subject in question being a new railway from the SWR at Carmarthen to Newcastle Emlyn and on to Cardigan town and harbour.[2] This was the Carmarthen & Cardigan Railway which would gain its Act of Parliament in 1854. Frederick George Saunders, who had replaced Captain Nenon Armstrong as secretary to the SWR following his disappearance with £5,000, referred to the application being made to Parliament by an independent company to construct a broad-gauge line, in connection with the SWR, from Carmarthen to Newcastle Emlyn, with a view to its ultimate extension to Cardigan and that it, '... cannot fail to be an important adjunct to the main line of the South Wales Railway'.[3] The last broad-gauge railway company incorporated in south Wales was to be the Ely Valley Railway which obtained its Act of Parliament on 13 June 1857 to build a railway from Llantrisant on the SWR to Tonyrefail and Penygaig with branches to Gellyrhaidd and Brofiskin.[4] This chapter attempts to chronicle the three south Wales railways of this period, lines that came late into the career of Brunel and indeed were not to be completed in his lifetime. None of these lines resulted in major engineering works, although the South Wales Mineral Railway (SWMR) is worthy of mention for the route it took to bring coal down from the colliery to the shipping place. In this period, the last decade of Brunel's lifetime, the SWR and its allies were also constantly engaged in fighting standard-gauge incursions or the threat of broad to standard-gauge conversions, including that by the most recent broad-gauge company on the scene, the Ely Valley Railway.[5]

A line clearly seen as a branch to the broad gauge in south Wales was the SWMR, a line with a tramroad antecedent in the shape of the Glyncorrwg Railway, otherwise known as 'Parsons Folly'. The Glyncorrwg Railway was a late entry as far as tramroads were concerned and sought to tap the mineral resources of the upper Afan Valley, running from Aberdulais, passing through Tonna, over the mountain to Tonmawr, up the side of the mountain and on to Blaencregan. It was built by Robert Parsons and Charles Strange between 1839 and 1843 in an attempt to reach Glyncorrwg, but Blaencregan was

Above: *The South Wales main line (centre) with the remaining section of the SWMR bridge at Briton Ferry. (Michael Hale collection)*

Left: *South Wales Mineral Railway seal. Incorporated in 1853 as a line from Briton Ferry to Glyncorrwg. (Courtesy of GWR Museum, Swindon)*

as far as it got before finances ran out. The high cost Parsons paid for Wayleaves to build his line meant that it ran at a loss. As already mentioned in Chapter 3, the SWMR was the first 'post crisis' broad-gauge railway to be incorporated in south Wales for a short line eleven and a half miles long on 15 August 1853. It was to run from a connection with the SWR at Briton Ferry to the Glyncorrwg mineral district, with a short branch from Baglan to coal mines at Fordecwyn. Isambard Brunel, in his biography of his father's life, had this to say about the SWMR:

> The South Wales Mineral Railway is another line of the same class [referring to the LVR]. It passes through a very heavy country, and has on it a self-acting incline of 1 in 9, ¾ of a mile long, worked by a rope, and a tunnel ⅝ mile long, and 470 feet below the surface.[6]

The Ynys-y-maerdy incline in use, a self acting incline of 1 in 9, three quarters of a mile long, which was worked by loaded coal wagons descending by a wire cable, controlled by a braked wheel at the top, which pulled up the empty wagons. (SKJ collection)

An access bridge crosses the lower part of the incline. (SKJ photograph)

Left: *Looking down the old incline.*
(SKJ photograph)

Below: *Bridge under the incline.*
(SKJ photograph)

The SMWR was the most 'unnatural' of all of Brunel's railways in that as a mineral railway it did not, for the major part, follow the natural course of a valley, which even his 'impossible' line, the Vale of Neath Railway, did. Beginning at Briton Ferry, the SWMR ran up the side of Baglan hill as the Ynys-y-maerdy incline and then down the other side to follow the Pelenna river as far as Tonmawr, turning right through Michaelston hill by the Gyfylchi tunnel to follow the Afan Valley to Cymmer and

Railway lines terminating at what was the entrance to Gyfylchi tunnel. (Michael Hale collection)

finally the Afon Corrwg to Glyncorrwg.[7] The principal work on the line was the self-acting Ynys-y-maerdy incline of 1 in 9, three quarters of a mile long, which worked on the self-acting principle that the loaded coal wagons descended by a wire cable, controlled by a braked wheel at the top, which pulled up the empty wagons.[8] Other works include the 1,109-yards-long tunnel at Gyfylchi, several under bridges and a flying arch access bridge at the summit; for the rest of the line the steepest gradients were 1 in 70. From Incline Top to Glyncorrwg the line was single track and about eleven miles in length, with passing places for trains at Tonmawr and Cymmer, three and a half and seven and three quarter miles respectively from Incline Top. Opened in stages between June 1861 and March 1863, it was one of the last of the Brunel lines to be completed, Robert Pearson Brereton acting as company engineer after Brunel's death. MacDermot states that there were delays in opening the line due to lack of capital and the failure of a contractor, '… the first 5½ miles from the South Wales Railway at Briton Ferry to the west of Gyfwlchau [sic] Tunnel were opened in June 1861'.[9]

In August 1861 a short extension to Briton Ferry docks was authorised. Briton Ferry dock was designed by Brunel and incorporated one of his wrought-iron buoyant gate designs.[10] The Briton Ferry Dock Co. had been formed in 1846 and although it obtained an Act of Parliament in 1851, no real progress on the actual dock was made until 1858.[11] In April 1852 the Briton Ferry Dock Co. opened a short branch from the SWR to a wharf on the river Neath; this was leased to the VNR so that it could ship the Aberdare steam coal then being worked.[12] Before the SWMR was opened, the Glyncorrwg Coal Co. leased the line for thirty years in 1855, the SWMR being worked by the Glyncorrwg Coal Co. until 1870 and then by its successors, the Glyncorrwg Colliery Co. Ltd.[13] It was to remain independent as a colliery line until 1908 when it was absorbed by the Great

Above: *The site of Glyncorrwg halt in the 1970s. (SKJ photograph)*

Left: *The remains of the SWMR (boundary marker) at Glyncorrwg in the 1970s. (SKJ photograph)*

Below: *Glyncorrwg as a working railway. (Michael Hale collection)*

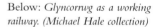

Western Railway. Four broad-gauge 0-6-0 tank engines, similar to those on the Llynvi Valley Railway, operated the traffic. In common with the broad gauge in south Wales, it was converted to standard gauge in May 1872.

The Port Talbot Railway had opened on 14 November 1898, the railway having authorisation to arrive at a working agreement with the SWMR in its 1896 Act. To facilitate this arrangement, a signal box was installed at Tonmawr for the traffic passing between the two

SWMR notice at Glyncorrwg.
(Michael Hale collection)

railways and by this time a small office and a weighbridge operated at Cymmer with telegraphic communication to both Incline Top and Glyncorrwg. These dealt with three trains a day each way, timed to pass at Cymmer unless special instructions were issued by the traffic manager at Briton Ferry or Glyncorrwg for the trains to be worked otherwise. The SWMR operated purely as a mineral line and was not designed for the conveyance of passengers and it operated no scheduled passenger services until 1918.[14] That was not to say, however, that passengers were never carried as from the time the line was opened it had been the custom to allow people residing in the neighbourhood to ride in the empty trucks or brake vans of the trains. Seen almost as a public service, due to the remote location of the termination at Glyncorrwg with its lack of public transport, this allowed easier access to the town of Neath, and its markets, some two or three miles distant from Incline Top. To maintain its status as a mineral line, no charges were made for this privilege and therefore no 'passengers' were carried. The only major accident that occurred on the SWMR was, ironically, due to this 'illegal' practice and involved a collision in the Gyfylchi tunnel on 16 August 1902 due to a breach of the standing instructions about where trains could pass each other.

Although the GWR had absorbed the SWMR in 1908, it was to be run by the Port Talbot Railway from that date, the latter company having taken over the running from the Glyncorrwg Colliery Co.[15] This arrangement resulted in some rationalisation and on 31 May 1910 the Ynys-y-maerdy incline was closed. The first closure of the line, it involved the abandonment of the line between Briton Ferry and Tonmawr Junction, traffic being diverted at the latter point on to the Port Talbot Railway.[16] A landslide closed the Gyfylchi tunnel on 13 July 1947, which was not reopened, and the only exit from the Glyncorrwg, now via Cymmer and Tondu over the GWR's line from Nantyffyllon in the Llynvi Valley (opened in 1878). The public passenger service, as far as the SWMR was concerned, operated between Cymmer Corrwg to North Rhondda Halt and Colliery, starting in 1918 and ceasing on 22 September 1930.[17] Unadvertised miner's trains continued until 2 November 1964 with the closure of the collieries, Barrie recording that the miner's trains comprised several four-wheeled coaches, which must have been the last of this wheel arrangement to be regularly used on British Railways.[18] The former incline has been incorporated into Jersey Park in Briton Ferry, the incline itself forming a scenic path up the hillside and a SWMR under bridge, at the bottom of the incline, taking on the appearance of park feature. In 1972 Glyncorrwg and its surviving colliery infrastructure was considered as a site for a major working museum for the Welsh mining industry. It was not to be, however, and the isolated township, in common with many mining villages in south Wales, continued its inevitable post coal decline.[19] Less than six miles away, however, at the Afan Argoed Country Park, the South Wales Miners' Museum was established to tell the story of coal mining in the Afan Valley.

The Carmarthen & Cardigan Railway (C&CR) was another railway in this period and a line with aspirations well beyond the reality of traffic based on rural agricultural trade. In December 1852 Brunel was approached by Owen Bowen on the subject of this proposal and Brunel's reply of 9 December 1852 restates the engineer's thoughts on the position of 'consulting engineer' (a position Brunel had made clear in an 1843 letter that is reproduced in the 1870 biography).[20] In the letter to Bowen in 1852 Brunel states:

> ... I never act as 'consulting' engineer particularly to lines of railway the general principle and details of which I have not had the opportunity of considering and determining myself before they were invariably fixed by parliamentary plans. And if the income should appear to be advantageous to the South Wales Rly the promoters may rely upon their cordial support without their being professionally engaged.[21]

In 1853 a prospectus was published for the building of a broad-gauge line and an Act of Parliament was granted in June 1856. It was intended to construct a line northwards from Carmarthen, along the Gwili Valley through the mountains at Alltwalis, and turn left at Pencader for Cardigan, where it was proposed to build a deep water port. A contract was signed by Jays of London, and the first sod was ceremonially cut at Myrtle Hill station, Carmarthen, by Capt. Lloyd at Dolhaiddyn in 1857, but the contract only allowed for the first eighteen miles of the line, as far as Llandysul. In November 1857 Brunel was forced to write to Owen Bowen, based on a conversation he had with the resident engineer, Mr Baxter, on the question of engineering expenses, for which the directors had expressed a wish to be fixed at a certain sum per mile:

> I beg to say, that I am willing to take upon myself all expenses for Engineering since the passing of the Act, incurring or to be incurred by me or my Assistants in the direction and superintendence of the Works; and including all my own professional charges, for a sum equal to an average of £350 per mile, assuming the Company to proceed with the Works in ordinary course, or at all events within the period defined by the Act. But should any unforeseen cause of delay render a suspension of the Works necessary, or prolong considerably the periods of execution, the above arrangement must be subject to modification – payment on account of this to be made from time to time, as I may require. In consequence of the great delays which have hitherto attended our proceedings considerable expenses have already been incurred since the passing of the Act, and much of the work connected with the setting out of the whole line and the preparation of plans, contracts etc have already been done. I must therefore now request a payment on account of £1,000.[22]

In January 1858 Brunel was forced to write again, complaining that he had not received anything from the C&CR Co. since the passing of the Act and that he had assistants' salaries and other expenses to pay, which amounted '... to more than the sum I have applied for...' The C&CR directors were even seeking a postponement of Brunel's claim, which Brunel refused to agree to, stating that the claim was for, '... money advanced by me and quite irrespective of my own Professional services'.[23] On 8 February 1858 Brunel wrote to the

The ubiquitous bridge rail being used as fence posts near Pencader, the abandoned line of the Carmarthen & Cardigan Railway crossing a farm access road in the background.

chairman of the C&CR, requesting that at the next meeting of the board (to be held on 10 February), some arrangements for paying for the past and future engineering expenses were made. He states that he cannot agree to incurring expenses and advancing money for the payment of salaries and wages, '... without some attempt on the part of the Company to reimburse me'.[24] From the passing of the Act up to 31 December 1857, Brunel confirms that he has incurred £1,459 in expenses, exclusive of any professional charge. This is broken down as upwards of £600 in actual pay checks or weekly wages to men engaged in setting out the line – one sum of £383 15s 1d being the amount of pay checks to workmen for a certain period, '... is all I have been able to obtain from the Secretary'.

No railway traffic would be seen on the C&CR in Brunel's lifetime, the line getting as far as Conwil some six and a half miles from Carmarthen, in its first phase, but it was destined never to link the places in its title. Services commenced on 3 September 1860; however, disputes over the hire of the locomotives from the SWR led to a suspension on 31 December 1860, and two locomotives were then hired from Sharp Stewart & Co., and the line reopened. The C&CR ordered two bogie engines, *Etna* and *Hecla* from Rothwell & Co., in 1864, locomotives that eventually found their way to the South Devon Railway in 1868 and 1872 respectively.[25] One of the C&CR's locomotives, *Hedley*, was to end up working a stonecrusher at Convil Quarry from 1893 to 1905 when it was moved and set up as a stationary engine at Neath Engineering Depot until 1929 where it was finally pensioned off to be cut up at Swindon.[26] Building the 985-yard-long Pencader, or Alltwalis Tunnel, was another factor that almost bankrupted the company.[27] C&CR's financial situation was made worse by their involvement in a mineral line near Kidwelly, and a receiver was appointed when debts exceeded £1 million. The C&CR was also associated with the Manchester & Milford Railway, whose final scheme involved building a standard-gauge line from Pencader Junction (with C&CR) to Llanidloes on the Cambrian Railways. It was not until 3 June 1864 that the line reached Llandysul, the line being converted to mixed gauge in 1866. In 1864 the C&CR was joined at Abergwili Junction by the standard-gauge branch of the Llanelly Railway from Llandillo, bringing with it the problems of break of gauge to Carmarthen. In 1866 the Manchester & Milford Railway gained access to Carmarthen in 1866, following the laying of a third rail from Pencader Junction to Abergwili Junction. The C&CR has the distinction of running the last broad-gauge trains in south Wales and was eventually sold to the GWR in 1881.[28] The end of the former C&CR came in 1973 with the closure of the remaining lines from Carmarthen to Felin Fach (on the Aberaeron branch) and Pencader to

Newcastle Emlyn on 30 September that year. However, a scheme was drawn up by the Teifi Valley Railway Society to reopen the line then still in use for goods trains. This led to the establishment of Gwili Railway Co. in 1974 and, following the granting of a Light Railway Order in 1977, the first steam-hauled services began at Easter 1978. The Gwili Railway continues to be the only steam standard-gauge railway operating in south-west Wales.

The last line in this section probably has the least connection with Brunel than any other railway; in fact, it is included only because it was built on the broad gauge and as such was the last broad-gauge railway to be incorporated in south Wales. This was the Ely Valley Railway (EVR), incorporated on 13 June 1857.[29] In fact, the railway had a pre-history linked with promoted and aborted schemes going back beyond the SWR itself, but in 1857 the EVR was an extension of the SWR that formed a junction at Llantrisant and ran to Penygraig. Those named in an engineering capacity are: John Pyne of Canford, Dorset, and Edward David of Radyr, Cardiff.[30] Neither of them had a profile of being a railway engineer; John Pyne was, in fact, the land agent, surveyor and steward to Sir Ivor Bertie Guest Bart, the son of Sir Josiah John Guest, who was to become the first Lord Wimborne. No doubt this appointment was through Guest's extensive commercial interests in the locality; even so he appears more experienced than Edward David of Radyr, known as a land agent and practical agriculturist.

The line was completed in August 1860 as a single-track, broad-gauge mineral line as far as Tonyrefail, continuing to Penygraig in 1862, a position that was less than half a mile or so off the TVR at Tonypandy. In 1877 the line was extended to the Cambrian Collieries at Clydach Vale and was to remain an independent concern, although leased by the GWR, independently of the SWR, from 1 January 1861.[31] This came about because the GWR had acquired one of the Ely Valley collieries for supplying its locomotives. The passenger traffic on the Ely Valley line survived until 1958, leaving Llantrisant with only the main line passenger traffic stopping service, and closure of the station followed in 1964. In 1860 the EVR attempted to promote a narrow-gauge line from Llantrisant to Cardiff, of which the TVR were implicated, although employing the cloak of an 'independent company', the TVR backed the Llantrisant & Taff Vale Junction Railway, incorporated on 7 June 1861 to convert the old Llantwit Fardre tramroad to build a line from the main line of the TVR near Treforest to a junction with the EVR at Maesaraul, one and a half miles north of Llantrisant. Running powers were granted over the EVR from the junction into Llantrisant and the powers to lay narrow gauge rails over that portion of the EVR.[32]

As already demonstrated by the situation of the EVR, the commercial interests of south Wales, particularly the mining industry, were now seeking a uniform gauge based on the standard gauge. Colliery owners complained about the fact that coal transhipped via the GWR (after 1863) to another district served by the standard gauge usually meant a second transhipment back to standard-gauge wagons. The GWR were under pressure to provide a standard-gauge connection to the outside world for colliery owners. All the initial interest shown in the broad gauge had long since dissipated, with only the 'spine' of the SWR maintaining the momentum, as demonstrated by these 'last lines'. Eventually it became clear to the GWR directors that the disadvantages of a 'break in gauge' were significant, and there was a steady introduction of the 'third rail' to allow the running of standard-gauge trains on GWR broad-gauge lines, but not, of course, vice versa. Gradually, as the demand for through traffic increased, the 'third rail' stopgap was abandoned and, despite Daniel Gooch's affection for the broad gauge, he saw that for commercial reasons the eventual removal of the broad gauge was inevitable.

The official recognition of a standard gauge for Great Britain did not mean that other gauges would not continue to be introduced and used in Wales. Gauges narrower than 4ft 8½in would be used extensively for new lines to provide transport for slate quarries to ports or feeding to standard-gauge lines, particularly in north Wales. In comparison, many felt that the broad gauge was not suitable for transporting the commodities, particularly natural resources such as coal, which Wales had in abundance:

> ... the old broad gauge system which, whilst adding to the comfort of passenger traffic, was wholly unsuited for goods, and especially in South Wales, where all the lines which had already been made were of the narrow gauge; it took a quarter of a century to convince the directors of the mistake they had made and induce them to correct it.[33]

Daniel Gooch's reported to shareholders in 1866:

> There is no doubt it has become necessary for us to look the matter of the narrow gauge fairly in the face. We have had within the past few days a memorial signed by nearly every firm of any standing in South Wales wishing that the narrow gauge might be carried out in their district, It is also pressing upon us in many other districts.

Five years later, in February 1871, the GWR directors proposed to convert to narrow gauge all the broad-gauge lines between Swindon and Gloucester and throughout south Wales, the work of conversion to be carried into effect as soon as the necessary narrow-gauge rolling stock could be obtained. The costs of such an exercise to carry out the alterations and conversion of the Permanent Way, was estimated at £226,000 with a further expenditure of £188,000 to provide the Locomotive, Carriage & Wagon Stock necessary to work the south Wales traffic on the narrow gauge. Thus, the full advantages of a uniform gauge would be available to the whole district through the proposal to:

> ... lay the mixed gauge from Didcot to Swindon, to convert to narrow gauge all the railways of the Company on which the broad gauge only at present exists between Swindon and Milford Haven, and to remove the broad gauge throughout those parts of the same district on which the lines are at present mixed gauge.

The proposals were accepted by the shareholders and signalled the final demise of the broad gauge in south Wales.

There were instances of railway gauge conversion before the ruling of the Gauge Commission in 1845, but not on the GWR or its associated broad-gauge companies. These were on what might be called the 'intermediate' gauges like the 5ft-wide gauge that George Bush almost had adopted on the TVR.[34] Railways that had adopted that gauge, the Eastern Counties and the Northern & Eastern Railways, converted their 5ft gauge to 4ft 8½in in September 1844, whilst in Scotland the Dundee & Arbroath and Arbroath & Forfar Railways changed from a 5ft 6in gauge to 4ft 8½in.[35] In Ireland, a uniform gauge of 6ft 2in had been recommended in 1838, but this was changed in 1841 when the 5ft 3in gauge was adopted, the Irish standard to this day. In the south west the London & South Western Railway (L&SWR) gained access to Devon and Cornwall through the acquisition of broad-gauge companies, and reached Exeter in 1860. Two years later it gained control of the broad-gauge north Devon route to Barnstaple, by leasing both the Exeter & Crediton and the Taw Valley Railways. For this incursion into broad-gauge territory, the L&SWR laid a third rail to allow the operation of standard-gauge trains, although broad gauge remained in place to Crediton until the final gauge conversion of the GWR in 1892. In 1862 the broad-gauge Somerset Central Railway and the standard-gauge Dorset Central Railway merged to form the Somerset & Dorset Joint Railway, the line between Evercreech and Burnham-on-Sea becoming a mixed-gauge line.

Even greater frustrations were to hinder the development of the broad gauge north of Oxford with the GWR's attempt to get to Birkenhead, all of which will not be repeated here as it has been well documented elsewhere.[36] However, there is an interesting sidelight on one of the overseas gauge conversions; in Canada the 5ft 6in gauge was adopted as the official gauge in the Province of Canada on 31 July 1851[37] and remained in use until the early 1870s. In November 1872 the Grand Trunk Railway began to change from 5ft 6in to standard gauge and a certain Edmund Phillips Hannaford (1834–1902) was to play a major role. Hannaford had begun working for Brunel as a draughtsman at the age of seventeen and was engaged for four years on the South Devon Railway.[38] He left for Canada in 1857, working as an engineer on the Grand Trunk Railway, becoming chief engineer in 1869. In this capacity he designed a number of important railway bridges and new lines and extensions. As mentioned, the Grand Trunk Railway had been built to the 5ft 6in gauge and, as chief engineer, Hannaford was responsible for converting 1,179 miles of track to the standard gauge of 4ft 8½in. It was tackled in three sections under Hannaford's planning, the longest interruption to traffic not being more than 15 hours.[39]

Back in Britain it might have been expected that the first conversion of Brunel's broad gauge would have been on the Bristol & Gloucester Railway, taken over by the standard-gauge Midland Railway in 1846. However, the Midland worked the line until June 1854 on the broad gauge but could not remove the broad-gauge rails because of the clause the GWR insisted on being included in the Midland's 1846 Amalgamation Act. This required that they maintained the broad gauge, which they did until 1872, despite the GWR never using the line.[40] After 1865 the directors of the GWR felt that they could not hold back the conversion of the broad gauge and began to plan for the narrowing of all broad-gauge lines. The first conversion from broad to standard gauge actually took place on the South Wales line of the GWR to accommodate the Pembroke & Tenby Railway's aspirations to extend its standard-gauge line past Whitland, where they had a junction with the GWR. The P&TR wanted to continue as an independent standard-gauge line to the Carmarthen & Cardigan Railway at Carmarthen and the Llanelly Railway and there access their connection to the London & North Western Railway's Central Wales line at Llandovery.[41]

With the P&TR contributing to the costs, the GWR agreed to convert their up main line to standard gauge for thirteen and a half miles between Whitland and Carmarthen Bridge, broad-gauge trains being run on the former down line. The work was completed on 1 June 1868 with P&TR goods trains running to Carmarthen. To quote MacDermot, 'Thus for nearly four years there were two single lines, one broad- the other narrow-gauge, side by side between Carmarthen Bridge and Whitland'.[42]

NOTES

1 University of Bristol, Special Collections, IKB Letter Book, p.107, letter to Owen Bowen 9 December 1852.

2 University of Bristol, Special Collections IKB PLB9, p.107, to Owen Bowen, 9 December 1852.

3 *Cardiff and Merthyr Guardian*, 4 March 1854, reporting on the half yearly meeting of the SWR.

4 The Bristol & South Wales Union Railway Portskewett branch would be authorised on 27 July 1857.

5 MacDermot, E.T. (revised by Clinker, C.R., 1964), vol.1, p.306.

6 Brunel, Isambard (1870, reprinted 1971), p.89, *The Life of Isambard Kingdom Brunel*, Longmans, Green & Co.: London, 1870, reprinted by David & Charles: Newton Abbot, 1971.

7 The 1in OS map. (seventh edition, 1947–48) shows a continuation of the SWMR running north-east for about another 1½ miles beyond the terminal point, serving other collieries further up the Corrwg Valley.

8 MacDermot, E.T. (revised by Clinker, C.R. (originally published 1927, first revised edition 1964)), p.233, *History of the Great Western Railway Volume II*, Ian Allen: London. It is stated that the 'engines travelled with the trucks'.

9 MacDermot, E.T. (revised by Clinker, C.R. (originally published 1927, first revised edition 1964)), p.233.

10 Brunel's dock works will be covered in vol.3.

11 Brunel, Isambard (1870, reprinted 1971), p.439.

12 MacDermot, E.T. (revised by Clinker, C.R. (originally published 1927, first revised edition 1964)), p.5.

13 Richards, S. (1976), *Rhondda & Swansea Bay Railway* and *South Wales Mineral Railway*, Ty John Penry: Swansea, p.4. The Glyncorrwg Colliery of the Glyncorrwg Colliery Co. Ltd closed in July 1925.

14 The SWMR section for this was Glyncorrwg to Cymmer and workmen's trains were run on the section from Cymmer to North Rhondda Halt, north of Glyncorrwg, see Richards, S. (1976), p.16.

15 Page, James (1979), *Forgotten Railway: South Wales*, David & Charles: Newton Abbot, p.106.

16 MacDermot, E.T. (revised by Clinker, C.R. (1927, first revised edition 1964)), p.233.

17 The Industrial Railway Society's records show that the Glyncorrwg Colliery of the Glyncorrwg Colliery Co. Ltd was closed in July 1925 and dismantled but that the SWMR ran north-east for about another 1½ miles to serve other collieries further up the Corrwg Valley (based on the seventh edition (1947–48) OS 1in map). See www.irsociety.co.uk/Archives/25/south_wales_mineral_railway.htm#Gyluchy

18 Barrie, D.S.M. (revised by Baughan, Peter E., 1994), p.192, *A Regional History of Great Britain*, vol.12, *South Wales*, David St John Thomas Publisher: Nairn.

19 Losing out to Big Pit near Blaenavon, although a mining museum has been established at the Afan Argoed Country Park.

20 Brunel, Isambard (1870, reprinted 1971). *The Life of Isambard Kingdom Brunel*, David & Charles reprint: Newton Abbot, pp.476–77. Letter on the position of Joint Engineer, 16 October 1843, as part of 'Mr. Brunel's Professional Opinions and Practice'. Also in Jones, Stephen K. (2005), p.121.

21 University of Bristol, Special Collections, IKB Letter Book, p.107, letter to Owen Bowen, 9 December 1852.

22 University of Bristol, Special Collections, IKB Letter Book, pp.361–2, letter to Owen Bowen, 6 November 1857.

23 University of Bristol, Special Collections, IKB Letter Book, pp.370–1, letter to Owen Bowen, 11 January 1858.

24 University of Bristol, Special Collections, IKB Letter Book, pp.15–16, 8 February 1858.

25 MacDermot, E.T. (revised by Clinker, C.R. (1927, first revised edition 1964)), p.277.

26 MacDermott, E.T. (revised by Clinker, C.R. (1927, first revised edition 1964)), p.282.

27 Blower, Alan (1964), p.108, *British Railway Tunnels*, Ian Allen: London.

28 MacDermot, E.T. (revised by Clinker, C.R. (1927, first revised edition 1964)), p.334. Broad gauge mileage at the end, 1 June 1872, stood at 18 miles 58 chains.

29 As already mentioned in Chapter 4, for a full account of the Ely Valley Railway see Chapman, Colin, (2000), *Ely Valley Railway: Llantrisant-Penygraig*, Oakwood Press: Usk,

30 Chapman, Colin (2000), p.11.

31 Amalgamation with the GWR took place in 1902.

32 For a full account of the Ely Valley Railway see Chapman, Colin (2000), *Ely Valley Railway*, Oakwood Press: Usk.

33 Jones, W. H. (1922), *History of the Port of Swansea*, Spurrell: Carmarthen, p.265.

34 Jones, Stephen K. (2005), pp.127–29.

35 Clinker, C.R. (1978), *New Light on the Gauge Conversion*, Avon-Anglia: Bristol, p.2.

36 See Day, Lance (1985), *Broad Gauge: an account of the origins and development of the Great Western broad gauge system*, and Awdry, Christopher (1992), *Brunel's Broad Gauge Railway*, Oxford Publishing: Oxford. www.bopcris.ac.uk/bopall/ref4918.html

37 The Legislature of the Province of Canada passed an act in 1851, which made 5ft 6in the standard gauge for new railways in the Province. This act, which was in force until 1870, stated that unless the 5ft 6in or 'Provincial Gauge' was used for new construction longer than 75 miles, the railroad would not be eligible for subsidies.

38 Min. Proc. Institution of Civil Engineers, vol.151, 1902–03, pp.411–9.

39 One theory has it that the first two locomotives for the Canadian portion of the road came second hand from the 5ft 6in gauge Arbroath & Forfar Railway in Scotland.

40 MacDermot, E.T. (revised by Clinker, C.R., 1964), vol.1, *History of the Great Western Railway*, vol.1. Ian Allen: London, p.110.

41 MacDermot, E.T. (revised by Clinker, C.R., 1964), vol.2, p.27.

42 MacDermot, E.T. (revised by Clinker, C R., 1964), vol.2, p.27.

11

BEYOND BRUNEL

'... THE CONTINUED EXISTENCE OF THE DOUBLE GAUGE IS A NATIONAL EVIL'[1]

The year 1868 saw the broad gauge and the standard gauge side by side following the accommodation of the P&TR between Whitland and Carmarthen. The next event of importance to south Wales was the laying of a third rail to provide mixed gauge from Gloucester to Grange Court and the whole of the Hereford Branch. In an article entitled 'Was Brunel's 7ft Gauge A Mistake?' published thirty years later in 1898, William Lancaster Owen (1843–1911), the son of William George Owen, gave his opinion. Owen was well placed for such an opinion, having been the engineer of new works for the GWR from 1885 when his father retired, until his retirement.[2] He trained under his father, who had become the chief engineer of the GWR from 1868 until he retired in March 1885. Owen was based at Swindon and, apart from three years as engineer to the Monmouthshire Railway & Canal Co. (1872–75), he worked for the GWR until retirement. One of Lancaster Owen's comments in the article, from which it is clear that he was not a supporter of the broad gauge, relates to John, later Sir John, Hawkshaw's recommendations back in 1839 that the GWR should abandon the broad gauge. Lancaster Owen comments, 'Alas! his far reaching recommendation was not accepted', and goes on to say:

> ... that had wiser councils prevailed, the Company would have been saved an after-expenditure of more millions than one would like to hint at, at a much earlier period of its career, in a position to develop to the utmost the colliery and manufacturing districts through which its line was constructed.[3]

He also gives Brunel's response to Hawkshaw's statement about the adoption of a uniform gauge on the GWR, which would allow the interchange of traffic throughout the whole of the railway system of the country. Brunel's reply to this suggestion was, 'Railway carriages and wagons must belong to the particular line upon which they run... it will never pay to trust them in the hands of others'.[4] Lancaster Owen also talks about the pressure on the GWR, having acquired the broad-gauge SWR and the standard-gauge West Midland Railway, which extended from Oxford, via Worcester and Hereford to Merthyr Tydfil and Swansea, the last two being the result of the Taff Vale Extension of the Newport Abergavenny and Hereford Railway and then standard-gauge connections to Middle Duffryn on the VNR enabling it to run through to Neath and Swansea.[5] Accepting that in these circumstances, for south Wales at least, conversion was necessary, it was important to gain experience of what a large scale conversion would involve. It was resolved, therefore, to narrow the broad-gauge line form Hereford to Grange Court, which would involve the laying of a third rail from Grange Court to Gloucester to provide a standard-gauge route from the north via Hereford to Bristol. The narrowing of Hereford to Grange Court was the task that would provide experience for the larger task ahead. Lancaster Owen was present as an assistant to J. Ward Armstrong[6] and says that it was rather a severe task, the line abounding in tunnels, sharp curves and steep gradients, '… and at this time was laid with at least half-a-dozen different descriptions of permanent-way in experimental lengths – some being of the "longitudinal system," others of the "cross-sleeper system," but all requiring workmen of varied experience and different classes of tools'.[7]

The operation took place in 1869, starting on a Sunday morning in June. The line was divided up into lengths of about four miles for each day's work, each length being sub-divided into quarter-mile sections for which gangs of about twenty platelayers were responsible. They were supported by a train of broad-gauge vans propelled by three locomotives, moving from the Hereford end four miles a day and providing the sleeping accommodation, kitchens, engineer's office and workshop facilities needed. On the following Monday the ordinary train service (standard gauge) was resumed. A number of important lessons were learnt, such as ensuring all standard-gauge switch and crossing work was laid in or assembled ready to be hauled in place before the closure of the line and what must have become obvious during the actual operation, to calculate beforehand and provide 'short' rails for curves in sufficient numbers, as:

Gauge conversion train at Grange Court, August 1869. (From The Railway Magazine, *vol. II, 1898)*

… during the narrowing period, seeing that when the outer rails of a curve are moved inwards they occupy a shorter length than when in their original position, and, consequently must be cut or replaced by 'short' rails.[8]

Overall, Lancaster Owen believed that the most important lesson was in organising the work so that no shifting of the men with their heavy tools and appliances should take place after commencement until the completion of the work. With the expertise gained it was now applied to the major work now proposed – converting the broad gauge in south Wales. This began in May 1872 or rather the night of Tuesday 30 April, when the up line was closed after the passing of a special engine from New Milford and, as the special engine passed each section, occupation of the up line was handed over to the engineers for conversion with single-line working commencing on the down line, which was divided into fourteen sections varying in length from five and a half to nineteen and three quarter miles. Crossing places for trains, worked by a pilot engine, were established at Haverfordwest, Whitland, St Clears, Carmarthen Junction, Llanelly, Landore, Neath, Bridgend, Llantrisant, Cardiff, Newport, Portskewett and Lydney. A total of 424 miles of broad gauge had to be converted, 188 miles of double and forty-eight miles of single. Saturday 11 May 1872 saw the last broad-gauge trains working on the former South Wales Railway. To quote from the GWR's printed instructions:

As the Broad Gauge Passenger Trains on the Saturday night finish their journeys they must be worked back empty as soon as possible to Swindon. The last of them must be despatched from New Milford at 9.15pm, or as soon as possible after the arrival of the 12.40pm train from Gloucester, due at 8.50pm. A Special Engine must follow that train (the last Up Train) with Inspector Langdon and a Permanent Way Official, who will distribute notices to all concerned on the way up to Grange, that all Broad Gauge Stock has been removed, and that the Broad Gauge Down Line can be no longer used. The Engineers will then at once proceed to form narrow gauge passing loops on the Down Line, and until they are completed, which will probably be not until the Tuesday, no Goods Trains must be run. The Passenger Trains can be run, however, on the Monday, by making use of an Up Siding at each Crossing Station as a passing place, and the Superintendents must arrange previously for the Engineers to have possession of an Up Line Siding long enough to take a Passenger Train at each Crossing Station, so that it may be narrowed in readiness. The first Down Train to traverse the Up Narrow Gauge Single Line will be the 12.50 Down Mail from Gloucester on the Sunday, and the first Up Train, the 4.0pm Up Mail from New Milford the same day, and these trains will be able to run without crossing places.

The special engine referred to in the printed instructions was the Victoria Class 2-4-0 engine, *Brunel*. The down line was completed on 22 May and double line working was reopened by a special engine from New Milford that evening. So after a period of fifteen years from the opening throughout of the SWR, the broad gauge had now disappeared from the south Wales line, with the exception of the C&CR which lingered for a further three months until their line could be re-gauged. As already mentioned, Lancaster Owen worked under J. Ward Armstrong, responsible to the chief engineer, W.G. Owen. Lancaster Owen was responsible for the part east of Cardiff and John Lean, of Neath, covered Cardiff and the west thereof.[9] No doubt fully aware of what the task of conversion meant and not wishing to go through the experience again, Lancaster Owen resigned before the final gauge conversion of 1892 with Loius Trench being appointed in February 1891 as Chief Engineer (the first since W.G. Owen's appointment).[10] By 1890 all of the Great Western lines were either 4ft 8½ in or mixed gauge except for the Taunton to Chard branch, the main line between Exeter and Truro, and a number of branch lines west of Exeter. Only a minority of trains between Paddington and Exeter were still broad gauge, although some broad gauge expresses like the 'Flying Dutchman' and the 'Cornishman' ran right through from Paddington to Penzance. The Chard branch was narrowed between 18 and 20 July 1891, leaving just the lines to the west of Exeter on which only broad-gauge trains could be run. Rather than disrupt traffic on the main line for a long period while the final sections were narrowed, the directors made the decision to bring in a large number of additional workers and convert the remaining 171 miles of broad-gauge track in a single weekend. The weekend chosen was from 20 to 23 May 1892, and at 9.45 a.m. on 21 May 1892 two locomotives ran with their train past the Swindon 'F' signal box, over the points and off the main line. With the passing of the train fifty-four years of broad gauge on the GWR had finally come to an end. Cardiff, however, would see a broad-gauge locomotive which, admittedly, had not travelled under its own steam, even after this when the pride of the GWR broad-gauge locomotive fleet, *Lord of the Isles*, came as an exhibit to the Cathays Park exhibition in 1896.[11] Lancaster Owen reflected on, 'what might have been' regarding the broad gauge, speculating on what sort of boiler and how much heating surface could have been provided for a broad-gauge engine, referring to the latest American practice, and what sort of payload such an engine would have, if such a load, '… were carried in the most up-to-date bogie wagons?'. With a carriage a little more than double the width of the gauge, say 15ft wide over all, '… what a commodious and elegant dining and sleeping car could have been placed on the road!'.[12]

Brunel, unlike his contemporary, Robert Stephenson, was destined never to become president of the Institution of Civil Engineers. Interestingly, the South Wales Institute of Engineers, which was formed in 1857, debated a proposal to make Brunel (and Robert Stephenson) honorary members at their first council meeting in 1858, but decided to postpone the matter until the Institute was deemed to be sufficiently mature.[13] One of Brunel's contemporaries and an associate in his Welsh work, Charles Blacker Vignoles, would go on to such an honour. What had happened to Vignoles in the meantime? Although he outlived Brunel and had numerous and wide-ranging commissions, his profile is not as well known. His temperament as engineer was to lose him a number of commissions due to his quick temper which often cost him support when he most needed it. European railways provided employment for him, as in 1853 when Vignoles was engineer for the line from Wiesbaden to Koln, although only the section to Rudesheim was completed. From 1854 he was appointed consultant for the Western Railway of Switzerland, designing the line from Lausanne to Yvedon, with his son Henry as resident engineer. The greatest challenge of all was the Tudela & Bilbao Railway, which was built between 1857–63 across mountainous territory for much of its 150-plus mile length. Vignoles himself, now well into his sixties, devoted much time to the project, with son Henry again acting as resident engineer. There were railways in Brazil for which a British company had the concession. Hutton carried out the surveys and was appointed resident engineer, with John Watson as contractor.

Earlier in his career he had embarked on a non-railway commission, even further afield, by designing and constructing the suspension bridge at Kiev in Russia. Vignoles' experience in this field dated back to the 1820s when he had assisted in projected bridge schemes across the river Thames. He discussed the idea of such a bridge with William Tierney Clarke, then designing the Szechenyi Bridge across the Danube in Vienna. In January 1847 Vignoles embarked on a journey of over 2,000 miles across Europe to St Petersburg to meet the Tsar and, with business partners, settle the terms for the concession to build the bridge and his own payment. Back in London in March, he worked on the design before returning to St Petersburg in July to finalise the contract. Vignoles' engineering work was accompanied by a variety of scientific interests, which contributed to his election to the Royal Society in 1855. A founder member of the (Royal) Photographic Society in 1853, he was responsible for having photographs taken of the Kiev Suspension Bridge – some of the earliest photographs taken as engineering records – and commissioned similar records of his overseas railways. At the Photographic Society's first exhibition, held on 4 January 1854, he was listed not as a photographer but as an exhibitor of some of Roger Fenton's photographs of the bridge at Kief. No photographs by Vignoles are known to exist.[14] Vignoles regularly attended the annual meetings of the British Association, giving a lecture on Atmospheric Railways in 1842, and a paper on suspension-bridge design for railways in 1857. At the age of seventy-six he was elected president of the Institution of Civil Engineers in 1869, recognising a lifetime of achievement which was to come to an end on 17 November 1875.

Sir Daniel Gooch did not see the final demise of the broad gauge. He remained chairman of the GWR until his death in October 1889. It was more than fifty-two years since he had first been associated with the broad gauge and he was spared the sad task of issuing the orders for its complete elimination. Towards the end of his life he records in his diary the loss of friends and colleagues that had been working with him and Brunel in shaping the GWR, such as on 18 May 1885 when he wrote the following in his diary:

> My old friend and brother officer on the Great Western since I joined the Co, Mr Owen, died on the 14TH of this month. He has for some years past been the chief engineer of the company. His serious illness began in Augt last and he has gradually got worse since that time. He resigned his position on the railway a couple of months ago. He was a good and trustworthy officer and much esteemed by all connected with the company. Year after year fewer of my old friends are left.[15]

Owen had been resident engineer at Chepstow when the tubular bridge was being constructed. Indeed, he had persuaded Brunel to act as godfather when his son was born there in 1850 and is why he was christened Herbert Isambard Owen (1850–1927).

A plaque recording the birthplace of Herbert Isambard can still be seen on Bell Vue House today in Chepstow. Sadly, the most potent reminder of Brunel's engineering work, the Chepstow tubular suspension bridge, is now longer extant although some important elements remain. It was to see in its centenary but even then a replacement was being planned. The non-symmetrical nature of the bridge has already been commented on, some observers making comments on other features, such as where the wrought-iron tubes of the bridge connected with the end bearings on top of the towers and were finished off with unusual architectural trimmings, 'They had the appearance of sad, unwinding swiss rolls and were constructed partially of timber with sheet zinc cladding'.[16] By the time of the Second World War the factor of safety with regard to stresses incurred by increasing loadings caused by heavier locomotives and rolling stock was approaching unity, or in other words, no margin of safety. Looking back on the situation, Sir Allan Quartermaine, the last chief civil engineer of the GWR and the first chief civil engineer of the Western Region of British Railways, made the following comment on the truss design pioneered at Chepstow and developed at Saltash, 'The finished truss forms a remarkably rigid structure, but has presented successive chief

Renewing the land spans at Chepstow. (Courtesy of Fairfield-Mabey Ltd)

Renewing the land spans at Chepstow. The cracks in the cast-iron piers and the use of wrought-iron straps or bands was noticed and commented on by, of all people, G.B. Airey, the Astronomer Royal, who first visited the bridge in 1852. (Courtesy of Fairfield-Mabey)

1891 advertisement for Edward Finch and Co. (SKJ collection)

engineers, bridge engineers and their assistants with an extremely difficult problem in stress calculation'.[17]

On 4 April 1944 the right-hand side main girder of the down line gave way but it was spotted in time to prevent any collapse under the passage of a locomotive. Single-line working at severely restricted speeds was allowed on the up line and repairs were quickly put in hand. Lees than three weeks later double-line working was resumed, although subject to a 15mph speed limit.[18] The life of the bridge, however, was now limited and it was only a matter of time, the first work taking place in 1948 with the replacement of the six 100ft 'land spans'.[19] In 1962 it was decided to replace the river spans of the bridge with the local company of Fairfield Shipbuilding & Engineering Co. Ltd being responsible for the fabrication and erection of inverted warren trusses to replace Brunel's tubular spans. Interestingly, the company continues and operates in Chepstow today as Fairfield-Mabey Ltd and are the successors to Finch & Hayes, the original builders of the bridge in 1849–53, which became Edward Finch & Co. when they decided to stay in Chepstow. Percy Berridge, an engineer with first-hand experience of bridge engineering on the GWR and Western Region of

BR tells the story of the replacement of Brunel's Chepstow Bridge is his book *The Girder Bridge After Brunel and Others*, including the 'discovery' of the origin of the cast-ironwork of the portal tower having come from, '... the Irish Engineering Co. and was made at the Seville Ironworks in Dublin...' Berridge believed that Brunel had learnt about this particular ironworks when he went across to Ireland in connection with the rescue of his SS *Great Britain* after it had gone ashore in Dundrum Bay in September 1846.[20] Curiously, no Irish ironworks of any reputable significance were shown as being in existence on a map published as part of the 1847 Enquiry into the Dee Bridge collapse, but Brunel must have come across this works and been suitably impressed by it during his stay in County Down, ironwork that could be delivered by sea from Dublin direct to the worksite at Chepstow. In 1962 the main spans of the bridge were replaced but the new bridge was still supported on Brunel's cast-iron piles and piers, supplemented by some new piles.

At the other end of the 'Welsh' SWR, Neyland, as the terminus of the broad gauge, was also subject to change. At the end of the nineteenth century the GWR decided to revert back to the original choice of port for the south Wales line by constructing a new port at Fishguard, the new harbour being formed by blasting away the cliff and using the rock for a breakwater and forming the harbour itself. With the opening of Fishguard on 30 August 1906, New Milford reverted to its old name of Neyland and the Irish crossing ceased to operate out of Neyland. This name remained in use throughout the remainder of the operational life of the railway. As a locomotive shed Neyland retained its facilities but under the Beeching plan closures were announced for all sheds in west Wales, with the withdrawal of steam on 9 September 1963. Later that year, on 2 December 1963, goods facilities were withdrawn from Neyland and on 15 June 1964 the last passenger train ran. A temporary railhead allowed materials needed for the new Gulf Refinery during construction, but with the completion the remaining rails were lifted, leaving a desolate site. The nearest railway station, and now the terminus, is the town of Milford Haven itself, Colonel Greville's prediction in 1855 that if the railway didn't go to Milford Haven at first they would be forced to go to it eventually coming true true.[21] Today, however, although the branch line, depot and station have disappeared, the site was regenerated in the 1980s as Brunel Quay and boasts the only statue of Brunel in Wales.

Curiously, there was a north Wales terminus of the broad gauge, although that is probably too grand a description for was the last complete section of broad-gauge line to survive. It was, in fact, a section of railway that was completely isolated from the rest of the broad-gauge network, built to facilitate the construction of the New Harbour at Holyhead, an engineering project that attracted the attention of a wide range of engineers, including James Walker, the chief engineer to the Admiralty, but was to be entrusted to James Meadows Rendell CE, of Westminster, whose design included a breakwater 5,100ft long, from Soldier's Point to Platter's Buoy with a 2,100ft-long pier from Salt Island, enclosing an area of 316 acres, three quarters of a mile long. The estimated cost was £700,000, the work being undertaken by the contractors Messrs J. & C. Rigby of London, supervised by G.C. Dobson, the resident engineer. The work began in January 1848 and it took twelve months to lay down the lines to the quarries, erecting stages and other necessary preparations. This was to keep an average of 1,300 men employed during the main construction phase.

Cut-up sections of the Fairfield-Mabey's 9ft-diameter wrought-iron tube in Fairfield Mabey's yard. (SKJ photograph)

Sections of the tube saddle of the old bridge in Fairfield Mabey's yard. This photograph was taken when the author was being shown around the works in 1978, escorted by Henry Llewellyn Warren. (SKJ photograph)

Above: *Construction of the Holyhead breakwater. (SKJ collection)*

Left: *View of the breakwater in 2005. (Owen Eardley photograph)*

The Royal Family were in Holyhead on September 1853 on the occasion of a visit to Ireland. They took the opportunity to view the improvements to the facilities, conducted on their tour by James Meadows Rendel, one of the contractors from Messrs Rigbys of London. They also inspected the adjacent quarries where a spectacular blast was arranged for their benefit. Stone was blasted from the slopes of Holyhead Mountain in lots of no less than 50,000 tons at a time. The material was then loaded onto large iron tip wagons on the broad-gauge railway and trundled along the breakwater to the tipping site. At the time of this royal visit, the harbour improvement construction known as 'The Great Breakwater' had extended over 4,000ft into the bay. In September 1857 it had reached out to 7,000ft with some 6 million tons of stone having been tipped and 1,200ft of superstructure built up to the level of high-water springs. In terms of the rail gauge chosen for this line, the opportunity had been taken to pick up a section of broad-gauge line, which would enable larger and heavier stone to be transported. Limestone was brought from the Moelfre quarry with schistus quartz extracted from Holyhead Mountain; this is a metamorphic rock which has changed by heat and which presents signs of faults and folding.[22] The breakwater railway ran from the quarry on Holyhead Mountain along the breakwater, with a branch along the seafront to Salt Island, where an eastern breakwater was planned and also to the inner harbour near the current station. The work was very hazardous and claimed the lives of over forty men between 1849 and 1852. In 1913 the stretch along the breakwater was converted to standard gauge and the broad gauge in Wales, indeed the whole of Great Britain, was finally brought to an end.

The broad gauge was one example linked to Brunel. A more obvious one, perhaps for Holyhead, was the visit by Brunel's last and ill-fated steamship, the PSS *Great Eastern*. In June 1857 Captain Harrison of the *Great Eastern* visited Holyhead together with officials of the Great Eastern Co. to find out if the new harbour could be used as the departure point for their first transatlantic crossing.[23] Steaming up from Weymouth in October 1859, she arrived too late in the year for an Atlantic crossing and returned to Southampton to winter. Nevertheless, the Great Eastern party were warmly welcomed and entertained at the Royal Hotel by the LNWR directors. Crowds occupied all vantage points to see the great ship and fifteen packed excursion trains arrived in just one day. The Royal Family were again in Holyhead at this time and Prince Albert and his guest, the French Prince Napoleon, were amongst the notabilities eager to inspect Brunel's magnificent vessel, although its designer had died a few weeks earlier on 15 September 1859.[24]

Meccano advertisement from the 1960s – back to the Great Eastern in volume three! (SKJ collection)

NOTES

1   Williams, Frederick S. (1885 sixth edition), *Our Iron Roads: Their History, Construction and Administration*, Bemrose & Sons: London, p.231. Williams quotes this as the opinion of the Gauge Commission who expressed concern that the break of gauge was a 'very serious evil'.

2   Owen, Lancaster (1898), p.515, *The Railway Magazine*, vol.II, January to June 1898, *Was Brunel's 7ft. Gauge A Mistake?* In his article he styles himself as 'Chief Engineer (Retired), Great Western Railway' but MacDermot, states that W.G. Owen '… had no successor, new works being left in the charge of his son, Lancaster Owen…' MacDermot, E.T. (revised by Clinker, C.R. 1964), vol.II,

p.193, for the second part in vol. III, July to December 1898, his title is 'Chief Constructive Engineer (Retired)'.

3   See Jones, Stephen K. (2005), p.128, regarding the Hawkshaw recommendations and Owen, Lancaster (1898), p.515, *The Railway Magazine*, vol.II, January to June 1898.

4   Owen, Lancaster (1898), p.515, *The Railway Magazine*, vol.II, January to June 1898.

5   See Chapter 8.

6   MacDermot, E.T. (1927, first revised edition 1964), *The History of the Great Western Railway*, vol.II, Ian Allan: London, p.29. MacDermot comments about the dates in *The Railway Magazine* article as being far from accurate.

7   Owen, Lancaster (1898), p.516, *The Railway Magazine*, vol.II.

8   Owen, Lancaster (1898), pp.517–8, *The Railway Magazine*, vol.II.

9   MacDermot, E.T. (1927, first revised edition 1964), p.32, vol.II.

10 MacDermot, E.T. (1927, first revised edition 1964), p.267, vol.II.

11 Allen S.W. (1918), *Reminiscences,* Western Mail Ltd: Cardiff.

12 Owen, William Lancaster, p.39, *The Railway Magazine*, vol.III, '*Was Brunel's 7ft Gauge A Mistake? Part 2*', July to December 1898.

13 South Wales Institute of Engineers (2006), p.13, Sesquicentenary Brochure 1857–2007, Cardiff.

14 Morris, Richard, Photo Historian (Royal Photographic Society Historical Group), Autumn 1994, (105), pp.25–6.

15 Wilson, Roger Burdett (1972), *Sir Daniel Gooch: Memoirs & Diary*, David & Charles: Newton Abbot, p.342.

16 Sealey, Anthony (1976), p.174, *Bridges and Aqueducts*, Hugh Evelyn: London.

17 Quartermaine, Sir Allan (1959), p.12, *I.K. Brunel – The Man and his Works*, British Railways (Western Society) London Lecture and Debating Society, Session 1958–59, No.456.

18 Berridge, P.S.A. (1969), p.85, *The Girder Bridge After Brunel and Others*, Robert Maxwell: London.

19 Berridge, P.S.A. (1969), p.86. Berridge notes that these were among the last examples of riveted girderwork to appear on the Western Region of British Railways.

20 Berridge, P.S.A.,(1969), pp.53–54 & 131.

21 Rees, J.F. (1954), p.57, *The Story of Milford*, Cardiff. Chapter 7.

22 *Schistus* means 'easily cleaved' in Latin, in that it is fairly easy to break up, in contrast to both granite and quartzite.

23 Jones, Norman; Robinson, Tony & Carr, Carolyn (2001), p.8, *Holyhead's Royal Visit*, Foxline (Publications) Ltd: Clerkheaton.

24 Jones, Norman, Robinson, Tony & Carr, Carolyn (2001), p.9.

INDEX

Colour plates in bold italic

Abandonment
  of possible routes, 58
  of Bristol & South Wales Junction Railway (B&SWJR), 72
  of SWMR line between Briton Ferry and Tonmawr Junction, 233
  of Tenby and Pembroke Dock Branch, 169
Aderdare, Baron, see Bruce
Aberdare, 20, 59, 76, 77, 86, 111, 177-179, 183, 185, 186, 188, 190, 194, 196-200, 204-206, 231
  Canal, 205,
  timber all-over roof station, 198, *33*
Abergavenny, 22, 58, 59, 61, 62, 176, 197, 242
Abermawr, 165, 167, 170, *32*
Abernethy, James, 223
Accidents
  derailments on South Wales Railway, 74, 160, 164
  collision with Brunel's carriage, 92
  due to possible ground conditions, 130
  fatal accident to railway navvy, 154
  at Swansea north dock, 195, 199, 212, 213, 216, 217
Adare, Lord, 129, 131, 149
Admiralty, 11, 42, 44-46, 70, 78, 79, 162, 248
Airey, G.B., 247
Anglesey
  Amlwch, 39, 40, 52
  Mona, 39, 40
  Parys Copper Mountain 39, 40
Archer, Henry 35-37, 45, 51, 54, 188
Armstrong
  J. Ward, 242, 244
  George, 52
  Nenon, 56, 227
  William, 199
Baden-Powell, Mrs H.G., *19*
Barlow, Frederick Pratt, 70
  Peter, 41, 42, 45, 65
Barlow rail, 126, 157, 159, 160, 168, 169, 191, 195, 203, 213
Barrow, Sir John 78, 79, 87, 226
Batchelor, John, 116, 123 *23*
  James Sydney, 116
Bath, 15, 19, 26, 27, 31, 33, 118, 200, 216, 206
Benson, Starling, 214, 217-219, 224, 225
Board of Trade, 131, 141, 184
Borough of Newport, 100, 101, 104, 122
Bowen, Owen, 227, 234, 239, 240
Boxes for coal (containers), 194, 213
Braithwaite, John, 39, 52

Brecon, 19, 21, 25, 59, 61, 191
Brereton, Robert Pearson, 231, 253
Bridges and Viaducts, 26, 38, 51, 70, 71, 79-82, 91, 116, 139, 152, 155, 162, 167-169, 182, 213, 246
  bascule, 163, 169
  bowstring girders, 102, 103, 109
  Bridgend, Coity Road, (SWR), 133, 134
  Britannia Bridge, 47-51, 88, 121, 128
  Carmarthen Bridge (SWR), 239
  Goitre Coed (TVR), 12, 14, 16, 32
  Landore viaduct (SWR), 11, 142-147, 199, *25-28*
  Llansamlet flying arches (SWR), 138, 140, 141, 151
  Loughor viaduct (SWR), 14, 154, 157-159, *31*
  Menai Suspension Bridge, 42, 46, 51
  Neath swing bridge (R&SBR), 139
  Newbridge Viaduct, Pontypridd (TVR), 14
  Resolven cast-iron aqueduct (VNR), 186
  Severn proposed swing bridge, 81,
  Seiont Bridge, Caernarvon, *3*
  timber bridges drawbridge, 70, 71
  Usk bridge, 99
  Windsor Bridge (GWR), *15*
  Wye bridge at Chepstow, tubular suspension bridge (SWR), 89, 94-97, 246 *9, 11, 14*
Bridgend, 4, 12, 14, 59, 60, 76, 112, 127, 128, 130, 131, 132-134, 150, 185, 219, 221, 222, 224, 243
  station *24*
Bridgewater ironworks, 186
Bristol, 11, 13, 15, 16, 25-28, 30, 31, 33, 34, 43, 57, 64, 66, 67, 72, 77-79, 83, 85, 86, 92, 93, 121, 123, 126, 141, 142, 151, 156, 162, 173-175, 178, 191, 204, 206, 213, 224, 225, 226, 238, 239, 240, 242
Briton Ferry, 26, 77, 135, 136, 139, 140, 149, 150, 180,185, 197, 206, 213, 228, 230, 231, 233
Brogden, John, 87, 222, 244
Brown, Captain Sir Samuel, 36, 38
Bruce, Henry Austin, 197, 199, 206
Brunel,
  Marc Isambard 25, 38-41, 52, 53, 63
  Isambard Kingdom 6-13, 22-32, 54-56, 58-60, 62-66, 80-82, 90-92, 116-120, 138-142, 166, 168, 170-174, 182, 210-214, 222-224, 243-254, *1, 3-4, 7-8, 11, 13, 15-16*
  Brunel Beds (geological), 168
Brunel University, 247 *12*
Brunton, William, 26, 27, 141, 214, 224
Bullo Pill, 84
Bush, George, 65, 116, 155, 156, 174, 175, 214, 217, 225, 238
Bute, Marquis of, 20, 70, 109, 110, 113, 128, 129, 131, 148, 149, 174, 182, 221
Caernarfon, 51, 53
Cambridge, 33, 53

Canals, 7, 28, 60, 80, 81, 137, 176, 194, 196, 198, 208, 209, 214
Cardiff, 5, 9, 22, 26, 29, 32, 51, 59-62, 65, 67, 109, 111, 112, 114-116, 119, 121, 125-127, 221
  Board of Health, 115
  Butetown, 121
Cardiff Arms, 118
  Cardiff Arms Hotel, 120
  Cardiff station (SWR), 119 *18*
  Castle, 117
  Coal Exchange, 121
  Millennium Stadium, *21-22*
Cardigan town, 227
Carmarthen, 21, 56, 59, 61, 62, 70, 160, 162, 206, 211, 213, 215, 224, 227, 234, 235, 239
Chambers, William, 70, 156, 158, 159, 175
Chartists, 18-20, 31, 100
Cheltenham, 9, 27, 28, 118
Chepstow, 57, 59, 60, 62, 70, 98, 127, 152, 172, 245-247
  Bellevue House, 90, 91
  station, 89, 94, *8-9*
Wye bridge (tubular suspension bridge), 89, 94-97, 246, *9, 11, 14*
Chester, 44, 46, 47
Chadwick, William, 51
Cirencester, 15, 28
Clarbeston, 166
Clark, George Thomas, 100, 111, 122-124, 127, 128, 149, 206
Clarke, William Tierney, 38, 41, 245
Claxton, Captain Christopher, 47, 50
Clunderwen/Clynderwen station, 164, *30*
Coaches, mail, 100, 109
Coal, 3, 9, 21, 23, 32, 40, 76, 131, 139, 140, 195, 199, 218, 209, 211, 213, 221, 222, 234, 236
Cockett station, 155
Coffin, Walter, 22, 23, 32
Collister, John, 46
Condor, Francis Roubiliac, 33, 161, 175
Cordell, Alexander, 196, 206
Cowbridge, 126-127, 134, 224
Crawshaw, William, 24, 28, 29, 197, 206
  Bailey, 28
Cwmbran, 34, 67
Cymmer, 230, 233
Cynon Valley, 26, 59, 184
Bwllfa Colliery, 186, 195
  Bwllfa House, 186, 195
  Dare Valley, 192-194, 195
Dargan, William, 41, 43
Dean, William, 125
Dinas Bridge Fire Brick Works, 191
Dixton, Vicar of, 82
Downing, George, 14, 44
Drummond, Captain Thomas, 42
Ericsson, John, 39
Fairfield-Mabey Ltd, 13, 97, 121, 246-247, 249, *11*
Fenton, Roger, 245
Finch, Edward D., 95, 96, 144, 247
  Finch & Heath, 95
  Finch & Willey, 95, 247
Fishguard, 163, 167, 171, 248
Frere, George, 12
Gatcombe, railway carved through, 84
Gauge, 9, 67, 62-65, 237, 238, 251
Broad (7'o ¼"), 8, 11, 14, 20, 30, 46, 47, 64, 66, 69, 71, 72, 75-78, 98, 127, 136, 139, 143, 155, 195, 177, 199, 185, 217, 221-244, 227, 228, 232, 234-239, 241-244, 248, 250
Commission, 50, 237, 251
Glamorganshire canal bridge (Rhydycar), *34*

Gloucester, 9, 26, 67, 75, 78-82
  Gloucester Journal, 224
  station, *5*
Glyncorrwg, 228, 31-233
Gooch, Daniel, 17, 18, 65, 66, 195, 196, 237
Graham, Sir James, 131, 149
Grange Court, 73, 98, 241, 242
Great Britain (SS), 248
Great Eastern (PSS), 128, 169, 251
Greville, Colonel, 169, 248
Guest, Lady Charlotte, 16, 18, 24, 31, 32, 33, 100, 111, 131, 135, 149, 152, 153, 174, 197, 206
  Sir Ivor Bertie, 236
  Sir Josiah John, 20, 21, 24, 26, 32, 70, 110, 111, 131, 135, 149, 152, 153, 197, 206, 236
Health, Local Board of, 100, 113, 115, 131, 135, 158
Haverfordwest, 72, 152, 166, 167, 169
Hock Crib, 79-81
Holyhead, 25, 35-37, 42, 44-47. 50. 51, 54, 71, 88, 127, 248, 250-251
Horsley, John Callcot, 17
Howlett, Robert (photograph of Brunel), *27*
Hutton, Dr. Charles, 37, 38
Institution of Civil Engineers (ICE)/ICE Wales, 13, 14, 23, 37, 52, 86, 121, 130, 151, 240, 244, 245,
Incline, 66, 68
  Box, 16, 30
Gloucester & South Wales Railway (proposed), 62
Glynneath (VNR), 188, 189, 197, 205
Hownes Gill, 66
Merthyr tunnel (VNR), 191
Mona tramroad (proposed) 40
Taff Vale Railway (mainline), 16, 30
Ynys-y-maerdy (SWMR), 11, 228-231, 233
Ireland, 9, 10, 12, 25, 28, 35-37, 41-45, 51, 53-55, 58, 61, 64, 66, 72, 78, 130, 131, 154, 159, 162, 165, 167, 238, 248, 250
  Berehaven, 43
  Cork, 35
  Dublin, 35, 36, 42, 44, 45, 53, 248
  Kingstown, 41, 42, 45, 64, 76
  Skibbereen, 6, 152, 165, 174
James, Evan, 30
Jones, B., 156
  Rhys W., (VNR), 179, 214
  Samuel, 218, 219
  William, 116
Kemp, James, 29, 34
Landore, 72, 139, 142, 144, 151, 156, 207, 216, 243
  station, 144
  viaduct, see Bridges & Viaducts
Lean, John, 244
Lewis, Weston Dillwyn, 28, 135
  Richard alias Dic Penderyn, 31
  William, 128-131, 141, 148, 152, 174
Liverpool, 16, 25, 32, 35, 38-40, 42, 45, 46, 59, 95, 110, 119, 142, 209, 214, 142, 209
Llandysul, 234, 235
Llansamlet, 138, 140, 141, 151
Llewelyn, John Dillwyn, 94, 95
Locke, Joseph, 44, 53, 66
Locomotives,
  Brunel, 243
  Corsair class, 196
  Fenton, Murray & Jackson &Co., 106
  Firefly class, *26*
  Hedley, 235
  Lord of the Isles, 244
  Novelty, 39

Royal George, 38
Rob Roy, 74
Taff and Rhondda, 65
Sharp Roberts & Co., 64, 65, 68
Trevithick, 8, 52, 208, 209
Victor Emanuel, 107
Victoria Class, 107, 243
Waverley, 74
Loughor station, 158
Maps,
 railway companies associated with Brunel in south Wales, **7**
 railway development, **3**
 railway proposals in north Wales, **2**
McAlpine, Hon. Sir William, 13, **13**
MacDermot, E.T., 27, 30, 31, 33, 67, 84-87, 150, 151, 175, 205, 206, 225, 226, 231, 239, 240, 251, 252
McNair, Captain, 222, 223
Maesteg, 220-222, 225
Margam, 116, 118, 128, 130, 131, 134, 135, 150
Madocks, Alexander, 35
Merchant & Williams (contractors), 132
Merthyr Tydfil, 13, 24, 31, 39, 75, 109, 110, 123, 124, 139, 178, 179, 190, 199-201, 203, 205, 208, 241
 Dowlais, 18, 22, 31, 58, 59
 High Street station, 200-203
Milford Haven, 26, 28, 29, 58, 60, 61, 77, 78, 167, 237, 248
 New Milford (Neyland), 74, 169, 171-173, 243, 248
Monmouth, 18, 25, 29-31, 58-62, 70, 72, 75, 79, 82, 86, 87, 89, 151
Morgan, David, (Cardiff draper), 104, 122, **23**
Neath, 22, 32, 59-62, 67, 135-137, 139, 140, 144, 150, 151, 152, 176-180, 184, 185, 186, 188, 197, 199, 204, 205, 207, 231, 233, 242-244
Neath Abbey Iron and Coal Co., 21, 140, 151, 178, 204
Newnham, 29, 59, 60, 62, 79-81, 92,
Newport, 11, 18, 19, 26, 29, 31, 55, 57, 59-62, 77-79, 82, 84, 98-108, 110, 112, 115, 118, 121, 122, 139, 149, 152, 159, 243, 25
 station and carriage sheds, 105, 106, 108, **17**
Newtown, 37, 115, 118, 125
Neyland, 74, 169, 171-173, 243, 248
Ormerod, George of Sudbury Park, 89
Owen, George Wells, 84
 Lancaster, 241-244, 251, 252
 Sir Isambard, 51, 90, 245
 William George, 12, 36, 84, 88, 90, 91, 142, 159, 174, 241, 244, 245, 251, **3**
Oxford, 36, 37, 54, 224,238, 241
 Canal, 39, 40
Packet stations, 35, 36, 43, 45, 46
Page, James, 214
Pembroke Dock (Pater), 59-61, 70, 77, 78, 131, 169, 171, 173
Pim, James, 45, 46
Pontypridd, 14, 101
Porthcawl, 76, 219, 221, 222
Porthdinllaen, 10, 24, 35-37, 44-47, 50, 51, 54, 55, 78, 88, **1**
Price, Henry Habberley, 26, 27, 140, 141, 214, 224
 Joseph, 21, 140
Purdon, Wellington, 46
Purton, 57, 84, 87, **5**
Pyle, 127, 134, 135, 149, 150, 222
Railways
 Aberdare Railway, 20
 Aberdare Valley Railway, 196
 Birmingham lines, 19, 21, 25, 28, 36, 46, 88
 Bridgend Railway, 221
 Bristol & South Wales Junction Railway (B&SWJR), 72, 77

Bristol and South Wales Union Railway (B&SWUR), 72, 78, 86, 123, 239
British Railways, 246
Cambrian lines of 1833, 25, 26
Cardiff Railway, 29
Carmarthen & Cardigan Railway (C&CR), 77, 164, 227, 234, 235, 239
Cheltenham & Great Western Union Railway (C&GWUR), 9, 10, 28, 79
Cork & Waterford Railway, 76
Crewe Railway, 44
Dare Valley Railway, 193
Forest of Dean Railway (Bullo Pill), 29, 72, 75, 77, 79, 80, 82, 84, 85, 87
Dublin & Kingstown Railway, 41, 42, 45, 64, 76
Duffryn Llynvi & Porth Cawl Railway, 219-221
Eastern Counties Railway, 39, 52
Ely Valley Railway (EVR), 78, 86, 227, 236, 240, 254, 255
European railways, 244
Gloucester & Cardiff Railway (proposed), 29, 61
Gloucester & Dean Forest Railway, 71, 75, 77,
Gloucester & South Wales Railway (G&SWR), 9, 10, 28, 29, 34, 57, 58, 78, 79, 84, 118, 176, 204, 210
Glyncorrwg Railway, 227
Great Western Railway (GWR) Bath to Bristol Railway, 26, 27
GWR Bill, 28, 63
Hereford Railway, 72, 176, 242
Liverpool & Manchester Railway, 16, 38, 43, 219
Llynvi Valley Railway L&VR), 76, 219, 220, 222, 232
London & North Western Railway (L&NWR), 66, 172, 239
London & Windsor Railway, 27
Maesteg, Bridgend & South Wales Junction Railway (proposed), 221
Midland Counties Railway, 41
Midland Railway, 76, 219, 238
Mona tramroad (proposed) 40
Monmouth & Hereford Railway, 72, 75
Monmouthshire Railway & Canal, 60, 77, 241
Newport, Abergavenny & Hereford Railway, 21, 22, 176, 197, 242
Oystermouth Railway, (see Swansea & Mumbles Railway)
Port Talbot Railway,
Preston Railway,
Rhondda & Swansea Bay Railway, 139, 209, 239
Rhymney Railway, 119
Rumney Railway, 60
Runcorn Gap Railway, 41
Severn Railway Company, 27
Severn & Wye Railroad, 82
Sheffield & Manchester Railway, 52
South Wales Junction Railway, 72, 76
South Wales Mineral Railway (SWMR), 77, 135, 221, 227, 228, 230-232, 239
South Wales Railway (SWR), 9, 11, 25, 55, 56, 69-72, 74-78, 80, 82, 84-86, 92, 100, 103, 104, 109, 113, 115, 117-119, 125-128, 130, 132, 134, 135, 139, 140, 142, 144, 150-153, 155, 156, 158, 161, 164, 168, 170-176, 178, 182, 185, 188, 195, 196, 199, 204, 208, 210, 214-219, 221-224, 227, 228, 231, 235, 236, 239, 241, 243, 248, **3**, **6**, **8-10**, **12-14**, **16-20**, **24**, **28**, **30-32**
Southampton Union Railway, 72
Stanhope & Tyne Railway, 66, 68
Swansea Harbour Railway, 199, 211, 216, 223
Swansea & Mumbles Railway (see also Oystermouth Railway), 208, 209-211, 224

Swansea Vale Railway, 21, 76, 199, 214, 215, 217, 218, 225
Swansea Valley Railway, 76, 204, 218
Taff Vale Railway (TVR), 7, 9-13,15, 19-23, 30, 41, 55, 59, 65, 85, 86, 109, 112, 113, 127, 149, 185, 200, 204
Thames & Severn Railway,
Vale of Neath Railway (VNR), 7, 192, 194, 195, *33-34*
Waterford & Limerick Railway, 43, 89
Waterford, Wexford, Wicklow & Dublin Railway, 56, 72, 76, 77
Welsh Midland Railway, 21, 32, 217, 218
West Midland Railway, 241
Railway branches, 9, 21, 26, 27, 31, 59, 82, 112, 144, 176, 199, 214, 216, 227
Briton Ferry Dock Co., 213
Carmarthen and Cardigan, 236
Ely Valley, 227
Forest of Dean, 29, 33, 72, 75, 79, 80, 84
GWR branches, 244, 248
Holyhead Breakwater branch, 248, 250, 251
Llantwit Vadre, 221, 225
Llanelly Railway, 235
Milford, 78, 167-169, 171, 173
Portskewett branch (B&SWUR), 78, 98, 239, 243
Rhondda (TVR), 21, 22, 113, 118
proposed SWR branches, 214, 216, 218
SVR branches, 219
Wigan Branch Railway, 41
Rastrick, John Urpeth, 35, 38, 52, 89, 98
Rebecca, 19, 31, 111, 123, 131, 135, 159, 164, 175
Rendel, James Meadows, 248, 250
Rhondda Valley, 14, 21, 22, 113, 118, 124
River Loughor, 154, 158
    Neckar, 24, 33
    Pelenna, 230
    Rhondda, 14
    Saltash, 11, 82
    Seiont, 88, *3*
    Severn, 11, 27, 29, 37, 55, 56, 71, 72, 75, 78-84, 86-88, 91, 104, 118, 123, 139, *6*
    Taff, 12, 14, 20, 59, 72, 111, 113-117, 125, 126, *19-22, 34*
    Tawe, 71, 142, 144, 199, 207, 209-211, 214, 216-218, *25*
    Thames, 25, 27, 28, 33, 39, 40, 52, 53, 123, 224, 245, *15*
    Towey, 70
    Usk, 11, 26, 29, 55, 62, 78, 86, 99-103
    Wye, 11, 70, 82, 88, 89, 91, 93-95, 98, 173
Roberts, Richard, 64, 65, 68
Roch, Nicholas, 16, 70, 173-175
Royal Institution of South Wales, 13, 215
Russell, Clark 209, 223, 224
    John Scott, 128
    Charles, 152, 153, 218, 225
St Clears, 19, 164, 243
St Petersburg, 245
Schenk, A.J., 222, 223, 226
Smyth, Captain WHR, 87
South Wales Hotel, 171
South Wales Institute of Engineers, 13, 244, 252
Spooner, James, 36
Stephenson, Robert, 20, 24, 47, 50, 64, 66, 68, 74, 89, 128, 179, 182, 244
    George, 25, 36, 38, 39, 41, 44, 52, 64
Stroud, 28, 123
Swansea, 11, 13, 19, 21, 22, 26-29, 40, 55-62, 71, 76, 77, 82, 92, 98, 109, 116, 127, 135, 139, 142-144, 147-157, 159, 174, 178, 179, 184, 195, 197, 199, 207-219, 223, 224, 242, 253, *29*

Canal, 143, 208
Docks, 199, 210, 213-215
station, 147, 148
Swindon, 10, 11, 15, 54, 107, 235, 237, 241, 243, 244
Talbot, Christopher Rice Mansel, 116, 130, 134, 135, 149, 150, 152, 153, 172, 174, 217, 218, 225
    William Henry Fox, 116, 124, 153
Telford, Thomas 27, 36, 44, 53, 86, 135, 139, 214
Tenby, 72, 169, 171
Thomas, John, 50, 54
Tonmawr, 227, 230, 231, 233, 253
Trench, Louis, 244
Trevithick, Richard, 40, 52, 208, 209
Treweek, James, 40
Tunnels,
    Aberdare or Merthyr (VNR), 178, 185, 188, 190, 191
    Alltwalis or Pencader, 235
    Box (GWR), 15, 16, 142
    Channel, 9
    Cockett Swansea (SWR), 153-155
    Edge Hill (L&MR) 39, 52
    Goitre Coed (TVR), 16
    Gyfylchi (SWMR), 228, 230, 231, 233
    Haie Hill (SWR), 81, 84, 85
    Monmouth (proposed), 75, 82
    Neath (proposed), 139, 150
    Newport (High Street), 108
    Newport (Stow Hill), 98, 101, 104, 110 *16*
    Nottage (LVR), 222
    North Wales (proposed), 44
    Pencaedrain (VNR), 178, 188, 189
    Severn, 11, 81, 82, 104, 123
    Soudley (SWR), 84
    Swansea (High Street), 216
    Thames. 25, 26, 30, 39-41, 52, 53, 123, 224
    Wapping (L&MR), 16
    Woodhead (S&MR), 43
Vale of Neath Railway, Handbook, 150, 180-182, 184, 188, 205
Vignoles, Charles Blacker, 22-25, 27, 31-33, 35, 37, 38, 39, 40-46, 50-54, 64, 82, 89, 98, 121, 244, 245, *1-2*
    Henry 24
    Hutton 24, 245
Villiers, Lord, 188, 197, 205
Vivian, Henry Hussey, 40, 52, 209, 210
    John Henry, 40, 52, 67, 70, 209-211,
Warren, Henry Llewellyn, 121, 249
Walker, James, 38, 41, 44-47, 52, 53, 78-81, 86, 87, 98, 248
Wallace, Alfred Russel, 177-179, 183, 184, 188, 189, 204, 205
Whitland station, 171, 238, 239, 241, 243
Williams, Archibald, 32, 109, 122
    Charles, 29
    Contractor, 132
    Frederick S., 251
    Hugh, 164
    John, 162
    Joshua, 188, 191, 197, 206
    Richard Price, 22, 32
    Zephaniah, 19, 115
Winstone, John, 116
Woodhouse, Thomas Jackson, 41
Wye Bridge see Chepstow
Ynys-y-maerdy incline, 229-231, 233
Yockney, S.W., 139, 150